INTERNATIONAL SERIES OF MONOGRAPHS IN
PURE AND APPLIED BIOLOGY

DIVISION: **ZOOLOGY**

GENERAL EDITOR: G. A. KERKUT

VOLUME 38

ECHIDNAS

ECHIDNAS

BY

MERVYN GRIFFITHS

PHOTOGRAPHY BY

E. SLATER

PERGAMON PRESS

OXFORD · LONDON · EDINBURGH · NEW YORK
TORONTO · SYDNEY · PARIS · BRAUNSCHWEIG

Pergamon Press Ltd., Headington Hill Hall, Oxford
4 & 5 Fitzroy Square, London W.1
Pergamon Press (Scotland) Ltd., 2 & 3 Teviot Place, Edinburgh 1
Pergamon Press Inc., 44–01 21st Street, Long Island City, New York 11101
Pergamon of Canada Ltd., 207 Queen's Quay West, Toronto 1
Pergamon Press (Aust.) Pty. Ltd., 19a Boundary Street, Rushcutters Bay,
N.S.W. 2011, Australia
Pergamon Press S.A.R.L., 24 rue des Écoles, Paris 5e
Vieweg & Sohn GmbH, Burgplatz 1, Braunschweig

First edition 1968

Library of Congress Catalog Card No. 68-21385

PRINTED IN GREAT BRITAIN BY A. WHEATON & CO., EXETER
08 012650 2

CONTENTS

ACKNOWLEDGEMENTS

MY BEST thanks go to Dr. Imre Kaldor for the estimations of iron in echidna milk; Mr. Frank Knight for the line drawings; Mr. W. Vestjens for the entomological analysis of echidna scats; Mr. Adam Inglis for the amino-acid analysis of ants and termites; and to Messrs. R. Leckie, L. MacLean, and R. Coles for technical assistance. I should also like to thank the Executive of the Commonwealth Scientific and Research Organization for permission to write this book, and I am greatly indebted to Mr. J. H. Calaby for invaluable advice and information, to Mr. P. Magi for help in translation of German texts, to Mr. D. L. McIntosh for his assistance in reading proofs, and to Mr. and Mrs. George Lonzar who gave much assistance in taking echidnas with pouch young.

CHAPTER 1

EXTERNAL ANATOMY, TAXONOMY, AND NATURAL HISTORY

EXTERNAL FEATURES

The type specimen of the spiny anteater, *Tachyglossus aculeatus aculeatus*, was introduced to biologists by George Shaw (1792) with these sonorous words:

> Totum corpus superius cum cauda spinis contegitur validus et longioribus, quales omnino sunt hystricus vulgaris, nisi quod vice circulorum qui alternatim albi nigrique, plerumque albeant, apicibus altius nigro tinctis, quodque albedo a nigredine separetur annulo parvo sordide aurantio.
>
> *Myrmecophaga aculeata*
> Character Genericus
> Dentes nulli
> Lingua teres, extensilis
> Os augustatum in rostrum
> Corpus (plerisque) pilis tectum
> Character specificus
> *Myrmecophaga aculeata cauda brevissima.*

Shaw had no idea of the real nature of the beast he had described and he admitted, if it was not a species of *Myrmecophaga* (eutherian anteater), that the resemblance would be

> A most striking instance of that beautiful gradation so frequently observed in the animal kingdom by which creatures of one tribe or genus approach to those of a very different one. It forms a connecting link between the very distant genera of *Hystrix* and *Myrmecophaga*; having the external coating and general aspect of the one with the mouth and peculiar generic characters of the other.

An elegant enunciation of the principle of convergence in 1792.

Morphologically the hairs and spines he describes are mammalian entities and chemical analysis (Gillespie and Inglis, 1965) shows that the spines contain α keratins characteristic of rhinoceros horn, sheep horn, porcupine quills, finger-nails and so on. Proteins extracted from the α keratins contain much cystine, a fact that is of significance in connection with the nutrition of echidnas (p. 54).

On the sides of the body the spines point backwards but on the

1

dorsum they are directed towards the mid-line while those at the mid-line converge and cross one another alternately forming a handsome pattern. At the hind end of the body the spines are grouped into two semicircular rosettes over the stubby tail. One of our convict artists, Thomas Watling (Rienits and Rienits, 1963), portrayed these and indeed the external anatomy, accurately and attractively about the year 1794.

Between the spines on the dorsum is a thick pélage of hair of which Hausman (1920) finds that there are all gradational states from the finest of hair on the venter to the largest and most robust of spines on the back. The hairs are flattened in shape as they are in *Ornithorhynchus*; Spencer and Sweet (1899), however, observed a singular feature in the muscles attached to the hairs and spines of *Tachyglossus*: the arrangement of the muscle bundles of the hairs and spines follows the usual course from the superficial part of the corium obliquely downwards to their attachments to the hair follicle group or to the spine follicle, but the muscle is striated and not smooth as it is in *Ornithorhynchus* and other mammals.

The limbs and ventral surface are free of spines but they are clothed with hair which ranges in colour from light brown to black in different specimens; and some echidnas taken around Canberra have a striking patch of white hair on the chest. All the hairs occur in bundles consisting of one stout principal hair surrounded by 8–10 hairs of lesser diameter—the Nebenhaare of Römer (1898). The central part of the ventral surface of both the males and the females is relatively free of hair and at the antero-lateral margins of this area are to be found two small hairy patches, the milk areolae.

Maurer (1892), de Meijere (1893), Römer (1898), and Spencer and Sweet (1899) are agreed, on morphological and embryological grounds, that the spines are modified hairs since both spines and hairs develop in the same way from thickenings in the epidermis of the pouch young, each thickening growing down into the dermis carrying the stratum germinativum before it. In this way a long downwards extension of tissue is achieved and, at the bottom of the downgrowth, a dermal papilla which projects upwards into the extension. The cells of the distal part of the papilla form the germinal point from which the anlage of the hair or spine grows upward through the mass of the extension. The tip of the dermal papilla cornifies and as growth at the germinal point proceeds the tip breaks the surface of the epidermis and acquires a black colour due to deposition of melanin. Each hair or spine in cross-section, at the appropriate level, consists of external and internal root sheaths, a keratinized cuticle, a cortex, and a central medulla, as they do in any other mammal. Hausman (1920), and Wildman and Manby (1938) have described the pattern of scales on the keratinized cuticle.

The Nebenhaare are formed by a process of budding off from the anlage of the principal hair and at this stage they could be taken for developing sebaceous glands (Römer, 1898). However, the latter form as outgrowths from the principal hair follicle at a later stage and they are identical with the sebaceous glands found in other mammals, consisting of a solid matrix of cells in which ill-defined cavities develop and communicate with a space around the hair. This space leads to the exterior and serves for the passage of the greasy secretion of the gland to the surface of the skin and hairs. The spines are not furnished with sebaceous glands, and sweat glands are not found in the skin of *Tachyglossus* except for a few in the pouch area (Gegenbaur, 1886; Pinkus, 1906).

The ear appears as an area on the side of the head where the spines are parted to show a hairy hole. In some echidnas a definite external pinna is present, in others it is inconspicuous. Tucker (1966) has shown that the pinna is quite large and is buried for the most part in a muscle which he calls the panniculus carnosus but which is really the platysma (see p. 83, Fig. 33).

The small beady eyes are situated almost at the base of the snout and they look forwards; echidnas are reputed to have poor eyesight. The elongated snout is naked and bears two nostrils at its anterior end on the dorsal surface. These external features are best seen in the young echidna (Fig. 1). The snout is sensitive, tactile, and strong enough to be used upon occasions to dig out scarab larvae from pastures and to crush them to make them suitable for ingestion through the small mouth.

The limbs are short and stout; the manus is broad and pentadactyl, the digits being armed with strong spatulate claws. The hind limb also bears five toes of which the claw on number 1 is short, that on number 2 is long, and is used as a grooming toe, which, owing to the outward torsion of the tibia and fibula and the almost horizontal disposition of the femur, can be inserted between the spines on almost any region of the body. The claw on number 3 is as long, or even longer, than that on number 2, while the claws on numbers 4 and 5 are quite short. On the inside of the ankle in all males and in some

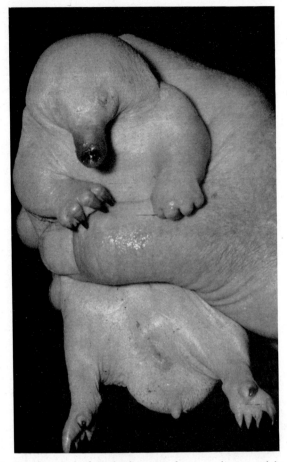

FIG. 1. Pouch young of *Tachyglossus aculeatus aculeatus*, weight 307 g, length 18·0 cm, showing nostrils at end of snout, cloacal aperture, stubby tail, and forwardly directed eyes (Griffiths, 1965b). (Reproduced from *Comp. Biochem. Physiol.*)

females is a hollow perforated spur 0·5–1·0 cm long from the base of which a duct leads up the leg to a gland buried among the muscles just below the knee. Jones (1923) says this is about the size of a pea, but we have found large glands about 2 cm in diameter in males taken during the breeding season. The spur and its glandular apparatus is not poisonous as it is in *Ornithorhynchus* at certain times of the year (see Calaby (1968) for a review of the subject).

There is only one hole for the passage of faeces, urine, and eggs (Fig. 1), hence the word monotreme, to distinguish platypuses and echidnas from other mammals; an inadequate criterion of distinction, I might say, since some dasyurid marsupials are cloacate and monotreme, and all marsupials are one-holed in the sense that the excretion and reproduction products pass out through the one sphincter. However, there are many references in the literature to Monotremata, so it looks as though we are stuck with it. There is no scrotum and the testes are internal.

The largest *T. aculeatus aculeatus* I have taken weighed 6·5 kg; Jones (1923) records that an "average" South Australian echidna was 400 mm long.

TAXONOMY

A classification of the mammals based on Simpson's (1945) and accepted by many zoologists is as follows:

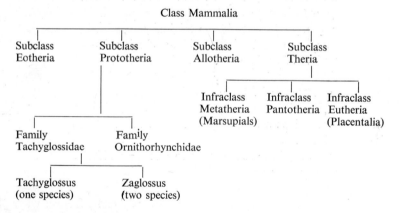

Gregory (1947) argues that the marsupials and the monotremes are closely related and should be grouped together as a subclass of the Mammalia—the Marsupionta. His views will be discussed later.

Tachyglossus aculeatus

The nominate race of the echidnas is *Tachyglossus aculeatus aculeatus* (Shaw) and there are five other subspecies, if one wishes to consider the Tasmanian echidna as a subspecies (Rothschild, 1913). Iredale and Troughton (1934) give it specific rank and, *inter alia*, give the authorities and synonymy of the Australian Tachyglossidae.

The various subspecies of *T. aculeatus*, their distinguishing characteristics, and their type localities are listed in Table 1.

The validity of those subspecies is not a matter of certainty since the numbers of animals examined have been small and since the characters used to distinguish the races—length of 3rd claw relative to the 2nd, hairiness, colour of hair, size of body and so on, are doubtless subject to variation within local populations. Four animals only were examined for the erection of *T. a. lawesii* (Ramsay, 1877), three for *T. a. ineptus* (Thomas, 1906) and nine for *T. a. acanthion* (Collett, 1885). Since then 15 echidnas (Tate, 1952) and a further three (Johnson 1964) have been examined critically and have been assigned to the subspecies *acanthion;* I have had the opportunity to examine one specimen of a West Australian echidna which agreed with Thomas's description of *T. a. ineptus. T. a. multiaculeatus* would appear to be a good subspecies since no variation was noted within the group of 30 specimens originally examined (Rothschild, 1905). Recently I examined 22 echidnas of this subspecies at Kangaroo Island and found no variation within the group save that only two had the light golden-coloured hair that Rothschild describes, the others had brown hair. I have no intention, however, of erecting a new species of *Tachyglossus* as Laurie (1952) did for *Zaglossus*, when she was given a brown specimen of *Z. bartoni bartoni*, which is usually black.

Thomas (1885) in an endeavour to test the validity of the subspecies of *T. aculeatus* examined nine Tasmanian, seven New South Wales, four Queensland, and two Papuan echidnas, and a few of doubtful origin. These specimens unfortunately came from a wide variety of localities and many of them lacked essential data (skins only); however, he arrived at the general conclusion that vagaries of soil and climate have modified the proportions of claws, snouts, and hair length of *Tachyglossus* at the extremes of its range. That conclusion did not prevent him, 21 years later, from describing *T. a. ineptus* on the basis of the dimensions of these same characters in three specimens.

In view of the fact that all specimens which have been examined taxonomically are the results of opportune collecting from widely

TABLE 1

Distinguishing characters and type localities of the subspecies of Tachyglossus aculeatus

Claw on 3rd digit elongated and as long as that on the 2nd digit		Claw on the 3rd digit short, less than half the length of that on the 2nd digit	
Subspecies	Type locality	Subspecies	Type locality
T. aculeatus aculeatus. Pélage on back relatively short, spines evident.	New Holland = Sydney, N.S.W.	*T. aculeatus multiaculeatus.* Profusion of long thin spines projecting well beyond a thick pélage.	Southern part of South Australia
T. aculeatus setosus. Pélage soft, thick, and woolly. Spines relatively few and obscured by pélage.	Tasmania	*T. aculeatus ineptus.* Long stout spines on back, no pélage of hairs on dorsum at all.	Southern Cross Western Australia
		T. aculeatus acanthion. Hairs or bristles on back very short and scarce, spines long and stout.	Rockhampton, Queensland
		T. aculeatus lawesii. Spines long and stout, pélage of brown hair well developed.	Port Moresby, Papua

E—B

separated localities, it is possible that the characters used for discrimination of subspecies vary clinally. For example, it is possible
that on mainland Australia hairiness increases gradually from north
to south. If this is so there would seem to be no point in using
trinomial nomenclature, but for physiologists interested in thermoregulation, for example, there is a point in using some way of speci-
fying whether or not the experimental animal had hair; at present
then it may be just as well to retain trinomial nomenclature.

Distribution of the subspecies of Tachyglossus aculeatus

Tachyglossus aculeatus setosus occurs throughout Tasmania and
one of the earliest records of echidnas was of this subspecies at
Adventure Bay (Tobin, 1792); it is also known to occur on King
Island and Flinders Island in Bass Strait to the north of Tasmania.
Three well-defined colour varieties are found on Flinders Island:
chocolate, brown, and a creamy off-white. "Aculeated anteaters"
were also taken by Matthew Flinders (1798) on nearby Cape Barren
Island.

T. a. aculeatus is found throughout Victoria, New South Wales,
and southern Queensland as far north as Munduberra (Tate, 1952).
This place is only 220 miles south of Coomooboolaroo where eight
of Collett's *T. a. acanthion* were collected by Lumholtz. Since Semon
(1894a) did much of his collecting in the Munduberra district and
since a hind limb of one of his specimens described by Hochstetter
(1896) is undoubtedly that of *acanthion*, it is possible that animals
with the characteristics of either or both subspecies occur there and
that some of the work of Semon and colleagues has been done on
acanthion. Collett's echidna is found as far north as Iron Range on
Cape York Peninsula (Tate, 1952) and it has been taken at Arnhem
Land and Groote Eylandt (Johnson, 1964) in the Northern Territory.
Echidnas occur in other parts of the Northern Territory including
the north coast and in desert country to the south. I have examined
three echidnas from these areas and found that they can be referred
to the subspecies *acanthion*.

According to Wood Jones (1923) *T. a. multiaculeatus* is found in
the far north of South Australia as well as in the southernmost parts
(Rothschild, 1905). Wood Jones records it on Kangaroo Island
which is only 8 miles from the mainland of South Australia. I have
found it to be abundant on that island, taking no less than six on
one day.

There is little information on the distribution of *T. a. ineptus*: apart from Thomas's specimens collected at Southern Cross, one specimen, already mentioned, has been taken at Maylands, a suburb of Perth, and echidnas have been observed in recent years at Mileura (p. 19), Port Hedland, and Woodstock, which were probably *ineptus*.

Mr. Hobart Van Deusen of the Archbold Expeditions of the American Museum of Natural History has very kindly given me his list of specimen records of *T. a. lawesii* in New Guinea; the localities are as follow:

Territory of Papua:

Lake Daviumbu (Middle Fly River)
Tarara (Wassi Kussa River)
Mabadavan (on the coast)
Dagwa (Oriomo River)
Mt. Leonard Murray
vicinity of Port Moresby
Rigo (Kemp Welch River)

Territory of New Guinea:

Kassam (Kratke Mountains)

It has also been taken at Apimuri in the Kratke Mountains (Laurie, 1952) and at Goroka (G. George, pers. comm., 1965).

T. a. lawesii appears to be common since it is offered for sale as food in the Port Moresby market at the rate of 15s. each (Garbi, pers. comm., 1965).

Zaglossus

This genus, which is restricted to the island of New Guinea and nearby Salawati Island, differs from *Tachyglossus* in that the snout is curved and is proportionately much longer; the distal part of the tongue is armed with spines and the body is longer and bigger; Rothschild (1913) records that a specimen of *Zaglossus bartoni bartoni* was 1000 mm long and Laurie (1952) states that a specimen of the same subspecies weighed 21·75 lb. The nominate race is *Z. bruijni bruijni* and Cabrera (1919) gives a synonymy and authorities for the genus. Thomas and Rothschild (1922) have revised the genus and the result of their labours is the following key:

1. Number of claws 3 or 4   2
   Number of claws 5   7
2. Head whitish; body dark   3
   Head dark like body   4
3. Black–brown; hair shorter, spines more
       exposed   *Z. bruijni bruijni*
   Yellowish-brown; hair longer, spines mostly
       concealed   *Z. bruijni pallidus*
4. Hair very long and thick, spines concealed   *Z. bruijni villosissimus*
   Hair sparse, spine much exposed   5
5. Spines and hair blackish   *Z. bruijni nigroaculeatus*
   Spines white or whitish   6
6. Spines on underside; smaller; claws slenderer   *Z. bruijni goodfellowii*
   No spines on underside; very large; claws
       large and heavy   *Z. bruijni gularis*
7. Skull longer, rostrum thicker   *Z. bartoni bartoni*
   Skull shorter, rostrum more slender   *Z. bartoni clunius*

The validity of the subspecies of the two species is again a matter of uncertainty, as it is in the case of the races of *Tachyglossus*, since the numbers of animals examined were small, the distinguishing characters are external anatomical features subject to variation, and in some cases the type localities are not certain; *Z. bruijni goodfellowi* would appear to be free of that stigma since it is the only echidna known to have spines on its ventral surface and it is geographically isolated on Salawati Island, West Irian.

Distribution of the species of Zaglossus

Zaglossus bruijni bruijni is known only at the type locality: the Arfak Mountains, West Irian. *Z. bruijni nigroaculeatus* was found at the Peninsula of Onin, West Irian; *Z. bruijni villosissimus* at Geelvink Bay, West Irian.

Z. bartoni bartoni was found originally at Mt. Victoria, Papua; it has since been found at the Bubu River district in N.E. New Guinea (Laurie, 1952). Van Deusen (pers. comm.) has records of *Zaglossus* taken from Lake Habbema in West Irian, from Telefomin, the headwaters of the Watut River, the Saruwaged Mountains in the Territory of New Guinea, and from various places in Papua as far east as Mt. Maneru. He has collected widely in Papua—New Guinea and he strongly suspects that when enough material is brought together in one place that it will be found that there is but one variable species of *Zaglossus*.

NATURAL HISTORY

Although echidnas have been known to biologists for upwards of 174 years, no one, with the exception of S. J. J. Davies (p. 19), has been able to carry out a planned study of their natural history since they are cryptic and for the most part uncommon (even Semon's (1899) best aborigine working with a dog could collect only 3–4 a day) and they apparently have no predictable habits and movement patterns that would facilitate their study. Consequently the little that is known about their natural history is the result of observations made during opportune encounters and made on captive animals. What was doubtless the first of those observations was published by Shaw (1792); he stated that his specimen had "been found in the midst of an anthill for which reason it was named by its first discoverers the ant-eating porcupine".

Echidnas move about at any time of the day or night, although Bennett (1860) and Semon found they were nocturnal; in hot weather they may well sleep all day and forage at night. Recently I took, at Kangaroo Island in September, 14 echidnas over a period of 6 days between the hours of 10 a.m. and 6.15 p.m.; a few months earlier, in the summer in central Queensland, three echidnas were taken at midnight fossicking in a Mitchell grass plain. Calaby (1966) observed, in a rainforest in northern New South Wales, echidnas abroad in daytime and at night.

Published data on what echidnas eat are few: Bennett records that they eat ants and ingest much dirt at the same time. Semon found that they eat a variety of small insects, principally ants and some earthworms. Jones (1923) thought that the staple diet of *T. a. multiaculeatus* was a small ant, *Camponotus nigrescens*. An account of some studies on the food of echidnas is given on p. 25 and since little is known of the subject the results are given in detail.

Echidnas appear even to be more uncommon than they are because of the inaccessible nature of the places they choose to hide in and because of their fantastic ability to dig vertically into the ground and cover their own backs with dirt when disturbed. Semon (1899) writes of echidnas being taken from self-made burrows and Johnson (1964) describes the extraction of two echidnas from the end of a burrow 8 in. high, 6 in. wide and at least 5 ft. long. On the rare occasions I have found echidnas buried they have been in a dish-shaped excavation at the base of a tree or a stump rather than in a

burrow as such; the excavations were camouflaged with leaves,
bark (Fig. 2) or even charcoal from a burnt stump.

In some localities, notably Kangaroo Island, echidnas are common,
even abundant and during October and November echidnas in the

FIG. 2. Echidna buried at foot of Eucalyptus tree in dense scrub at
Kangaroo Island.

Australian Capital Territory cease to be cryptic and invade the
suburbs of the city of Canberra. The reason for this is quite unknown
but it is of considerable help to us in planning our work to know
that a good supply of echidnas will be available at that time. In one
memorable week in October we took 19 echidnas from Canberra
gardens and streets in response to telephone calls from householders.

The animals were of various sizes and were nearly all males. Semon (1899) also found the anomalous sex ratio of 3 males to 1 female among the echidnas systematically tracked and caught by his aborigines; since the highest prices were paid for females it is probably true to say that the males greatly outnumbered the females in the population.

Habitats

The fact that *Tachyglossus aculeatus aculeatus* can live at sea-level near the coast of New South Wales, and that *Zaglossus bartoni bartoni* can live at an elevation of 8000 ft. in the mountains of New Guinea, is remarkable but one might expect that the genetic differences reflected in differences of anatomy would also be apparent as differences in physiology enabling each to live in its proper habitat. But *T. a. aculeatus* displays a singular virtuosity in its adaptation to different habitats. The echidnas observed by Calaby (1966) enjoyed a climate of hot moist summers and warm dry winters. The mean annual rainfall in parts of the area was 60 in. and in others 30 in. giving rise to a luxuriant growth of rainforest with a high tree density and a closed interlacing canopy. This contrasts with two other localities where echidnas live. One of these is Tero Creek, an arid plain favoured with intensely hot summers where day temperatures run as high as 112°F in the shade and frequently they are not much cooler in the nights; surface soil temperatures reach 132°F and the mean annual rainfall is 8 in. (during 1964 only 3 in. fell). The area has cool winters and severe frosts can occur. The stony and sandy soils support a meagre vegetation of various grasses, shrubs, and stunted trees. The other habitat of echidnas (Wimbush, pers. comm.) consists of ridges and valleys at an altitude of 5000–6000 ft. above sea-level in the Mt. Kosciusko area in the Australian Alps. The climate is severe, annual precipitation ranges from 70–90 in. and much of that is snow (Calaby and Wimbush, 1964). The mean temperature for the hottest month is between 50° and 55°F and the mean air temperatures for the three coldest months seldom rise above freezing. The vegetation is a heath community which has been described by Costin (1954).

The one factor common to all those habitats is the presence of ants. Termites occur at Tero Creek and in rainforest but not at 5000 ft. in the alps. Since ants and termites are about 70% water it would appear that echidnas could live anywhere that their prey could live and that just about covers the whole of Australia including the deserts. This versatility is no doubt also related to the echidna's homoiothermy and to its ability to hibernate.

Body temperature

Some temperatures recorded from the cloaca and from the abdominal cavity via a small incision in the body wall of freshly caught echidnas are quoted from Miklouho-Maclay (1883) and from Semon (1894a) in Table 2. These give an idea of the temperatures that might be expected in free-living echidnas in winter and early summer.

TABLE 2

Cloacal and abdominal temperatures of echidnas of various ages and sexes. Data of Miklouho-Maclay (1883) and Semon (1894a)

Animal	Cloacal temperature (°C)	Abdominal temperature taken through small cut in body wall (°C)	Air temperature (°C)	Time of year
Grown ♀	26·5	29·0	21·5	Sept. 15
Grown ♀	29·5	31·5	22·0	Sept. 16
Grown ♂	30·5		18·0	Aug. 2
Grown ♀	31·5		18·0	Sept. 28
Pouch young 90 mm long	31·0		24·0	Sept. 29
Pouch young 69 mm long	34·2		22·5	Sept. 29
Year-old ♀	34·0	36·0	31·5	Oct. 20
Unspecified		26·9	20·0	July 9

Wardlaw (1915) made detailed records of the temperatures of seven specimens of *T. a. aculeatus* studied at different seasons of the year, and found that in autumn, spring, and summer they showed a daily variation between morning and afternoon temperatures of about 3°C. This was also the amplitude of the variation of the morning and afternoon air temperatures, but the changes in echidna temperatures were not always in the same sense as those of the atmosphere. Outside the winter season the body temperatures were fairly constant (30–33°C); air temperatures from early spring to the middle

of summer varied from 13·8° to 36·8°C. This exhibition of homoiothermy is superior to the precarious thermoregulation of many
eutherian mammals such as the sloths and the prosimians; *Bradypus
tridactylus* has erratic thermoregulation and central temperature of
only 32·5°C at an ambient temperature of 22·6°C (Almeida and
Fialho, 1924), while the temperatures of lemurs and tarsiers may
vary continuously throughout the year from 18° to 35°C (Bourlière
and Petter-Rousseaux, 1953; Bourlière, Petter, and Petter-Rousseaux,
1956); *Cheirogaleus medius* is frankly poikilothermic for months on
end at ambient temperatures of 21–27°C. Members of other eutherian
orders display similar hypothermia and imperfect thermoregulation,
but despite this information the curious notion prevails that the
temperature regulation of echidnas represents a stage of quasi-
poikilothermy intermediate between the poikilothermy of reptiles
and the immaculate homoiothermy of eutherians and metatherians,
and that this has a bearing on phylogeny and the evolution of
homoiothermy. No doubt this stems from some experiments of
Martin (1903) and of Robinson (1954) which demonstrated that heat
regulation of *T. aculeatus* deteriorated at an ambient temperature of
35°C and above, whereas the regulation of a small selection of
Eutheria and Metatheria, which happened to possess good, functional, sweat glands, was superior under the same conditions. Since
Tachyglossus is furnished with very few sweat glands, of which
nothing is known about their functions, it might be better, if one
is interested in the phylogenetic implications, to compare the heat
tolerance of echidnas with those of eutherians that have few or no
sweat glands, such as the rodents *Spermophilopsis, Citellus, Sciurus,
Jaculus*, and the prosimian *Galago* (Chew, 1965). It would also be
very interesting to learn something of the heat tolerance of *Zaglossus*
which has many well-developed sweat glands distributed over its
body (Kolmer, 1929).

Martin's elegant studies established just how echidnas do regulate
their temperature; they do not pant and they have few sweat glands
so that evaporative cooling cannot be of prime importance, and they
apparently exhibit no vaso-motor adjustments aimed at heat loss
but they do regulate temperature by regulation of heat production.
The production of heat, as measured by the production of CO_2 is
proportional to the difference in temperature between the echidna
and the environment. Martin found that the percentage increases in
CO_2 production, when the difference in temperature between the

animal and the environment varies from 10° to 20°C, were as follow
for echidnas, marsupials, and eutherians:

>   Echidnas   72%
>   Marsupials (*Dasyurus, Trichosurus, Bettongia*) 50%
>   Eutherians (cat, rabbit)   16%

This shows that mechanisms other than heat production are used
in higher mammals for temperature regulation.

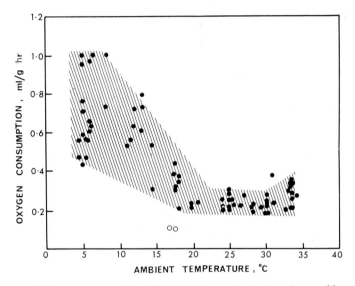

F<small>IG</small>. 3. Oxygen consumption of *Tachyglossus aculeatus* at various ambient
temperatures. Each point represents a 30-min. period. The two open circles
represent values from a hypothermic and apparently torpid animal. (From
Fig. 5, Schmidt-Nielsen, Dawson, and Crawford (1966), *J. Cell. Comp.
Physiol.* **67**, 67.)

Since those words were written, a study of temperature regulation
in three specimens of *Tachyglossus aculeatus* of unknown origin by
Schmidt-Nielsen, Dawson, and Crawford (1966) has come to hand.
They found, at an ambient temperature of 24°C, that the mean deep
temperatures recorded by thermocouples inserted into the intestine
were 30·0°, 31·1°, and 31·6°C. The range in a stable animal was
1·9°C and in the most variable was 4·1°C. In response to low ambient
temperatures the body temperatures were maintained in the usual

range of 29–32° and at 34°C, the highest ambient temperature to
which they were exposed, body temperature rose to and stabilized
at 3°C above ambient. One animal exposed to an ambient temperature of 5°C for 12 hr. exhibited a drop in temperature of 10°C over
that time and a great increase in oxygen consumption during the
first hour of exposure and maintained an elevated irregular rate of
O_2 consumption during the 12 hr. In spite of this increase in O_2
consumption the temperature continued to fall and even at the end

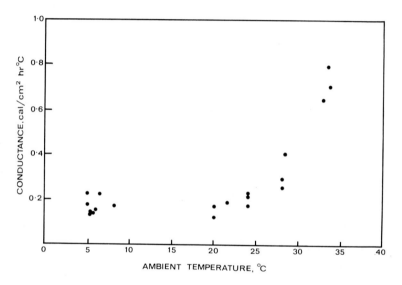

Fig. 4. Conductance of *Tachyglossus aculeatus* at various ambient temperatures. (From Fig. 6, Schmidt-Nielsen, Dawson, and Crawford (1966),
J. Cell. Comp. Physiol. **67**, 68.)

of the exposure when the body temperature had fallen to 21°C the
O_2 consumption was twice as high as the normal resting value at
31°C body temperature.

At a body temperature of 31·8°C the O_2 consumption of the
echidnas was 0·217 ml O_2/g hr. and at 5° higher it increased to
0·313 ml O_2/g hr. This gives a Q_{10} of 2·1 which is similar to the Q_{10}
values found for other mammals. Additional determinations of O_2
consumption over a range of 4–33°C were made. At thermoneutrality
the normal resting metabolic rate was found to be between 0·20 and

0·25 ml O_2/g hr and the lower critical temperature to be 20°C (Fig. 3). From those data it appears also that the metabolic rate at low temperatures is approximately linearly related to the temperature.

Schmidt-Nielson *et al.* also determined the rate of heat flow from the echidnas in terms of conductance. This is the rate of heat flow from the animal per degree temperature difference; the lower the conductance the more readily the animal can maintain its body heat; it is usually expressed as cal/cm² °C hr. At low ambient temperatures conductance is at a minimum presumably due to reduction of the peripheral circulation. The values for conductance of echidnas are given in Fig. 4. From this it is seen that the conductance at 20°C is 0·15 cal/cm² °C hr and no change in conductance was detected when the temperature was lowered to 5°C suggesting that vasoconstriction was already at a maximum at 20°C and that the rate of heat transfer could not be further reduced. Above 20°C there was a gradual increase in conductance and at 34°C conductance had increased to 0·7 cal/cm² °C hr and the 3°C core-ambient temperature difference was sufficient to dissipate the metabolic heat.

When the ambient temperature exceeds the body temperature the sole method left for dissipation of heat is evaporation. In the echidnas evaporation increased with increasing ambient temperature but an abrupt increase in evaporation exhibited by animals that can pant and sweat was not apparent. The evaporation that did occur in *Tachyglossus*, however, was useful and accounted for the dissipation of about a third of the metabolic heat production at 34°C.

The experiments of Schmidt-Nielson *et al.* offer no support for Martin's conclusion that echidnas cannot vary heat loss by vasomotor adjustments; there is agreement, however, that the principal mechanism of temperature regulation is variation in metabolic rate and Schmidt-Nielson's group has defined precisely the value of evaporative cooling. They conclude that if one extends the reasoning that mammals with low body temperature are "low" on the phyletic sense, "It follows that the chicken (40–41°C) should be placed above man." It seems more prudent to consider body temperature in the light of its meaning to an animal rather than to make it into a scale of evolutionary ascendancy where "high" implies "better".

The echidna's method of temperature regulation is trustworthy only up to 35°C. When exposed to higher temperatures the body temperature soon rises to 38°C and the echidna dies of heat apoplexy. This led Robinson (1954) to surmise that echidnas living in very hot climates would be inactive during the daytime and would probably retire to the equable climate of a burrow. Davies (pers. comm.) in a fascinating study of echidnas at Mileura on the Murchison River, Western Australia, found that that is exactly what they do. Mileura is favoured with an annual rainfall of about 9 in. and with air temperatures that vary from 32° to 111°F in the shade; echidnas live there in shallow caves in an area known as a breakaway. A breakaway consists of a hard lateritic cap overlying decomposed granite that erodes far more quickly than the laterite and as a result wind and water action forms caves and crevices of all sorts of shapes and sizes. In these caves Davies gathered literally pounds of echidna scats, indeed he swept the floors clean and in this way proved that echidnas used the caves continuously by subsequently house-cleaning for them now and again. Thermohygrograph readings recorded continuously inside a cave and at a distance from the caves in the shade in open air showed that the cave environment was greatly buffered compared with the changes in temperature and relative humidity that went on outside (Table 3). In addition to the information in the table it was noted that no diurnal temperature variation

TABLE 3

Temperature and relative humidity in caves inhabited by echidnas at Mileura, W.A., and temperature and relative humidity of the open air

15th day of month	Cave temperature (noon) (°F)	External temperature (°F)		Relative humidity (noon)	
		(Max.)	(Min.)	Cave	External
May	71	82	48	50	28
June	67·5	63	32	64	50
July	63	66	43	66	50
August	62	72	47	71	20
September	66	70	52	68	42
October	71	82	62	67	42
November	78	87	61	55	36
December	85	107	80	56	25
January	91	111	87	58	35
February	85	75	64 (cyclone)	72	60
March	88	101	80	67	32
April	80	100	70	60	46
May	73	78	60	57	44

was detectable but a steady change of only 2°F/week occurred and that the relative humidity did show a small diurnal variation of about 6%. From the caves the echidnas emerge to feed, and after rain when it is cool their diggings are particularly conspicuous. As Davies says "The echidna appears to have evolved a very satisfactory way of life in the Murchison. It has come to terms with the extremes of climate by avoiding them."

The echidnas observed by Davies were probably the virtually hairless variety, *T. aculeatus ineptus*, which would have imperfect insulation from extremes of heat and cold; it is possible that other echidnas, such as the Tasmanian species with its thick woolly pélage, can withstand the rigours of the environment by physiological, rather than by behavioural means (*vide* Bailey, 1951).

Hibernation

Echidnas hibernate like other mammals that have imperfect thermoregulation and hypothermia (*vide* Kayser's *dicta*, 1961). Lyman (1963) defines hibernators as warm-blooded animals "which abandon the warm-blooded state in an almost purposeful manner and sink into a torpor in which the body temperature approaches that of the protective cave or burrow". In the light of that definition echidnas qualify as hibernators since they become poikilothermic and torpid in winter and can go for a long time without food and water. Martin (1903) has recorded that his echidnas, kept in a shed in Melbourne, abandoned homoiothermy and became torpid, their body temperatures remaining only a few tenths of a degree above the ambient temperature. They maintained that condition during two successive winters from June to October, which, as the citizens of Sydney will attest, is the very best thing to do in a Melbourne winter.

Wardlaw (of Sydney) had occasion to observe hibernation in echidnas. It was found that homoiothermy was abandoned sporadically during the winter months, the animals becoming torpid for intervals of 2–10 days during which periods the temperatures of the echidnas remained only slightly higher than ambient. Wardlaw had the good fortune to observe echidnas entering and leaving hibernation and he found that the large falls in temperature heralding the onset of hibernation generally occurred between an afternoon observation of the temperature and the next morning observation; falls of temperature of 16–17°C occurred in this period of 20 hr.

Equally dramatic were the changes on arousal; on two occasions rises of 12° and 13·8°C took place in the short time of 4 hr. Coleman (1935, 1938) in her studies of a tame echidna recorded no temperatures but she found that it gave up eating for periods of up to 6 days. Over a period of 4 years of observations this echidna hibernated for 6 days in the 1st year, 117 days in the 2nd, 44 in the 3rd, and 29 in the 4th year.

Griffiths (1965a) found that two torpid echidnas abstained from food and water continuously for 64 and 72 days. The nitrogen excretion of those echidnas is discussed on p. 56.

Food and feeding habits

Shaw's echidna was found in the midst of an ant hill *ca.* 1790. In August 1962 Griffiths and Simpson (1966) found extensive diggings which had been made recently in a series of mounds of the meat ant, *Iridomyrmex detectus*. It was shown by opportune observations of free-living echidnas, and by planned observations of echidnas enclosed along with a meat-ant mound, that the diggings were indeed the work of echidnas. These mounds are roughly circular, domed, and vary in diameter from 1 to 6 ft and from 3 to 12 in. in height. A fair-sized mound has 10 to 20 openings each with a diameter of about 0·25 in., which lead into an extensive system of galleries and brood chambers which may extend downwards for more than 6 ft (Greaves, 1939). An area roughly half a mile by a quarter of a mile supported 193 of these colonies or mounds.

The climate of the area is for the most part mild, but severe frosts can occur in winter and occasionally temperatures rise to 95°F in the summer. Rain falls throughout the year but much of it falls in spring and summer and the average annual rainfall is about 30 in. Echidnas living in this reasonably equable climate attacked meat-ant mounds in late winter and spring only; the observations of echidnas actually burrowing into mounds were made in the springtime and all attacks took place in the afternoon between 3.50 p.m. and 5.15 p.m. The longest time taken in burrowing was 25 min. The process was actually one of feeding since faeces taken from these echidnas during the ensuing 2–3 days contained large quantities of *I. detectus* including a high proportion of winged forms (virgin queens and males).

The burrowing was different from the astonishing vertical subsidence usually exhibited by echidnas and involved a delving action

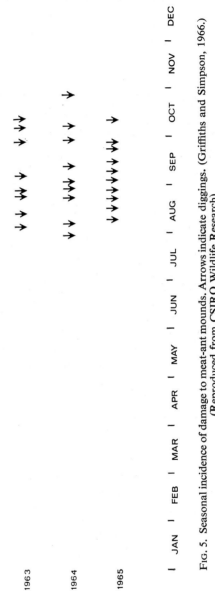

Fig. 5. Seasonal incidence of damage to meat-ant mounds. Arrows indicate diggings. (Griffiths and Simpson, 1966.) (Reproduced from CSIRO Wildlife Research).

of the forelimbs with the head and hunched shoulders directed into
the heart of the mound. From time to time the head would be withdrawn somewhat and then thrust back to the attack again. At the
end of feeding, one of the free-living echidnas gave a display of great
animation, rolling over, scratching furiously at his chest and abdomen
with the grooming toes to rid himself of tormenting ants.

The damage to the mounds was of three types: one was a small
conical hole 1–3 in. deep made by a thrust of the snout, another was
large, "echidna-sized", and characterized by a broad working face
conical towards the lowest region and ending in a snout hole. This
type of hole penetrates at least to the upper brood chambers. The
third type was a deep well-formed burrow shaped like a railway
tunnel with a flat floor and arched roof. These burrowings pene-
trated to the lower brood chambers and the greatest depth achieved
was 3 ft 6 in. As mentioned above, attacks on the mounds occur
only in late winter and spring of any year (Fig. 5). It should be
explained in connection with that figure that in 1962 much damage
was found during the period August–October but since it was not
possible to tell when the attacks commenced only the times of the
last attacks were indicated. Records of rainfall and temperature
showed no correlation with occurrence of attacks but it was noted
that 83% of all attacks, in 1963 for example, were made on the north
sides of the mounds which is the warm side in the southern hemisphere. Since the ants tend to move to this side of the mound in late
winter seeking warmth (T. Greaves, pers. comm.) some of the
mounds were opened from time to time to see what was going on.
It was found that before the onset of attacks the mounds contained many plump virgin queens as well as workers and males. The
queens appear in the deepest galleries at the beginning of winter
(Greaves) and they start to move towards the surface galleries in
early August; about the end of October they and the males swarm
and quit the mound for the nuptial flight. In 1965 (Fig. 6) virgin
queen and other castes were present in the surface galleries on
August 8 and the first echidna attacks were detected on August 15.
The last attacks took place on October 14, and on October 22 the
winged queens and males swarmed and left the mounds. Winged
virgin queens were not detected again until May 1966, and only in
small numbers in a few mounds.

Analysis of samples of the three castes of ants showed that total
lipids accounted for 47·2% of the dried weight of the virgin queens,

E—C

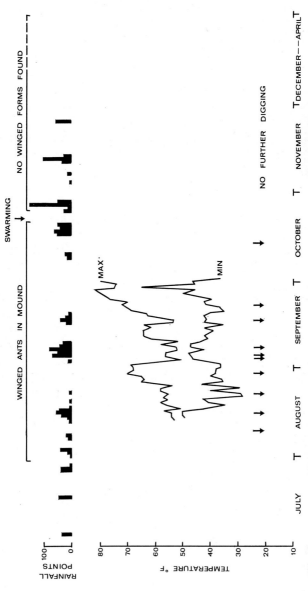

FIG. 6. Temperature changes, rainfall, incidence of winged forms of ants in the mounds, and incidence of echidnas feeding on meat ants during 1965 and 1966. Arrows indicate attacks on mounds. (Griffiths and Simpson, 1966.) (Reproduced from CSIRO Wildlife Research.)

9·6% of that of the males and 18·8% of that of the workers. In fact there was so much lipid of low melting point that the dried, ground up virgin queens looked wet all the time. Griffiths and Simpson concluded that echidnas attack meat-ant mounds only in the springtime because they want to feed on the virgin queens loaded with fat found there at that time. The mound would thus provide an energy-rich meal in a small accessible space at a time when the echidnas are probably emerging from hibernation. The fat content of the queens would be of peculiar importance to echidnas since Griffiths (1965a) found that carbohydrate, or an energy-rich proximate constituent of the diet, is limiting for growth in echidnas feeding on insects (termites).

The fact that echidnas in this part of Australia eat meat ants in the springtime does not mean that they are feeding solely on that species. Scats taken from echidnas at this time of the year exhibited the chitinous remains of many species of termites and ants (Table 4). Winged female and male ants of various species are found in scats throughout the year with the exception perhaps of November and January, thus an adequate supply of fat seems to be assured at most times.

For entomological analysis each scat was freed from dirt and sand by floating off the chitinous parts of the insects in water and collecting them by filtration. They were then suspended in alcohol. The relative proportions of ants to termites were determined by counting, along random transects, identifiable parts in thinly spread aliquots of each suspension. Twenty-seven out of 43 scats examined contained 80% or more ants and 19 of them contained ants only. On the other hand, no scat contained 100% termites and only 3 out of the 43 contained 80% or more termites. It would appear that *T. a. aculeatus* in the southern tablelands is principally an anteater.

The frequencies of occurrence of the species of termites eaten appear to be in proportion to their relative accessibility to the echidna. *Nasutitermes exitiosus* is an extremely common termite, while *Heterotermes ferox* and the two species of *Coptotermes* may not be common but because of their nesting habits they are much less accessible; thus *N. exitiosus* was found in 46% of the scats, *H. ferox* in 12% and *C. lacteus* also in 12% of them, while *C. frenchi* and *Amitermes neogermanus* were found once only.

As well as ants and termites, the occasional odd item turns up in echidna scats and stomachs; Semon (1899) found that Queensland

TABLE 4

The ants and termites found in faeces of Tachyglossus a. aculeatus taken in the southern tablelands of N.S.W. November 1963–November 1965

Month	Ants—Hymenoptera: Formicoidea		Termites—Isoptera		
	%	Species	Presence of winged forms	%	Species
January	80	Camponotus sp.,* Rhytidoponera metallica	Nil	20	Nasutitermes exitiosus
	61	Iridomyrmex sp.	Nil	39	Nasutitermes exitiosus
March	100	Camponotus sp.	Present	0	
	100	Iridomyrmex gracilis,* Camponotus clavipes	Present	0	
	100	Camponotus sp.,* Iridomyrmex sp., Rhytidoponera metallica	Present	0	
April	100	Iridomyrmex detectus	Nil	0	
	44	Pheidole sp.	Nil	56	Nasutitermes exitiosus
May	82	Iridomyrmex sp.,* Camponotus sp.	Present	18	Nasutitermes exitiosus
	100	Iridomyrmex rufoniger,* Iridomyrmex sp.,* Rhytidoponera metallica	Nil	0	
June	24	Aphaenogaster longiceps,* Iridomyrmex sp., Pheidole sp.	Nil	76	Heterotermes ferox, Nasutitermes exitiosus
August	100	Camponotus sp.	Present	0	
	100	Camponotus intrepidus,* Iridomyrmex rufoniger*	Present	0	
	100	Iridomyrmex sp.	Present	0	
	31	Camponotus sp.,* Pheidole sp., Rhytidoponera metallica	Present	69	Nasutitermes exitiosus, Coptotermes lacteus
	90	Iridomyrmex detectus	Present	10	Nasutitermes exitiosus
	56	Camponotus sp.,* Iridomyrmex sp., Rhytidoponera metallica	Present	44	Coptotermes frenchi
	46	Camponotus sp.,* Amblyopone sp.*	Nil	54	Heterotermes ferox, Amitermes xylophagus

Month	Ants present				Termites present
September	Iridomyrmex detectus,* Rhytidoponera metallica	100	Present	0	Coptotermes lacteus
	Iridomyrmex sp.,* Rhytidoponera metallica	15	Present	85	Nasutitermes exitiosus
October	Iridomyrmex nitidiceps,* unknown sp.	95	Nil	5	Nasutitermes exitiosus
	Unidentifiable	100	Present	0	Nasutitermes exitiosus, Coptotermes lacteus
	Iridomyrmex sp.,* Iridomyrmex darwinianus,* Rhytidoponera metallica, Pheidole sp.	40	Present	60	Nasutitermes exitiosus
	Iridomyrmex spp.,* Camponotus consobrinus, Rhytidoponera metallica	13	Present	87	Nasutitermes exitiosus
	Iridomyrmex spp.,* Rhytidoponera metallica, Camponotus sp., Melophorus sp.	96	Nil	4	Nasutitermes exitiosus
	Iridomyrmex darwinianus	30	Nil	70	Nasutitermes exitiosus
	Iridomyrmex sp.	100	Present	0	Amitermes xylophagus, Nasutitermes exitiosus
	Iridomyrmex sp.	89	Present	11	
November	Monomorium rubriceps	100	Present	0	Heterotermes ferox
	Iridomyrmex sp.	62	Present	38	Nasutitermes exitiosus
	Iridomyrmex sp.	74	Present	26	Nasutitermes exitiosus
	Polyrhachis femorata	100	Nil	0	Heterotermes ferox
	Iridomyrmex detectus,* Melophorus sp.	62	Nil	38	Heterotermes ferox, Nasutitermes exitiosus
	Iridomyrmex sp.	100	Nil	0	
	Iridomyrmex sp.,* Rhytidoponera metallica	77	Nil	23	
	Iridomyrmex sp.,* Rhytidoponera metallica, Pheidole sp.	100	Nil	0	
	Iridomyrmex rufoniger	80	Nil	20	
December	Iridomyrmex sp.,* Rhytidoponera metallica	100	Nil	0	Nasutitermes exitiosus, Coptotermes lacteus
	Iridomyrmex detectus,* Iridomyrmex sp.	100	Present	0	Nasutitermes exitiosus, Coptotermes lacteus
	Polyrhachis sp.	20	Nil	80	
	Iridomyrmex sp.	100	Nil	0	
	Iridomyrmex detectus,* Iridomyrmex sp.	81	Present	19	

* The species denoted by an asterisk account for more than 50% of the ants present.

echidnas sometimes ate earthworms and small beetles; parts of Orthoptera, and larvae of the cossid moth, *Xyleutes,* have been encountered. The latter are upwards of 3 in. long and as thick as a little finger; very likely they were crushed to a suitable consistency with the snout before ingestion. This is certainly their technique in handling thick scarab larvae found in pastures; the snout is thrust with a vigorous cork-screw action into the soft soil and the larva, presumably located by sense of smell, is squashed at the bottom of the hole made by the snout and it is then licked out by the tongue. Coleman (1935) observed similar behaviour in her tame echidna when it ingested beetle larvae.

Some echidnas appear to be indifferent to the presence of an observer and will obligingly range and feed for long intervals of time. When on the march for food the echidna has a busy inquisitive air sniffing and poking here and there with its snout (see p. 94) and suddenly it will dart from the line of march and dig rapidly removing stones if necessary with claws and snout and will lick up the exposed ants or termites as the case may be; the whole performance has an air of more than a little ferocity. A feeding ground used frequently by echidnas has the look of an area torn up by feral pigs (Fig. 7).

Unlike the southern tablelands echidna, the West Australian numbat, *Myrmecobius fasciatus,* otherwise known as the marsupial anteater, is principally a termite eater (Calaby, 1960). It is entirely possible, however, that echidnas elsewhere may have different food preferences and may eat far more termites than ants; the one scat of a Western Australian echidna that I have studied consisted of 93 % *N. exitiosus.*

Movements

In the previous section it was claimed that echidnas stop feeding on meat ants when the virgin queens leave the mounds but it could be argued that the echidnas also leave the area at that time and return in late spring, and that if they were in the area in summer they might well attack the mounds and eat worker meat ants. However, from evidence of the movements of some echidnas that were released in the study area, this is unlikely. Eleven echidnas collected from various parts of the Australian Capital Territory were identified by means of a numbered metal band clamped around a back leg and were let loose in the study area on the following dates: one on September 14, 1964, one on October 21, 1964, six on November 11, 1964, one on July 21, 1965, and two on August 31, 1965. Four of these were apprehended in the study area 350, 346, 40, and 28 days after release (Table 5). In spite of the fact that six echidnas were released on November 11, 1964, and the banding evidence indicates

FIG. 7. Feeding ground, riddled with nests of ants, much used by echidnas. Kangaroo Island.

that at least two of them would have stayed in the area until late December 1964, no meat-ant mounds were attacked until August 1965.

These banding returns and the fact that meat-ant mounds are visited in a definite area at a definite time year after year suggest that echidnas actually live for long periods in or near a given area. The results from further banding work tend to support that notion but there are exceptions; the results of the banding programme that have come to hand so far are summarized in Table 5. In addition to the 11 released at Mount Tidbinbilla 17 banded echidnas of various weights and from various places were released at Mt. Majura, a region of dry sclerophyll eucalyptus forest known to harbour echidnas. To date, three echidnas have been retaken, 240, 475 and 509 days after release in the same area. The one taken 509 days after release originally came from Mt. Majura.

Another series of releases were made at Gungahlin, situated about 3 miles from Mt. Majura, in cleared pastoral country; 34 animals were released here and of these 9 have been recaptured at intervals of 5–830 days after release and at distances of 0·5–11 miles away from the point of release. It should be explained that 7 of the re-captured echidnas had headed south to the city and had been cap-tured by townspeople; one eluded capture for 300 days and had probably been living in a nearby belt of sclerophyll eucalyptus forest. The eighth recapture, No. 28010, was noteworthy in that the echidna had been caught at a ranger's cottage on Mt. Majura and had been taken by a circuitous route through Canberra to Gungahlin, where it was banded and released; within 7 days it was recaptured back at the ranger's cottage, covering in that time at least 3·4 miles.

Doubtless many of the missing 25 echidnas headed north into sparsely populated rural country and have thus eluded capture. The fact that seven of the Gungahlin releases were found in the city area is not to be discounted as unnatural since echidnas invade the city from time to time as has already been noted. Nearly all of the banded animals that headed into the city were sub-adults, but seven of the total number released at Gungahlin were as big or were bigger than those recaptured at Mt. Tidbinbilla. Since none of these, with the exception of No. 26902, have been retaken near Gungahlin, despite the alertness of over 80 CSIRO staff located there, it suggests that the country around Gungahlin is simply unsuitable for echidnas and that they all moved out of the area with the exception of No. 26902.

On the whole the data indicate that when an habitat is suitable an echidna will stay put when released there, no matter how far it is from its usual home area; if it is not suitable the echidna will travel and try to find a congenial "Lebensraum".

Just how No. 28010 managed to return to where it was caught originally is a matter for conjecture; it may have homed or it simply

TABLE 5

Movements and body weight changes of echidnas banded and released at three different localities in the Australian Capital Territory

Place of release	Sex	Initial body wt. (g)	Number	Distance between point of release and point of recapture (miles)	Time interval between release and recapture (days)	Body wt. at time of recapture (g)	Change in body wt. (g)
Mt. Tidbinbilla	♂	—		0·5	350	5877	—
	♂	4200		Practically nil	346	4000	−200
	♀	3875		Practically nil	40	Not read	—
	♂	4075		Practically nil	22	3500	
				Practically nil	28 (recaptured 6 days later)	3425	−650
Mt. Majura	♀	4025		0·4	509	5000	+975
	♀	2850		Practically nil	240	3550	+700
	♀	3450		0·3	475	3250	−200
Gungahlin	?	1200	26901	1·5	5	1159	−41
	♂	2260	26902	0·5	39	2780	+520
	♂	1503	26906	1·4	5	1423	−80
	♀	1660	26910	1·0	27	1817	+157
	♂	1910	28005	11·0	148	1590	−320
	♂	1325	28024	1·5	5	1325	nil
	♂	1600	28025	2·0	300	1425	−175
	♂	1925	28010	3·4	7	2025	+100
	♀	2670	28007	1·3	830	3750	+1080

arrived there by chance, but in view of an experience described by Semon (1899) I incline to the view that echidnas have a well-developed "Ortsinn": one of Semon's blacks caught an echidna and carried it four miles back to camp enclosed in a sack, but during the night it broke out and decamped. On the following morning one of the blacks followed its tracks which led straight back to where it had been caught the day before, and where "the creature was found peacefully slumbering in its self-dug burrow".

The elapsed time between release and recapture and the distance travelled in that time (Table 5) give no idea of the rate of travel of echidnas; however, in one instance an echidna released at Gungahlin was followed at a discreet distance in a motor vehicle the milometer of which had been calibrated; the echidna travelled 0·8 mile in 1·75 hr and during that time it fed thrice and it was still moving smartly when the observations were called off. It is clear then that an echidna can travel quite long distances in a short time in search of a proper habitat.

Parasites

A list of the internal parasites of Australian mammals has been published by Mackerras (1958) and from this it is established that *Tachyglossus* harbours one sporozoan, *Theileria tachyglossi* (Priestley, 1915) which occurs in the blood; two cestodes which were found in the intestines, *Taenia echidnae* (= *Linstowia echidnae*) (Thompson, 1893; Zschokke, 1899), and *Cittotaenia tachyglossi* (Johnston, 1913) and two intestinal nematodes, *Nicollina tachyglossi* and *N. echidnae* (Baylis, 1930). Recently two more endoparasites have been reported: *Dipetalonema* sp., a new species of filarian nematode found in the subcutaneous tissues (Mackerras, 1962) and a new piroplasmid sporozoan (Backhouse and Bolliger, 1959) which occurs in the red cells of the blood. The multiplication of this parasite is by budding to form 8 daughter-cells; although the parasitaemia is usually low it can rise to high levels and in some animals 90% of the red cells are infected.

Tachyglossus also carries a number of ectoparasites including fleas, ticks, and mites. Authorities and synonymy for four of the fleas, *Echidnophaga ambulans ambulans*, *E. ambulans inepta*, *E. gallinacea*, *E. liopus*, are given by Hopkins and Rothschild (1953). Of these, *E. liopus* has been recorded from echidnas only and the other fleas mentioned have been found on various animals. *Bradio-psylla echidnae* (Jordan and Rothschild, 1922), another flea, has been taken from *Tachyglossus* in Tasmania, Victoria, and New South Wales; it has also been found on a marsupial, but there is no doubt that its proper host is the echidna.

Eight species of ticks (Acarina : Ixodidae) have been found on *Tachyglossus*: *Haemaphysalis humerosa, Aponomma concolor, Ap. tachyglossi, Ap. undatum, Amblyomma papuanum, Amb. australiense, Amb. echidnae,* and *Amb. moyi.*

Roberts (1963, 1964) gives the detailed taxonomy of these genera; of the eight species listed here, *Ap. tachyglossi, Amb. papuanum, Amb. australiense, Amb. echidnae,* and *Amb. moyi* have not been found on any animal other than echidnas.[1] A species of tick, *Ixodes zaglossi,* has been found on *Zaglossus bruijni* (Kohls, 1960).

Lice have not been detected on echidnas but a species of mite, *Mesolaelaps australiense* is found on *T. aculeatus acanthion* (Domrow, 1962) but it also occurs on many other mammals.

---

[1] Another species of tick, *Ixodes tasmani* occurs on a number of mammals, including *Tachyglossus a. setosus,* in Tasmania (Roberts, 1964, Rec. Q. Vic. Mus. Launceston). *Aponomma oudemansi* has been found on *Zaglossus.*

CHAPTER 2

INTAKE OF FOOD, DIGESTION, AND BODILY FUNCTIONS

INTAKE OF FOOD

The insect prey is picked up by the sticky tongue and transferred to the back of the buccal cavity where it is comminuted to a paste-like consistency by the grinding action of a set of spines at the base of the tongue against sets of transversely arranged spines on the palate (Home, 1802; Griffiths, 1965a). The tongue is absolutely necessary for the existence of the echidna for without it there is no other way it could catch and ingest its food. The muscles that bring about the grinding of the food have been described by Duvernoy (1830) and by Fewkes (1877). In cross-section (Fig. 8) the tongue is seen to contain two longitudinal cylindrical muscles which extend from their insertions at the sternum, right through the base of the tongue, to a point about one-third of the length from the tip. The two cylindrical muscles are the m. sterno-glossi which really consist of two muscles each: the m. sterno-glossus superior and the m. sterno-glossus inferior; both arise on the underside of the sternum and pass forward to unite to form the cylindrical muscle of each side of the tongue. Surrounding the two cylindrical longitudinal muscles inside the tongue are loose sheaths of circular muscles (Oppel, 1900). Since the base of the tongue is fixed, the contraction of these circular muscles deforms the longitudinal muscles so that they squirt forward and thus the tongue is extruded. The circular musculature does not contract uniformly along the tongue since high speed cinematography shows that definite annuli appear at intervals along the tongue during the extrusion phase, indicating that portions of the musculature contract more than neighbouring portions. Retraction is brought about by the relaxation of the circular muscles and the contraction of the sterno-glossi.

Outside the pharynx at a position just posterior to where the m. sterno-glossi enter the base of the tongue, those two muscles and

34

the posterior half of the tongue are covered by a series of transverse flat muscles. The superficial muscle of this series is the m. depressor mandibulae anterior (Schulman, 1906); this is very thin and arises from the raphe in the middle line, midway between the rami of the lower jaw, while the lateral portions are inserted into the maxillae. Beneath the superficial muscle is a larger, stronger muscle, the m. myloglossus (= mylohyoideus of Duvernoy and Schulman). This also arises from a common raphe with its fellow of the opposite side along the mid-line of the throat together with a deeper layer—the

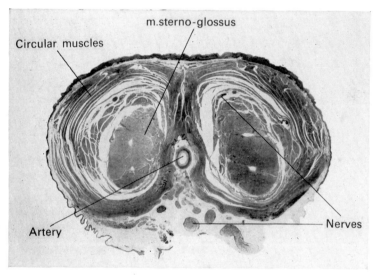

Fig. 8. Cross-section of proximal region of the tongue of *Tachyglossus a. aculeatus*. Heidenhain's iron haematoxylin. ×6·1.

m. annulus inferior. The m. myloglossus is inserted on the underside of the skull. The m. annulus inferior passes over the m. sterno-glossus of each side and is inserted by a strong attachment which also forms the back of the tongue. The contraction of all three of these transverse muscles presses the base of the tongue against the roof of the mouth.

A fourth transversely arranged muscle lies posterior to the myloglossal muscle. This is the m. stylo-glossus. Its origin is the stylo-hyal cartilage at its proximal end, just posterior to the ear tube. It forms with its fellow of the opposite side a loop which extends to its insertion in the median raphe. Contraction of this muscle can also press the base of the tongue against the roof of the mouth but it also has a posteriorly directed component combined with that of the sterno-glossi. This posterior pull is opposed by two m. genio-glossi (Fig. 9) which pull the base of the tongue forwards. The alternate

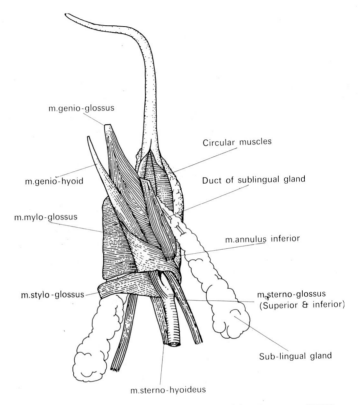

FIG. 9. Dissection of musculature of tongue. After Duvernoy (1830).

contraction of these two opposed sets of muscles produces the grinding action of the base of the tongue pressed against the roof of the mouth.

At the region which lies about one-third of the length of the tongue from the tip, the circular muscles are progressively replaced by radially arranged muscles which invade the sterno-glossi. The origins of the radial muscles are in the dermal layer found beneath the stratified epithelium of the tongue and their insertions are either in the form of median raphes or of connective tissue sheaths around the central bundle of blood vessels and nerves (Fig. 10). Thus the sterno-glossi near the tip are subdivided into 6–8 smaller longitudinal muscles. These, along with the radially arranged musculature, give extraordinary mobility to the anterior part of the tongue, endowing

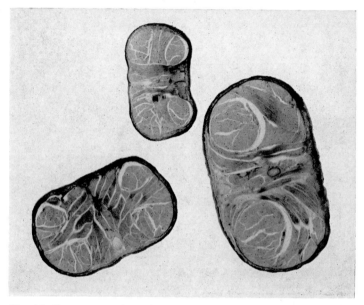

Fig. 10. Transverse sections of tongue at three different levels from the tip, showing progressive replacement of circular muscles by radially arranged muscles. Heidenhain's iron haematoxylin. ×9·8.

it with the ability to dart right and left, up and down, in pursuit of rapidly moving insects.

The tongue is covered by the usual stratified squamous epithelium which is thickest on the dorsal surface. Beneath the stratum germina-tivum of this epithelium is a layer of loosely arranged connective tissue; in between the two sterno-glossi, blood vessels and nerves pass from one end of the tongue to the other. At the hind end of the tongue in the mid-line just posterior to the spiny protuberance, two slits, forming a V, are found. These lead into deeply seated circum-vallate papillae (Fig. 11) in the trenches of which taste buds are found (Oppel, 1899). Large, well-developed glands of von Ebner discharge into the trenches around the papillae. It must be emphasized here that circumvallate papillae occur only in the tongues of mammals. As well as these papillae sets of papillae foliatae are found laterally and posterior to the horny protuberance; these are also equipped with taste buds but the foliate papilla is much smaller than the circumvallate type. All these sets of taste organs are situated

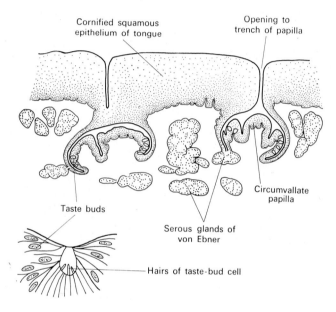

FIG. 11. Section of circumvallate papillae situated below the dorsal surface of epithelium of the tongue. After Oppel (1899).

precisely where they would receive a maximal stimulus, i.e. where the insect prey is crushed and homogenized.

The enormous tongue of *Zaglossus bruijni* has been described by Kolmer (1925) and from his account it is apparent that the organization of the muscles and the keratinous grinding apparatus are similar to those in *Tachyglossus*. The end of the tongue in *Zaglossus* is different in that it bears several rows of regularly arranged horny teeth which are directed backwards. It is also different in that the circumvallate papillae are situated at the surface of the tongue, not at the bottom of two slits in the epithelium as in the *Tachyglossus* tongue.

DIGESTION

In the buccal cavity the ground-up insects are permeated with saliva secreted by the sublingual, submaxillary, and parotid salivary glands. For some strange reason Owen (1847) failed to find the

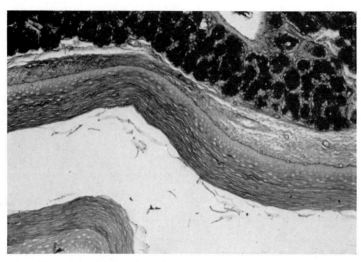

FIG. 12. Longitudinal section through portion of the alimentary canal showing the strongly stained Brunner's glands and the non-glandular stratified epithelium which is typical of the whole stomach lining. Periodic acid-Schiff stain. (Griffiths, 1965a.) ×102. (Reproduced from *Comp. Biochem. Physiol.*)

parotid glands, and called the sublingual the submaxillary gland. All three sets of glands have well-defined ducts (Hochstetter, 1896) opening into the buccal cavity, but the ducts of the sublingual glands are particularly noteworthy. Each gland is lobulated, roughly triangular in shape, and narrowest at the anterior extremity from which a large duct emerges and passes forwards to the interspace between the lower jaws (Owen, 1847). Here each duct divides into 8–10 branches which subdivide into branchlets and communicate with the buccal cavity by numerous openings situated along the greater part of the floor of the mouth. This affords an efficient method of lubricating the long tongue with the sticky mucus-like secretion so that the insect prey adhere to it. This is an extraordinarily effective method of ingesting food and a fair-sized echidna of about 3 kg weight can ingest 200 g wet weight of termites, enough to maintain growth if the echidna is kept in the laboratory, in a matter

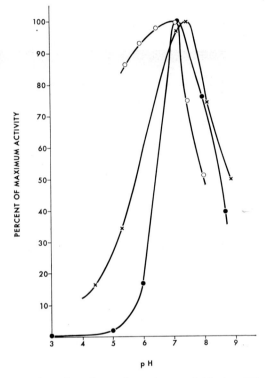

FIG. 13. pH Optima of amylase and proteinase activities in echidna succus entericus and of amylase activity in termite extract. O—O, Termite amylase. X——X, Amylase of succus entericus. ●——●, Proteinase of succus entericus. (Griffiths, 1965a.) (Reproduced from *Comp. Biochem. Physiol.*)

of 10 min; the distensible stomach accommodates a meal like this with ease. The whole inner surface of the stomach is lined with a stratified cornified epithelium (Oppel, 1896a) and there are no glands, fundic, cardiac, pyloric, or otherwise (Fig. 12); the pH of the stomach lining is about 7·3 and the pH of the stomach contents 2–4 hr after ingestion of a meal of termites (*Nasutitermes exitiosus*) does not fall below 6·2. The stomach lining has no intrinsic digestive enzyme activity, but the saliva contains an α amylase active at neutral pH so that doubtless the enzyme is active in the stomach, degrading glycogen in the homogenized insects permeated with saliva, to carbohydrates of low molecular weight. The termites themselves also have amylase activity with an optimum close to the pH of the stomach contents (Fig. 13); a circumstance that would also contribute to digestion of carbohydrate of high molecular weight.

The absence of glands from the echidna stomach would appear to be a monotreme specialization since the stomach of *Ornithorhynchus* is also lined with cornified stratified epithelium (Oppel, 1896a), but at least two other insectivorous mammals, *Onychomys torridus* (Horner, Taylor, and Padykula, 1965) and *Manis javanica* (Oppel, 1896b) have stomachs that are almost completely lined with cornified stratified epithelium, with the exception of a pouch of typical gastric tissue which communicates with the rest of the stomach through a small orifice. The stratified epithelium in the stomachs of all those animals could be an adaptation for the handling of rough insects interlarded with much dirt—the ratio of dirt to insects, by volume, in the scats of echidnas living in the southern tablelands was found to be 2:5. Horner *et al.* noted that *Onychomys* ate much dirt and Calaby (1960) also observed that the scats of *Myrmecobius fasciatus* contained a large proportion of sand and dirt, but *Myrmecobius* has no stratified epithelium whatever in its stomach (Griffiths, unpubl.), the stomach lining consisting of the usual fundic, cardiac, and pyloric glandular tissues. A stomach lining of cornified stratified epithelium is therefore not mandatory in insectivorous mammals ingesting dirt along with their insects, but it probably contributes to a more effective comminution of the hard insects—the grinding action of the dirt no doubt assisting greatly to that end.

The non-glandular epithelium of the stomach continues without interruption by a pylorus into a relatively narrow tube which corresponds in position to the duodenum in eutherian mammals. At this region a prominent set of Brunner's glands, situated between the stratified epithelium and the muscular layers, opens by a series of ducts into the pseudo-duodenum. At the posterior margin of the glands the stratified epithelium is replaced by numerous finger-like villi clothed by a columnar epithelium, many of the cells of which contain 1,2-glycol linkages which stain strongly with Schiff's reagent. This is the epithelium of the small intestine which, in an echidna of 3000 g body weight, is 11 ft long. The epithelium of the small intestine presents a uniform histology from the stomach to its union with the large intestine and rectum, and it is organized into typical glands of Lieberkühn (Oppel, 1897); the distal portions of the villi are covered with a simple columnar epithelium, the central parts of the gland are covered with goblet cells loaded with mucigens —the indian-club shaped bodies seen in Fig. 14, and the deeper parts of the gland or the crypts contain Paneth cells loaded with secretion granules.

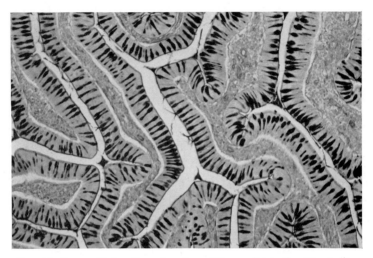

FIG. 14. Parasagittal section of portion of the small intestine. The Indian club shapes indicate goblet cells loaded with 1,2-glycol linkages. Periodic acid-Schiff stain. (Griffiths, 1965a.) ×117. (Reproduced from *Comp. Biochem. Physiol.*)

A small caecum, apparently an appendix (Diener and Ealey, 1965) about 1 in. in length, marks the commencement of the large intestine leading into the rectum which terminates at the cloaca. The length of the large intestine + rectum is approximately 16 in. The histology of the large intestine is similar to that of the small intestine, except that there are but few Paneth cells in the crypts of Lieberkühn.

The two great appendages of the gut, the liver, and the pancreas pour their secretions into ducts which combine, near their entrance into the small intestine, into a common pancreatic and bile duct that enters the small intestine at a point 10–11 mm posterior to the end of the pseudo-duodenum. Internally both the pancreatic and bile ducts are seen to be convoluted (Fig. 15) and, at the point of entrance of the combined duct into the intestine, a ring of glands, giving a positive reaction to Schiff reagent and identical with Brunner's glands, also opens into the small intestine. As far as I know these glands have not been noted before (Griffiths, 1965a).

The bile passed into the intestine contains bile salts which promote

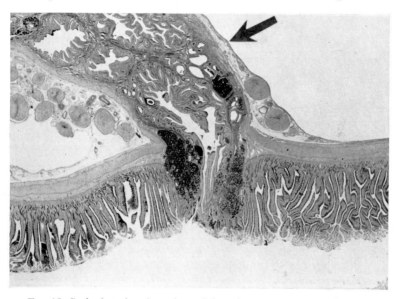

FIG. 15. Sagittal section through small intestine and portion of the combined pancreatic and bile duct. The mucigenous glands which discharge into the small intestine may be seen at the junction of the duct and small intestine. Ligation of the duct was carried out at the position indicated. Periodic acid-Schiff stain. (Griffiths, 1965a.) ×9·3. (Reproduced from *Comp. Biochem. Physiol.*)

digestion of fat by emulsification of triglycerides to form small droplets thereby increasing several-fold the surface exposed to the action of lipases. The bile salts have a hydrotropic effect on the fatty acids liberated by lipase and they also unite in the intestine with the fatty acids to form complex compounds which pass readily into the columnar cells of the intestinal villi. In the Eutheria the bile salts are principally the sodium salts of taurocholic and glycocholic acids; smaller amounts of bile salts formed from other C_{24} acids—deoxycholic and chenodeoxycholic—conjugated with taurine and glycine, also occur. In the bile of Carnivora taurocholic acid prevails; in rabbits, hares, and pigs, glycocholic acid is present almost exclusively; in ox bile sometimes taurocholate is in excess, sometimes glycocholate. However, in the bile of the marsupials so far examined and in that of monotremes, salts of C_{24} acids conjugated with glycine have not been detected (Bridgwater, Haslewood, and Tammar, 1962). Sodium taurocholate is the bile salt of *Tachyglossus* and *Ornithorhynchus* but it is accompanied by a trace of taurodeoxycholate in the latter (Bridgwater *et al.*).

The mucosa of the small intestine of *Tachyglossus* contains a number of disaccharidases (Kerry and Messer, unpubl.). These authors have very kindly allowed me to quote their results summarized in Table 6. From these data it is apparent that adult echidna intestine has maltase and isomaltase activities, very low lactase, cellobiase, and sucrase, but high trehalase activities. The latter observation is of particular interest since trehalose—a disaccharide containing two molecules of glucose—is physiologically important to insects and indeed it constitutes their principal blood sugar (Gilmour, 1965); thus the elaboration of an enzyme by the echidna intestine for the hydrolysis of that sugar is a necessity if all the carbohydrate in the diet is to be assimilated.

TABLE 6

Disaccharidase activity of intestinal mucosa in various mammals. Activity is expressed as μ moles of substrate hydrolysed/min/g wet weight of mucosa

	Tachyglossus (one adult animal)	Man (baby)	Ferret (adult)	Cat (adult)	Sheep (adult)
Maltase	3·3	9·5–28·0	14·0	20·0	1·4
Isomaltase	2·0	2·2–13·0	—	—	—
Sucrase	0·01	2·6–13·0	3·3	2·8	0·02
Lactase	0·0036	1·0–6·2	0·13	0·6	0·82
Cellobiase	0·028	0·2–1·0	—	—	—
Trehalase	5·4	0·6–2·8	2·8	0·0001	0·02

The succus entericus squeezed out from the small intestine posterior to the entrance of the combined pancreatic and bile duct has lipase, amylase, and trypsin-like activities, the pH optima for the last two being 7·5 and 7·2 respectively (Fig. 13). Water extracts

TABLE 7

Body weight, N_2 intake, faecal N_2, fat intake and faecal fat of a normal male echidna and of a female echidna with common pancreatic and bile duct ligated. Both ate 98–99 g Nasutitermes exitiosus daily.[a] Observations commenced 7 days after operation

Animal	Diet	Initial weight (g)	Final weight (g)	Number of daily observations	Average daily N_2 intake (g)	Average daily fat intake (g)	Average daily faecal N_2 (g)	Average daily faecal fat (g)	Dry weight of faeces pased daily (g)
Control	Live termites	2460	2471	4	2·40	2·32	0·38	0·66	7·7
Common pancreatic and bile duct ligated	Live termites[a]	2139	2142	9	2·38	2·32	1·34	3·48	18·5
	Deep-frozen termites[a]	2142	2156	8	2·41	2·34	0·83	2·50	13·8

[a] Ration sufficient to sustain growth at the rate of 10 g/day before operation.

of fresh pancreas have amylase activity and water extracts of acetone-
dried pancreas contain lipase (Griffiths, 1965a). In all probability
most of that amylase and trypsin-like activity of the succus entericus
is secreted by the pancreas, since it was found that the activity of
those enzymes was reduced to a very low level in the succus entericus
of an echidna whose combined bile and pancreatic duct had been
ligated 79 days before; the lipase activity, however, was almost
equal to that of normal succus entericus.

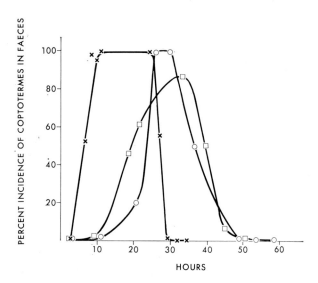

FIG. 16. Rate of passage of termites through echidnas and through
Isoodon macrourus. O——O, Male echidna, weight 2500 g. Fed 100 g *Coptotermes lacteus* at zero time and then 100 g *Nasutitermes exitiosus* 24 hr later.
□——□, Same animal a week later. Fed 200 g *Coptotermes* at zero time
and then 200 g *Nasutitermes* 24 hr later. X——X, Male *Isoodon*, weight
625 g. Fed 120 g *Coptotermes* at zero hr followed by 120 g *Nasutitermes*
24 hr later. (Griffiths, 1965a.) (Reproduced from *Comp. Biochem. Physiol.*)

The effects of the absolute lack of bile and of a deficiency of
digestive enzymes on the physical well-being of this echidna were
less than might be expected. A daily ration of about 100 g termites
either alive or deep-frozen enabled it to maintain body weight
(Table 7) and to exhibit lively behaviour in spite of a negative fat
balance and a large excretion of N_2 in the faeces. It may be argued in
explanation that the proteinases, lipases, and amylases of the termites

are active in the alimentary tract and provide assimilable food to the echidna, but termites heated to 80°C for 1 hr, and presumably lacking active enzymes, were equally effective as fresh termites in the maintenance of body weight. Another possibility, that termites contain quantities of free amino acids, cannot be discounted as an explanation of ease of assimilation, since some insects are known to possess large amounts of free amino acids in their tissues (Gilmour, 1961).

A third possibility is that ligation of the duct decreased rate of passage of the food; whether or not this is so it is certain that the digestive enzymes of normal echidnas have ample time to act on their substrates since the rate of passage of termites is slow. This was established by feeding echidnas a maintenance diet of a given amount of *N. exitiosus* daily and then giving one feed of a different termite, *Coptotermes lacteus*, followed by the usual maintenance feed 24 hr later. The *Coptotermes* served as a marker since the structures of the heads of the soldiers and of the jaws of the workers differ from those of *Nasutitermes*. The parts of the ground-up exoskeletons of both species appear in the faeces apparently unchanged so that it is possible to count directly the number of each species in aliquots of the faeces. The results are summarized in Fig. 16. Feeds of 100 or 200 g wet weight are cleared in about 2 days; a very slow rate compared with that through a facultatively insectivorous marsupial, *Isoodon macrourus* (Fig. 16). This animal has a glandular stomach very like that of a carnivorous eutherian (Oppel, 1896a); presumably the gastric digestion in the stomach permits a faster rate of passage than in the echidna which has no intrinsic stomach digestion. Another factor that one might suppose contributes to the slow rate of passage of food through echidnas is the great length of the intestine.

NITROGEN EXCRETION, N_2 RETENTION, AND GROWTH

Excretion

In 1898 Neumeister demonstrated that protein catabolism of echidnas is the same as that in the eutherian mammals, i.e. the principal end-product of that catabolism is urea. This was confirmed by Mitchell (1931).

Urea is synthesized from CO_2 and the NH_3 of the deaminated

amino acids derived from the "worn-out" protein by the following
series of enzymatic reactions:

(1) CO_2 + NH_3 + adenosine triphosphate → Carbamyl phosphate
(2) Carbamyl phosphate + aspartic acid → Carbamyl aspartic
   acid
(3) Carbamyl aspartic acid + ornithine → Carbamyl ornithine
   (citrulline)
(4) Citrulline + aspartic acid → Arginosuccinic acid
(5) Arginosuccinic acid → Arginine + fumaric acid

The arginine is hydrolysed to ornithine, which re-enters the cycle,
and to urea by the enzyme arginase whose presence has been demonstrated in echidna liver by Denton, Reich, and Hird (1963);[1] arginase
is not found in the livers of birds where uric acid is the principal
end-product of protein breakdown.

Urea accounts for 82–90% of the nitrogen in urine and, as one
might expect in a mammal, very little N_2 is excreted in the urine as
uric acid; the daily excretion is of the order of 10 mg and the serum
levels vary from undetectable amounts to $0·1$ mg per 100 ml. The
average blood urea level is 50 mg% (range 29–92). This is quite
unlike the partition of N_2 in the blood and urine of Sauropsida;
there, uric acid is the major nitrogenous constituent and the tissues
of those animals lack uricase, the terminal enzyme in a chain of
enzymes responsible for the degradation of purines in mammals.
Like most eutherians, echidnas possess uricase in their livers, which
oxidizes the uric acid to allantoin (Griffiths, 1965a).

As one might expect from the foregoing, the tachyglossid kidney
is a mammalian structure, in fact it resembles a rabbit kidney
externally and bears no resemblance to the lobulated organ found
in the Sauropsida (Figs. 17 and 49). Renal arteries and veins enter
the medial cavity or hilus of the kidney and from here the ureter
leaves it. The ureter communicates with a simple cavity in the kidney
called the pelvis into which projects one papilla only. From the
papilla collecting tubules radiate out forming an entity known as the

---

[1] The rest of the urea-cycle enzymes have just recently been demonstrated in
echidna liver (F. A. Hird, personal communication). The activities expressed as
μmoles product/hr/g fresh liver are as follow: carbamyl phosphate synthetase,
469–630; ornithine transcarbamylase, 16,500–22,800; arginosuccinate synthetase,
41–64; arginosuccinate lyase, 201–384; arginase, 18,650–21,300.

pyramid or the medullary substance, the widest part of the pyramid being capped with the "kidney" shaped cortex in which the dark knots of the glomeruli of the malpighian corpuscles can be distinguished. The medullary substance contains uriniferous tubules of the two kinds, the secretory portions which help form the urine and the

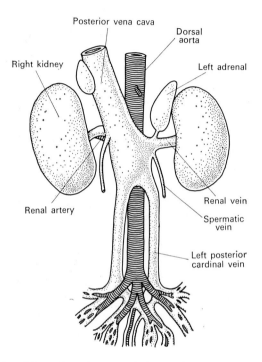

Fig. 17. Arterial supply and venous drainage of kidneys of *Tachyglossus aculeatus*. Probably a young specimen since the adrenals are relatively enormous. After Hochstetter (1896).

collecting ducts which unite to form large ducts, the "Sammel-gange" of Zarnik (1910), in the papilla. These communicate, through openings in the area cribrosa at the base of the papilla, with the pelvis and from here urine is led to the urogenital sinus by the ureters which enter at the dorso-lateral aspect of the sinus (Fig. 49). How the urine gets into the bladder which depends from the ventral surface of the urogenital sinus, is not known.

Finger-like projections composed of collecting tubules and

uriniferous tubules enter the cortex at various points forming medullary rays (Fig. 18).

Zarnik has used, with conspicuous success, the technique of maceration with strong acid for the study of isolated nephrons and their connections with the collecting tubules. Each nephron consists of Bowman's capsule, which surrounds a glomerular tuft of blood vessels, and the successive parts of the tubule leading away from Bowman's capsule: the proximal convolutions, the descending limb

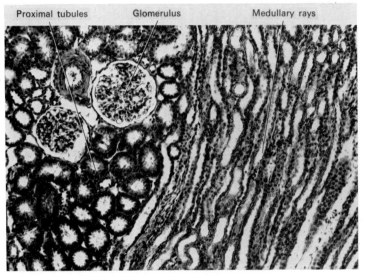

FIG. 18. Section of portion of kidney of *Tachyglossus a. aculeatus*. Haematoxylin and eosin. (Griffiths, 1965a.) ×111. (Reproduced from *Comp. Biochem. Physiol.*)

of Henle's loop, the thin segment of the descending limb followed by the ascending limb, and the distal convoluted tubule which is connected to the straight collecting tubule by the arched collecting tubule. In *Tachyglossus* and other mammals the proximal and distal convolutions are found within the cortex and the loops of Henle penetrate deeply into the medulla (Fig. 19). In this figure, which is taken from Zarnik's monograph, it can be seen that the large nephrons may have long, thin segments or short ones, and that one type of Henle's loop has no thin segment at all. The descriptions up to this point would be perfectly applicable to the kidneys of many

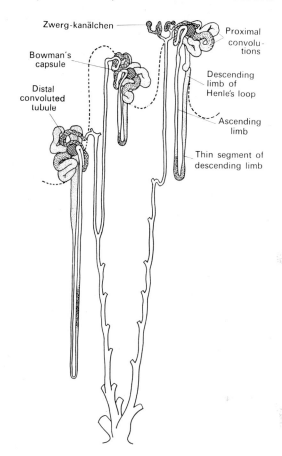

Zwerg-kanälchen

Bowman's capsule

Distal convoluted tubule

Proximal convolutions

Descending limb of Henle's loop

Ascending limb

Thin segment of descending limb

FIG. 19. Isolated nephrons and their connections with collecting tubes. Diagrammatic, after Zarnik (1910). Dotted lines indicate border between medulla and cortex.

primitive Eutheria, but as well as mammalion nephrons[1] the tachyglossid kidney exhibits the curious dwarf nephrons (Zwerg-kanälchen of Zarnik) that are to be found in the kidneys of many reptiles. They consist of a small Bowman's capsule and a short length of relatively uncoiled proximal tubule whose component cells have large nuclei and exhibit an embryonic appearance. The short tubule opens directly into a collecting tubule (Fig. 19). Zwerg-kanälchen

[1] See Appendix III.

are unknown in the kidneys of adult eutherians but they have been observed in those of the 2-day-old rat.

The blood supply and drainage of the kidney is entirely mammalian in that the renal portal system of the Sauropsida is not represented. Figure 17 shows the entry of the renal artery and the exit of the renal vein from the hilus of the kidney. The renal veins lead directly into the posterior vena cava. This drawing after Hochstetter (1896) is apparently based on the anatomy of a very young echidna since the adrenals drawn here are relatively enormous. An idea of their relative sizes and positions in an adult *Tachyglossus* can be formed from the photograph of a dissection of the male urogenital system reproduced in Fig. 49.

Retention

One item of the diet of *Tachyglossus aculeatus*, the termite *Nasutitermes exitiosus*, is about $8 \cdot 5\%$ N_2 w/w (dry), but a great deal of that N_2 is in the form of tanned protein and chitin and is not assimilated by the echidna (Griffiths, 1965a). This was shown by the fact that an intake of $4 \cdot 28$ g termite N_2/day gave a growth rate of 18 g/day whereas a much smaller intake of N_2, $2 \cdot 3$ g/day, in the form of eggs, milk, and termites, gave a growth rate of 26 g/day and greatly improved N_2 retention. Increases in weight and N_2 retention, similar to those obtained when milk and egg proteins are fed, can also be obtained if enough termite N_2 plus a supplement of glucose is fed. However, very large amounts of glucose must be ingested to elicit an effect; for example, an echidna receiving $3 \cdot 10$ g of termite N_2 and a supplement of 14 g glucose/day increased in weight at the rate of 7 g/day and excreted $2 \cdot 69$ g N_2/day. When the glucose supplement was increased to 28 g/day the increase in body weight was 25 g/day and the N_2 excretion $2 \cdot 50$ g/day. Thus the large daily intake of 14 g glucose had a sub-maximal effect on N_2 retention and the threefold increase in "growth rate", which occurred when the supplement was increased to 28 g/day, reflects deposition of fat rather than true growth involving proportionate increase in protein formation. In spite of the fact that large amounts of glucose are ingested in a matter of 15–20 min in experiments of this nature, very little glucose is excreted in the urine. This argues that echidnas have a high tolerance for glucose and the data summarized in Fig. 20 show that this is so. From these data it is seen that the tolerance of glucose

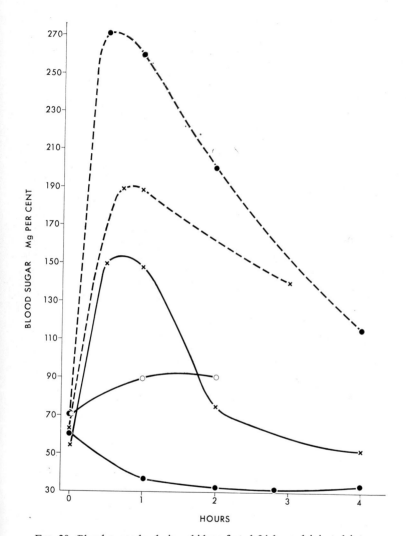

Fig. 20. Blood sugar levels in echidnas fasted 24 hr and injected intra-peritoneally with glucose in 25% solution or with regular insulin sub-cutaneously. ●‑‑‑●, Glucose. Dosage 1·67 g/kg body wt. 3000 g ♀. X‑‑‑X, Glucose; 1·50 g/kg body wt. 2260 g ♂. X——X, Glucose; 1·00 body wt. 2590 g ♀. O——O, Glucose; 0·26 g/kg body wt. 1900 g ♂. ●——●, Regular insulin; 3 units/kg, average curve from two echidnas. (Griffiths, 1965a.) (Reproduced from *Comp. Biochem. Physiol.*)

is very like that of carnivore eutherians. Practically no glucose appeared in the urine when the blood sugar rose to 190 mg% and only 0·81 g out of a total of 5 g injected, appeared in the urine when the blood sugar rose to 270 mg%. From this it may be concluded that the renal threshold of the echidna kidney for glucose is about 180 mg% which is the threshold level in man.

The fact that addition of carbohydrate to a natural food like termites improves growth infers that carbohydrate or some other energy-rich proximate constituent is limiting for growth so that complete assimilation of carbohydrate is necessary. Various mechanisms operate to that end: the absence of peptic digestion in the stomach and the high pH there probably facilitates fermentation of carbohydrates by prolonging action of salivary amylases and carbohydrases in the live food; a slow rate of passage of the food; a high renal threshold and good tolerance for glucose; the elaboration of trehalase for the digestion of the disaccharide trehalose found in insects.

However, it seems likely from some experiments in progress at the present time that cystine is also a limiting factor for growth. Analyses of amino acids in proteolytic-enzyme digests of *N. exitiosus* and

TABLE 8

The amino acids found in pronase digests of Iridomyrmex detectus *and of* Nasutitermes exitiosus *expressed as* μ *moles of amino acid/g dry insects*

Amino acid	Nasutitermes exitiosus	Iridomyrmex detectus
Lysine	174	72
Histidine	67	33
Ammonia	412	268
Arginine	114	100
Aspartic acid	270	167
Threonine	165	95
Serine	176	94
Glutamic acid	368	263
Proline	202	141
Glycine	290	163
Alanine	463	181
½ Cystine	trace	nil
Valine	232	103
Methionine	48	31
Isoleucine	145	93
Leucine	226	132
Tyrosine	144	47
Phenylalanine	103	44

Iridomyrmex detectus (worker caste only) show that very little or no cystine is detectable in digests prepared in this way. The actual process involved digestion of the dried and powdered insects with a solution of pronase, a potent proteolytic enzyme of bacterial origin, followed by denaturation of the liquor at 100°C and further digestion with pronase. The total digest liquor was then filtered, freeze-dried, hydrolysed, and analysed by the Moore and Stein procedure. The amino acids found and their concentrations expressed against dry weight of insects are listed in Table 8. With this type of digestion practically no cystine and relatively little methionine (which can be converted to cystine) could be found. An enzymatic digestion, rather than acid hydrolysis of the insects, was chosen since the latter would digest tanned protein and chitin as well as the protein available to the echidna. As a matter of interest it can be mentioned here that Hackman (1960) found that acid hydrolysates of the cuticles of two arthropods, one an insect and the other a crab, contained no cystine/cysteine and no methionine.

Furthermore, many insect systems such as grasshopper eggs when digested with acid are found to contain no cystine, and in the haemolymph of many insects cystine is not detectable but many other amino acids are found there in high concentration (Hackman, 1956; Gilmour, 1961, 1965).

With this information in mind the effect of a supplement of cysteine hydrochloride (readily oxidized to cystine) and of glycine on N_2 balance in an echidna fed *N. exitiosus*, was studied. A batch of termites sufficient for an experiment was thoroughly mixed and stored deep-frozen; thorough mixing is necessary since the N_2 content of termites can vary, thus different batches can have different N_2 contents. This means that the control and experimental period of feeding must be done on the one batch of termites. From Table 9 it is seen that the finding (Griffiths, 1965a), that glucose improves N_2 retention and rate of increase of body weight, is confirmed. Addition of cysteine hydrochloride to the diet effects a further increase in body weight and improves N_2 retention. Addition of glycine had no such effect, in fact it seemed to have a detrimental effect on growth, no doubt due to the "toxic" effects of amino-acid imbalance (see Harper 1964 for review of this subject). At present then the indication is that cystine or methionine is a limiting factor for growth in the termite-fed echidna; further work will show whether or not this is a statistical result.

E—E

TABLE 9
Nitrogen retention and growth rates in an echidna fed termites with and without various supplements

Number of daily observations	Initial weight (g)	Growth rate (g/day)	Diet (daily intake)	Total average daily N_2 ingestion (g)	Average daily N_2 excretion (g)
5	2520	−11	1·94 g termite N_2 +5 g glucose	1·94	1·91
5		+7	1·95 g termite N_2 +15 g glucose	1·95	1·77
6		+10	1·95 g termite N_2 +15 g glucose +40 mg cysteine N_2	1·99	1·75
			*New batch of termites*		
5	2609	+4	1·92 g termite N_2 +5 g glucose	1·92	1·70
6		+4	1·92 g termite N_2 +5 g glucose +60 mg glycine N_2	1·98	1·74
5		+21	1·92 g termite N_2 +15 g glucose	1·92	1·63
7		+12	1·92 g termite N_2 +15 g glucose + 60 mg glycine N_2	1·98	1·79

N_2 excretion in torpid echidnas

It has been reported (Griffiths, 1965a) that two echidnas that had been feeding well became torpid when kept in an unheated animal house during the winter. These two animals failed to eat for 72 and 64 days respectively, and their body temperatures, like those of Martin's hibernating echidnas (p. 20) were close to the ambient temperatures. During the last 2 weeks of the period of torpidity, details of body weight and N_2 loss were recorded and it was found that the daily N_2 loss was 40 mg and 50 mg/day/kg body weight respectively. They lost weight at the rate of approximately 7 g/day. Blood urea level was normal at 41 mg% but blood sugar levels of 50 and 44 mg% were below the minimum values recorded for normal echidnas (Griffiths, 1965a). At the end of their fast each echidna fed well and put on weight rapidly.

The rate of loss of nitrogen in these two echidnas was very like the rate of loss in the hibernating woodchuck, which excretes between 29 and 50 mg/day/kg (Carpenter, 1938). The average loss in body weight of 3·8 g/day/kg sustained by the echidnas is also comparable with the loss of 2·07–3·29 g/day/kg that Rasmussen and Rasmussen (1917) found in woodchucks.

CHAPTER 3

SKELETON

EARLY CHONDROCRANIUM

Semon (1894) described the development of echidna embryos and pouch young and identified the various stages by numbers. In the stage 44 embryo Gaupp (1908) found that the chondrocranium consists of two parachordal cartilages fused in the mid-line to form a basal plate from which occipital arches arise at the postero-lateral corners and at the other end two trabeculae are attached to its antero-ventral margin, while at the lateral corners of its anterior edge are found two processes, the pilae antoticae. Laterally and at the posterior end of the chondrocranium two auditory capsules in a pre-cartilagenous state are situated, with their cochlear portions in contact with the lateral edges of the basal plate.

The hindmost parts of the trabeculae exhibit projections to the side forming a processus alaris which is the proximal part of the ala temporalis in other mammals. There is no indication of an ascending process in *Tachyglossus*, but in *Ornithorhynchus* there is a condensation of cartilage at the distal end of the processus alaris corresponding to a rudimentary ascending process (de Beer and Fell, 1936). The absence of an ascending process or lamina ascendens has led to the idea that the ala temporalis is absent in *Tachyglossus* (Jollie, 1962). However, Terry (1917), quoted by Gregory and Noble (1924), in a study of the development of the skull of the cat, showed:

> that the "differences between the independent ala temporalis of the cat and the continuous ala of the mole are apparent rather than real", and that this conception supports the homology of the ala temporalis of placental mammals with the ala temporalis of *Echidna*.

Terry also states:

> whether the lamina ascendens of the cat should be regarded as an independent element in origin, or continuous with the basis cranii is a question which could be answered either way from the evidence here presented, and would be purely a choice of interpretations.

58

Two occipital condyles are already present as rudimentary bosses on the hinder surface of the base of the occipital arches.

DEFINITIVE CHONDROCRANIUM

This is achieved by stage 48a and from the Gaupp–Ziegler model (Fig. 21) it is seen to be a well-chondrified structure not unlike that of the hedgehog.

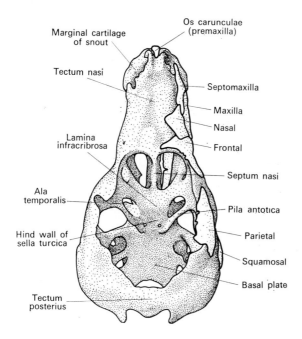

FIG. 21. Gaupp–Ziegler reconstruction of the definitive chondocranium of *Tachyglossus aculeatus*, stage 48a. After Gaupp (1908).

The occipital arches are connected one to the other by the tectum posterius and the foramen magnum is thus formed. The auditory capsules are anchored to the basal plate by a basi-vestibular commissure. Each capsule consists of a canalicular portion (dorso-postero-lateral) and a cochlear portion (ventro-antero-medial). Of the auditory ossicles of the middle ear Doran (1878) wrote, "I hardly need remind the anatomist that, as far as the ossicles are concerned, the Monotremata wear a perfectly mammalian uniform, having malleus, incus, and stapes." The development of those ossicles as seen in the chondrocranium at this stage is identical with that in the chondrocraniums of metatherians and eutherians, that is Meckel's cartilage exhibits three cartilages plastered onto the caudal surface of each ramus, and close by is a small three-cornered ossification the angular (=tympanic) lying medially to the hind end of the ramus. Two of those cartilages and the bone are repeating an episode in that marvellous transformation of the anlagen of three bones that once occurred in the lower jaw of therapsid reptiles: the quadrate, the articular, and the angular into the incus, malleus, and tympanic respectively. The other cartilage forms the stapes the base of which will be attached to a membrane filling in the fenestra ovalis. The stapes takes the form of an imperforate columella identical with that found in many metatherians and in the eutherian *Manis javanica* (Doran, 1878).

The incus at this stage is in cartilaginous contact with the crista parotica which is a forwardly projecting process on the pars cochlearis of the capsule. Later in development in *Tachyglossus* it is ossified but it is smoothed out and incorporated into the general contours of the adult periotic bone. However, in the chondrocranium the laterohyal cartilage of the visceral arch skeleton becomes attached to the crista parotica to form the hyoid arch of the adult larynx (Göppert, 1901). In addition to the hyoid there are three pairs of branchial arches.

The orbital cartilage is attached to the central stem of the chondrocranium by a preoptic connection of cartilage and by the pila antotica. In front the orbital cartilage is attached to the roof of the nasal capsule by the sphenethmoid commissure and posteriorly to the parietal plate and to the auditory capsule by the orbitoparietal commissure.

The processus alaris now takes the form of a well-developed projection, the ala temporalis, directed outwards and upwards from the fused trabecular plate.

The nasal capsules are well chondrified with complete roofs and sides and are furnished with maxilloturbinal and ethmoturbinal cartilages. The nasal septum formed at an earlier stage by a medial dorso-ventral growth of the trabecular plate, forms the internal walls of the capsules. At its posterior margin the septum is continuous with a horizontally placed plate of cartilage, the lamina infracribrosa, which forms a large part of the anterior wall of the brain case.

In the chondrocranium of *Ornithorhynchus* the eye cup is seen to be surrounded by a delicate but well-defined sclera of young cartilage (de Beer and Fell, 1936), but it has not been described in the chondrocranium of *Tachyglossus*, nevertheless it is probably present at this stage since the sclerotic cartilage is present in the eyes of adult echidnas (O'Day, 1938).

A number of dermal bones are found investing the definitive chondrocranium. These are as follow:

The premaxillae are fused in the mid-line and at this junction is a dorsally situated knob of bone formed from the fusion of two os carunculae. The egg-laying Amniota possess either an egg tooth or a caruncle but the monotremes with their flair for the bizarre have both. The egg tooth is present at birth which is at stage 46 in *Tachyglossus* but it has disappeared from the chondrocranium by stage 48a.

The maxillae have ascending portions that cover the lower parts of the paries nasi, palatine processes that project inwards, but which at this stage fail to meet on the mid-line, and zyogmatic processes that extend backwards to similarly named processes of the squamosals. The latter are small pieces of bone lying against the auditory capsules. The paired nasals are attached to the roof of the nasal capsules, and rudimentary frontals and parietals are present.

Meckel's cartilage itself is covered on its ventro-lateral surface by the dentary. The triradiate tympanic, which is situated medially to the hind end of that cartilage, will support the embryonic tympanic membrane at a later stage of development.

Reptilian and mammalian characters of the chondrocranium

From time to time in this and succeeding chapters various structures in monotremes will be compared with those in living Sauropsida and it will be pointed out that some of those structures in the two groups are identical or similar; this does not imply that they are homologous, it only emphasizes the fact that we cannot compare the soft parts of monotremes with those of therapsid reptiles since the latter are extinct.

As Gaupp (1908) pointed out the early chondrocranium of *Tachyglossus* is very like those of reptiles since it has recognizable separate trabeculae while in other mammals the dual origin of the trabecular plate is obscured by the early appearance of the central stem of that plate.

The pila antotica is present in reptiles and the Prototheria but fails to appear in the chondrocraniums of Metatheria and Eutheria. In the reptiles and birds it gives rise to the laterosphenoid (= pleurosphenoid) bone (Gregory and Noble, 1924; de Beer, 1926; Goodrich, 1958), but in *Tachyglossus* ossifications of the pilae antoticae are incorporated into two straps of bone along the sides of the sella turcica in the basisphenoid complex of bones.

The sclerotic cartilages around the eye cups occur in birds and reptiles but as far as is known they occur only in monotremes among the mammals.

Apart from these reptilian structures, the chondrocranium is essentially mammalian in all other respects. It exhibits paired occipital condyles; the nasal capsule is furnished with ethmoturbinals as well as maxilloturbinals; the laterohyal cartilages of the visceral skeleton are attached to the cristae paroticae; Meckel's cartilage is replaced by a single bone, the dentary; and the relations of the stapes, incus, malleus, and tympanic are identical with those of other mammals. The fact that the stapes is an imperforate columella is not of great significance since this is the case in many Metatheria and in *Manis javanica*, while it is a perforated stirrup in the Gymnophiona and in the Geckonidae.

By far the outstanding mammalian character of the tachyglossid skull is the modification of the cavum epiptericum. In the reptile chondrocranium, between the side wall on the inside and the palatoquadrate with its processus ascendens on the outside, is enclosed a space partially floored by the basitrabecular and basal processes which was called the cavum epiptericum by Gaupp (1900). The cavum has anterior, lateral, and posterior openings, and through it pass the internal jugular vein, the orbital and facial arteries, and the profundus, trigeminal, and facial nerves.

In the mammal (including monotreme) chondrocranium, with the expansion of the brain, the original side wall posterior to the orbit ceases to chondrify and is reduced to the condition of a membrane through which the nerves pass into the cavum epiptericum. This latter is now included in the cranial cavity because a new lateral wall has evolved. In the chondrocranium this side wall is represented by the ala temporalis and a sphenoparietal membrane which later becomes ossified (see p. 65).

ADULT SKULL

The bones of the skulls of adult *Tachyglossus* and *Zaglossus* (Gervais, 1878) are thin and strongly ossified so much so that they tend to fuse together and the sutures between them to disappear. The enormous brain case is limited to the occipital and parietal region, and the anterior part of the skull is projected into a long snout, with a pronounced aquiline curve in *Zaglossus*, flat to slightly retroussé in *Tachyglossus*, with the nares at the distal end.

There are two occipital condyles formed from the exoccipitals and the floor of the brain case is formed by the basioccipital and a sphenoid complex consisting of a fused basisphenoid, presphenoid (van Bemmelen, 1901), and of the paired ridge-like ossifications of the pilae antoticae; presumably the latter are the homologues of laterosphenoids.

Anterior to the brain case the floor of the skull is formed from the vomer, the hind end of which overlays the lamina terminalis presphenoidei. The anterior part of the floor of the brain case is formed by the mesethmoid which is an ossification of the anterior wall of the brain case including the median nasal septum and by the posterior walls of the nasal capsules and the lamina infracribrosa which is now attached at its upper and anterior margin to the cribriform plate. This is pierced by a large number of pores and it extends forward from the top of the transverse mesethmoid so that it has a horizontal disposition; branches of the olfactory nerves pass through the pores from the nasal epithelium to the fore-brain. The olfactory organs are very large and well developed: from the cribriform plate depend seven vertical endoturbinals and a large number of ectoturbinals which are collectively known as the ethmoturbinals, and in addition there are sets of nasoturbinals and maxilloturbinals.

The elongated upper jaw is made up of two bones on each side: the premaxillae and the maxillae. The former are incurved at their distal ends, meeting to form a lacuna through which the external nares communicate with the exterior. There are no teeth on the jaws and anlagen of teeth never appear during ontogeny.

The roof of the mouth is a very long false palate formed by flat extensions of the maxillae and palatine bones meeting in the mid-line ventral to the true roof of the mouth. This arrangement forms the nasal passage. At the rear end of the palate are the internal choanae situated beneath the posterior margins of the palatines which are without thickened rims—a condition very like that in the palate of the marsupial anteater, *Myrmecobius fasciatus*. Palatal vacuities do not occur in *Myrmecobius* nor in tachyglossids. Abutting on to the rear ends of the palatines are the large "echidna pterygoids" on either side and dorsal to these are the "mammalian pterygoids". This distinction between two types of pterygoids arose from Gaupp's (1908) discovery of a separate bone in *Tachyglossus* ventral to that usually called the pterygoid. He concluded that it is homologous with the reptillian pterygoid, but as Goodrich (1958) points out, the pterygoid bone in many mammals may be formed of two elements separate during development, one a dorsal element of dermal bone and a ventral one the "pterygoid cartilage". However, from its histological characters it appears that the latter gives rise to dermal bone and Goodrich concluded, therefore, that there are probably two dermal elements related to the basitrabecular region in all mammals: the dorsal mammalian pterygoid and the ventral echidna pterygoid which persists as a separate bone only in the adult echidna.

No one has pointed out any reason for the retention of these large ventral pterygoids but it seems likely that they have developed in connection with the echidna's peculiar method of trituration of its food. This is achieved, as we have seen, by the grinding action of a set of keratinous spines mounted on the dorsal surface on an eminence situated at the posterior end of the tongue. This keratinized knob is as wide as the bridge of bone formed by the combined pterygoids and palatines and it fits very well the contours of that slightly dished palatal region. Insects passed to the back of the buccal cavity by the prehensile tongue are crushed and homogenized between the keratinous spines and the series of spiny ridges on the epithelium which is applied directly to the pterygoids and palatines.

There are no jugals and since echidnas do not have the big muscles associated with chewing, the malar arch is reduced to a thin bar formed from a backwardly projecting process of the maxilla which joins the anterior zygomatic process of the squamosal. The lower jaw consists of a dentary bone also reduced to a splinter, but at the ventro-posterior end of each ramus is a vestige of an angle (the "echidna angle" of Patterson 1956; see p. 223), and on the posterodorsal aspect is an indication of a coronoid process (Fig. 91). The condyles are elevated relative to the coronoid processes and articulate with small depressions in the squamosals.

The roof of the skull is formed by the supraoccipital, paired parietals, frontals, and nasals. The remainder of the sides of the brain case is formed by the squamosals, orbitosphenoids, alisphenoids (van Bemmelen, 1901), and the periotic bones.

The alisphenoids of mammals are not to be confused with the reptilian alisphenoid which is an old name for the ossification of the

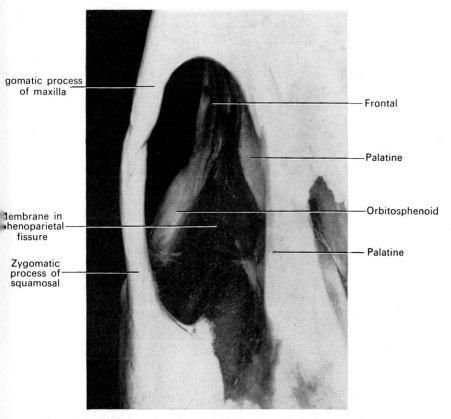

FIG. 22. Ventral view of portion of skull of a young *Tachyglossus aculeatus multiaculeatus*, weight 400 g., length 20·5 cm. The sphenoparietal fissure is filled with a membrane only. ×5·8.

pila antotica which we have seen gives rise to the laterosphenoid or pleurosphenoid. The mammalian alisphenoid is an ossification of a distinctly different cartilage of the chondrocranium—the ala temporalis. The ossification of that cartilage, and its ascending process, in most reptiles including Therapsida (lost in Crocodilia and Ophidia)

66 ECHIDNAS

gives rise to the epipterygoid, and in Goodrich's (1958) opinion there is little doubt that Broom's (1914) contention that the mammalian alisphenoid is derived from the epipterygoid of lower tetrapods is correct. However, in spite of the fact that an ala temporalis is present in the chondrocranium of the echidna (p. 58), Watson (1916) held

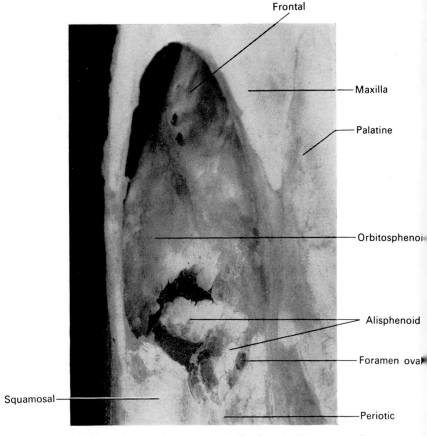

FIG. 23. Ventral view of portion of skull of *Tachyglossus a. aculeatus*, weight 3000 g., showing an invasion of bone from the ala temporalis region into the membrane of the sphenoparietal fissure. ×3·7.

that alisphenoids are not present in echidnas since he believed that the large gap in the brain case of the young echidna, the spheno-parietal fissure, is filled by the gradual growth forward of an ossification which is always continuous with the anterior ossification of the otic capsule and that only very late in life is there any connection of this ossification with the ala temporalis. However, Watson must have had immature material to work on, since in a properly prepared skull at the right stage, it can be seen that the sphenoparietal fissure is filled in by a membrane (Fig. 22) into which, later, there is an invasion of bone from the ala temporalis region of the skull (Fig. 23),

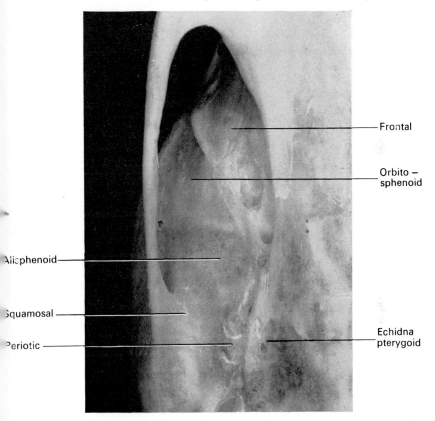

FIG. 24. Ventral view of portion of adult skull of *Tachyglossus a. aculeatus*, weight 5500 g. ×2·9.

i.e. the sphenoparietal fissure is being filled by a true alisphenoid. In older skulls it can be seen that the fissure is filled by bone (Fig. 24), somewhat as van Bemmelen (1901) drew it in his text figure 4B. This he called the alisphenoid and I am in agreement with his interpretation but I cannot detect the sutures as he draws them; the whole mass of bone in this region is fused together. It might be pointed out that this description of the alisphenoid development agrees well with Watson's own remarks about the human alisphenoid to the effect that it is "A good example of a bone which is undoubtedly one

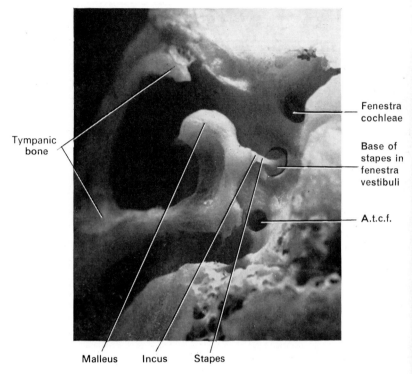

FIG. 25. *Tachyglossus aculeatus* ventral view of ear ossicles *in situ*. A.t.c.f. Apertura tympanica canalis facialis (Canalis Fallopii). ×7·2.

morphological entity arising partly as an ossification replacing a cartilage and partly as an extention of ossifications from the cartilage in membrane."

Periotic bone of the adult skull, bony labyrinth, membranous labyrinth, and ear ossicles

The auditory capsule is invested with a single bone, as is the rule in mammals, called the periotic which probably represents the fusion of two reptillian bones, the prootic and the opisthotic. At its postero-lateral aspect the periotic bears a large mastoid process, the pars

mastoidea which abuts onto the orbitosphenoid, the parietal, the
supraoccipital, and onto the external occipital. The ventro-medial
portion of the periotic is the pars petrosum. The periotic houses the
acoustic and vestibular organs which have been described by
Alexander (1904), and Simpson (1938) has described in detail the
structures of the bones surrounding and enclosing those organs. The
external ear tubes are like two great flexible ear trumpets leading from
the exterior downwards to the tympanic membranes lodged behind
the glenoid depressions. These trumpets are stiffened by two longitudinal strips of cartilage from which arise a series of transverse

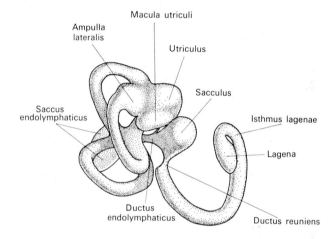

FIG. 26. Membranous labyrinth of a young *Tachyglossus aculeatus*, stage
51. After Alexander (1904).

rib-like cartilages. The tympanic cavity lying dorsal to the membrane
is a large, domed cavern, the entrance to which is surrounded by the
tympanic bone; this has achieved a horse-shoe shape but it still shows
a vestige of the triradiate shape it bore in the chondrocranium and it
now supports the tympanic membrane blocking off the entrance to the
cavern (Fig. 25). At the posterior end of the tympanic cavity is a
hole surrounded by a membrane supporting the base of the stapes,
this is the fenestra vestibuli (= f. ovalis) which leads into another
cavity, the vestibule, and this in turn communicates with the bony
labyrinth. The bony labyrinth is simply the osseous cavities which
house the semicircular canals or membranous labyrinth and which is
lined with endosteum and, together with the vestibule, is filled with

perilymph. Thus the perilymph bathes the outside of the membranous labyrinth and it also fills the scala vestibuli and scala tympani
of the cochlea. In passing it may be mentioned that the semicircular
canals have the smooth rounded outlines of mammalian canals and
exhibit no sign of the angularity of the reptilian labyrinth (Gray,
1908).

The cochlear aqueduct, a channel in the osseous labyrinth,
extends from the scala tympani to the subarachnoid space (Denker,
1901).

An endolymphatic sac situated at the endocranial surface of the
periotic communicates by means of a ductus endolymphaticus, which
passes through a bony canal the aqueductus vestibuli, with the
saccule and utricle of the membranous labyrinth. Thus endolymph
passing through the ductus endolymphaticus from the sac fills the
semicircular canals and also, via a duct of fine calibre the ductus
reuniens, fills the scala media (ductus cochlearis) of the cochlea.
These structures are to be seen in Fig. 26 which is a copy of Alexander's drawing of the membranous labyrinth in a stage 51 pouch
young.

The cochlea and its surrounding bony fossa cochleae is curved and
exhibits a spiral three-quarter turn, a condition lying between that of
a straight cochlea in reptiles and the mesozoic mammal *Triconodon*
(Simpson, 1928), and that of the many complete spirals of eutherian
cochleae. The scala media is an outgrowth of the membranous
labyrinth passing down the centre of the cochlea; it is somewhat
triangular in section (Fig. 27) and forming one side of the duct and
separating its cavity from that of the scala vestibuli is a delicate
vestibular membrane (membrane of Reissner). The roof of the
triangular duct is the stria vasculosa which presumably has the
trophic function that it has in other mammals. Its electrical properties
will be discussed on p. 112. Forming the third side of the duct
and separating its cavity from that of the scala tympani is the
robust basilar membrane. Lying on the inner side of the basilar
membrane and running its entire length is the organ of Corti. As
already mentioned, the scala vestibuli and scala tympani are filled
with perilymph; this is retained in the scala tympani by a membrane
in another window at the base of the cochlea—the fenestra rotunda
which looks through into the cavum tympanum as does the fenestra
vestibuli. At the distal end of the cochlea just before its termination
is a construction, the isthmus lagenae and at this point the scala

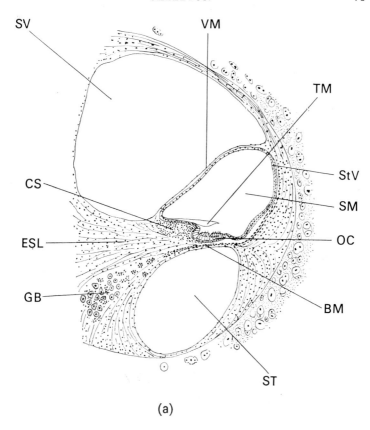

(a)

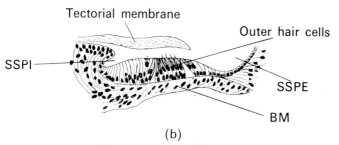

(b)

FIG. 27. (a) Transverse section through the cochlea of a young *Tachyglossus aculeatus*. BM, basilar membrane; CS, crista spiralis; ESL, external spiral ligament; GB, ganglion basilare; OC, organ of Corti; SM, scala media; SV, scala vestibuli; StV, stria vascularis; ST, scala tympani; TM, tectorial membrane; VM, vestibular membrane. (b) Transverse section through organ of Corti. BM, basilar membrane; SSPE, sulcus spiralis externus; SSPI, sulcus spiralis internus. After Alexander (1904).

vestibuli and scala tympani communicate with one another through a small hole, the helicotrema. The scala vestibuli, however, extends a little further and ends blindly near the tip of the cochlea. At this tip is found an interesting structure the lagena (Fig. 26) which appears to be identical with that in the cochlea of reptiles and birds (see Pumphrey, 1961). In *Tachyglossus* it takes the form of an ovoid macula situated at the end of the scala media and consists of a proximal layer of nerve fibres (Alexander's neuro-epithelium), and a distal one of tall epithelial cells provided with hairs which project into a layer of gelatinous substance that lines the internal surface of the macula. The jelly contains minute bodies, the otoconia or otoliths. Among the mammals only the Prototheria exhibit this lagenar macula in the cochlea.

The tympanic cavity is the air-containing space which lies between the tympanic membrane and the fenestra vestibuli (oval window) and which houses the three auditory ossicles. The first of these, the malleus, has a long manubrium which is attached to the inner surface of the tympanic membrane. The head of the hammer is connected to the incus by a tiny articulation and the incus in turn is articulated to the top of the columelliform stapes whose base is clamped to the membrane of the oval window (Fig. 25).

As Doran (1878) and Gregory (1947) recognized, the malleus, incus, and stapes of the monotremes are very like those of *Phascolomys* (wombat) and *Phascolarctos* (koala).

Laryngeal skeleton

This skeleton surrounds and supports the larynx situated between the pharynx and the top end of the trachea; it is made up of ossified and cartilaginous elements the essential morphology of which has suffered little change since the stage 48a development of the hyobranchial skeleton.

The body of the hyoid portion is a transverse ossified piece called the basihyal copula to which are attached anteriorly the two hypohyal, and laterally, the first two ceratobranchial ossicles. At the posterior end of the basihyal copula is a crescent-shaped cartilaginous thyroid copula which bears two pairs of ossicles, the 2nd and 3rd ceratobranchials, and posterior to these is a large cricoid cartilage, but there is no evidence from its ontogeny in *Tachyglossus* that it is a derivative of a 4th branchial arch.

The basal parts only of the hyoid arch, i.e. the hypohyals, are ossified and the distal cartilaginous portions known as the laterohyals are fused to the auditory capsules at the cristae paroticae.

The monotreme laryngeal skeleton is primitive in that there are two pairs of ceratobranchials attached to the thyroid whereas in the Eutheria there is only one pair formed by the fusion of those two pairs of ceratobranchials, but in the Metatheria the dual nature of the thyroid ceratobranchials is witnessed by the foramen on either side (Goodrich, 1958).

APPENDICULAR SKELETON

This exhibits that curious mosaic of frankly reptile and mammal characteristics found in the chondrocranium. The pectoral girdle is that of a reptile and the pelvis would be at home in a marsupial. The vertebral formula varies with the author but Gregory (1947) after careful appraisal concludes that there are 7 cervical, 15 dorsal, 3 lumbar, 2 sacral, and 2 sacrococcygeal vertebrae; a formula well within the limits of tolerance for marsupials and theriodonts.

Pectoral girdle

In *Tachyglossus* this consists of 2 scapulas, 2 coracoids, 2 clavicles, 2 procoracoids (epicoracoids) and a median interclavicle (Fig. 28 (a)); the dorsal scapula, and ventral coracoid and procoracoid form a unit on one side, tied to the rib cage dorsally by the scapula, and tied to the sternum ventrally by the united coracoid and procoracoid. The glenoid cavity is a wedge-shaped excavation at the union of scapula and coracoid. The paired clavicles are laid along the cross-member of the T-shaped interclavicle; this in turn is united posteriorly to the sternum while the cross of the T is clamped anteriorly to the scapulas. This triple binding of all elements of the girdle, together with the robust, generous proportions of the component bones, provides a tremendously strong suspensorium for the stout forelimbs, and it accounts for the echidna's powers of digging and limpet-like attachment to various objects and surfaces. The pectoral girdle of *Ornithorhynchus* conforms to this description but that in *Zaglossus* almost passes belief; as an extra precaution that nothing will come apart the epicoracoids overlap (Gervais, 1878), the right overlying the left, and since their union is somewhat asymmetrical the interclavicle is displaced a little to the right of the mid-line (Fig. 28 (b)). On the whole the monotreme pectoral girdle is very like that in the dicynodont reptile, *Kannemyeria* (Pearson, 1924).

The humerus in both genera of tachyglossids is a short and strong bone expanded at both extremities and twisted half round on itself. The proximal end exhibits a convex border, the middle part of which forms the articular surface which so fits into the glenoid cavity that it has a horizontal disposition and because of the torsion of the bone the distal end is vertical. The distal articular surface is convex for the articulation of the concave articular surfaces of the radius and ulna. These two bones are in contact and firmly connected together

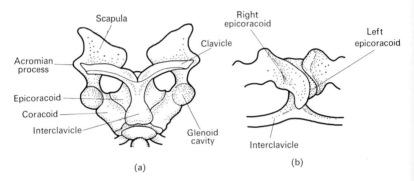

FIG. 28. (a) Pectoral girdle of *Tachyglossus aculeatus*. After Gregory (1947). (b) Pectoral girdle of *Zaglossus bruijni*. After Gervais (1878).

throughout their length. The distal articular surfaces are both expanded and broad for articulation with the large manus. In *Tachyglossus* all five digits are well developed and bear claws; in *Zaglossus bruijni bruijni* digits 1 and 5 are much reduced and bear no claws while digits 2, 3, and 4 are armed with claws (Gervais, 1878), but *Zaglossus bartoni bartoni* has claws on all five digits.

Pelvic girdle

This consists of the usual three elements, the dorsal trihedral ilium, the ventro-posterior ischium and the ventro-anterior pubis. The symphysis of these three bones is incomplete and a foramen is present for the reception of the trochanter of the femur rather than a depression at the union of the three pelvic bones as happens in other mammals. The pubis and ischium are widely separated by an obturator foramen, and both bones contribute equally to the symphysis which unites the pelvis ventrally. The anterior margin of each pubis bears an epipubic or marsupial bone which projects forwards. The base of each epipubic bone extends along the whole anterior face of each pubis where it is movably articulated as it is in the marsupials; in fact the epibubic bones in tachyglossids are essentially like those of wombats and koalas.

The anterior extremities of the ilia extend forwards and dorsally to unite closely with the two sacral vertebrae.

The femur is short, broad, and flattened, and is inserted horizontally and widely everted so that the knee is above the level of the acetabulum. The insertion of the fibula and tibia is such that the conventional lateral position of the fibula is twisted through an arc of 90° so that the fibula faces backwards and the pes is at right-angles to the body, and since the claws are strongly curved they actually face backwards instead of forwards. In the tarsus a supernumerary bone is articulated to the posterior part of the astragalus and it supports the spur.

The five digits of the pes bear claws in all the tachyglossids with the exception of *Zaglossus bruijni* which bears claws on digits 2, 3, and 4 only.

CHAPTER 4

THE CENTRAL NERVOUS SYSTEM

ANATOMY OF THE BRAIN

The brains of vertebrates are built on a tripartite plan and are divisible into fore-, mid-, and hind-brains. These primary divisions consist of various parts as follow:

The fore-brain or prosencephalon is divided into two parts, the telencephalon and the diencephalon or between-brain. The mid-brain or mesencephalon has no subdivisions and the hind-brain or rhombencephalon consists of the metencephalon and the myelencephalon.

The diencephalon, mesencephalon, metencephalon, and myelencephalon constitute an entity known as the brain stem which conforms to the segmental organization of the spinal cord and from which emerge the cranial nerves, numbers III to XII.

Ziehen (1897, 1908) published a detailed study of the whole central nervous system of *Tachyglossus*, and Abbie (1934) made a complete restatement of the microscopical anatomy of the brain stem; I have drawn heavily on these works in the following description of the brain.

The brain of echidna compared to that of reptiles and birds exhibits many structures that proclaim it to be essentially mammalian. The cerebellum in the metencephalon is much enlarged and is divisible into a number of lobes whose surfaces are thrown into folds which results in an increase in the quantity of superficial grey matter or cortex. A band of nerve fibres joins the two sides of the cerebellum one to another, passing ventral to the rest of the mesencephalon; this is the pons Varolii (Fig. 29). It is characteristic of mammals and is developed in connection with the hypertrophy of the neopallium in mammals as compared with that in reptiles. It is a peculiarity of the Prototheria that the pons lies wholly posterior to the insertion of the Vth or trigeminal nerve which in both *Ornithorhynchus* and *Tachyglossus* is enormous and ribbon-like in shape (Fig. 30).

76

The roof of the mesencephalon is distinctly mammalian also, since it bears four prominences, the corpora quadrigemina or superior and inferior colliculi (Fig. 31) instead of the two optic lobes of lower vertebrates. The floor of the mesencephalon contains two main bundles of fibres which pass up and down from the brain and spinal cord; these run in the ventral portion of the rhombencephalon dorsal to the pons Varolii and diverge right and left in the region of the infundibulum forming the crura cerebri or cerebral peduncles (Fig. 30). The floor of the infundibulum posterior to the attachment of the hypophysis exhibits an unpaired mamillary body.

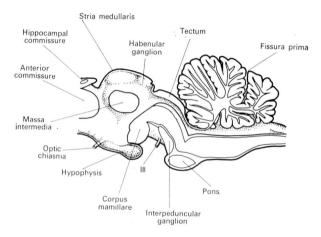

FIG. 29. *Tachyglossus*; median longitudinal section through the brain stem and cerebellum. After Abbie (1934). (Reproduced by permission of the Royal Society.)

At the anterior end of the telencephalon the olfactory bulbs are attached by short peduncles to the anterior poles of the pyriform cortex. Each bulb is a large flattened mass partly overlapped by the anterior poles of the hemispheres; inside the cranium the bulbs project forward and rest their ventral surfaces on the horizontal cribriform plate through the numerous openings of which the olfactory nerve fibres pass to the ventral surfaces of the bulbs.

The outstanding character of the telencephalon and indeed of the whole brain is the enormous size of the cerebral hemispheres which is largely due to the hypertrophy of the gyrencephalic neocortex. The pattern of sulci has not been homologized satisfactorily with those of higher mammals, apparently for the reason (Smith, 1902) that the brain exhibits a fronto-caudal compression and as a consequence of this the sulci on the outer convexity of the hemisphere run more or less transversely and continue over the dorsal angle on to the medial surface. In passing it may be noted that the brains of *Ornithorhynchus* and of the opossum *Didelphys* are lissencephalic, i.e. the neocortex is smooth and exhibits no gyri.

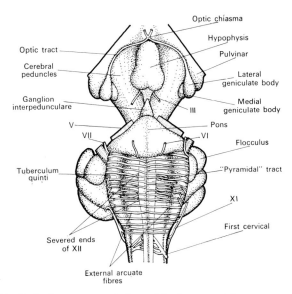

FIG. 30. *Tachyglossus*; ventral view of brain stem. After Abbie (1934). (Reproduced by permission of the Royal Society.)

The brains of echidnas, like those of most marsupials, lack the connecting commissure of the neocortex—the corpus callosum—but the dorsal commissure which links together the hippocampuses in reptiles is retained in the mammals, including *Tachyglossus*, as the hippocampal commissure.

Spinal cord and medulla oblongata

The spinal cord in mammals, unlike that in birds and reptiles, seldom extends through the entire length of the vertebral canal, the caudal part of the canal being occupied by the filum terminale. The echidna spinal cord is no exception to the general rule and it ends about midway through the canal. In the platypus it is longer and extends to the sacral region; possibly this difference in anatomy is connected with the ability of the echidna to roll itself into a tight ball.

The spinal cord has two main functions: firstly, it is the seat of many reflex centres controlling the muscles of the trunk and limbs, and secondly, it is a path of conduction between these centres and the co-ordination centres in the brain. In general the fibre tracts, both ascending and descending, in the spinal cord are phylogenetically old

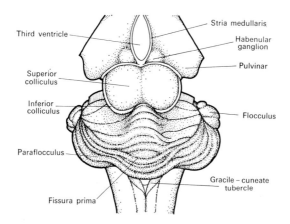

FIG. 31. *Tachyglossus*; dorsal view of brain stem and cerebellum. After Abbie (1934). (Reproduced by permission of the Royal Society.)

but in *Tachyglossus* and the other mammals, along with the development of the neo-cortex, a tract of fibres for the projection of impulses from the telencephalon directly upon the spinal cord makes its appearance. This is the pyramidal tract which according to Abbie (1934) passes from the cortex through the cerebral peduncles and collects at the ventral surface of the medulla oblongata into a relatively thin bundle of fibres (Fig. 30). The tract then decussates at the extreme caudal end of the medulla oblongata and the prevailing course of the fibres from there is in the dorsal funiculi of the cord. That this tract is indeed the pyramidal tract is disputed (Goldby, 1939; see p. 85).

The cord insensibly swells into the medulla oblongata, the ventral

surface of which is very broad, and from here cranial nerves V–XII
emerge. The eminence formed by the gracile and cuneate nuclei is
seen as a large swelling at the anterior end of the dorsal funiculus of
the cord (Fig. 32).

The medulla oblongata contains the fibre tracts connecting the
higher parts of the brain with the spinal cord and the primary sensory
and motor nuclei of eight of the cranial nerves as well as the co-
ordination centres between these sensory and motor nuclei. The
most important co-ordination centres are the inferior olive and
the lateral reticular nuclei; the olive receives numerous fibres from

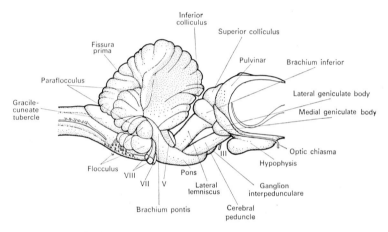

FIG. 32. *Tachyglossus*; lateral aspect of the brain stem and cerebellum.
After Abbie (1934). (Reproduced by permission of the Royal Society.)

the gracile and cuneate nuclei and some from the descending root
of the vestibular nerve.

From the olive, the gracile, and the cuneate, nuclei secondary
fibres pass out to the arcuate fibre system; fibres also pass directly
from the descending root of the vestibular portion of the VIIIth
nerve to the arcuate system. This consists of external and internal sets
of fibres; the external forming a continuous transverse layer over the
ventral surface of the medulla oblongata and in places gathering into
definite fibre bundles (Fig. 30). The external arcuate fibres also receive
a contribution from the descending root of the trigeminal nerve and
from the tractus temporo-trigeminalis (see p. 81). A special nucleus,

the nucleus arcuatus trigemini, is the intermediary for the interrelation of these cerebral trigeminal, and vestibular impulses, the secondary fibres passing from the nucleus to the external arcuate system. A series of arcuate nuclei lying among the arcuate fibres also assist in this function.

The internal arcuate fibres can be divided into dorsal and ventral sets. The dorsal are derivatives of the descending vestibular root and pass to the longitudinal fasciculi. Here many of the fibres terminate but some pass beyond and reach the nucleus arcuatus trigemini of the opposite side. The ventral internal arcuate fibres, like the external, also arise from the gracile and cuneate nuclei and from the descending vestibular root.

In general the function of the whole arcuate system is to transmit cerebral, trigeminal, and vestibular impulses to the corpus restiforme of each side and thus to the cerebellum. The corpus restiforme arises around a core of dorsal spino-cerebellar fibres. This body of fibres is enlarged by contributions of external and internal arcuate fibres, and of dorsal external arcuate fibres from the gracile and cuneate nuclei of the same side. It also receives fibres from the gracile and cuneate nuclei of both sides, the inferior olive, the arcuate nuclei, the nucleus arcuatus trigemini, the spinal fifth root, the tractus temporo-trigeminalis, the descending vestibular root, and probably from the nucleus reticularis lateralis.

THE CRANIAL NERVES AND THE MOTOR FUNCTIONS OF THE BRAIN

There are 12 pairs of cranial nerves in *Tachyglossus* (classified by Roman numerals). The olfactory nerve (I) arises from sensory cells of the olfactory epithelium as fibres which unite to form many small nerves which enter the olfactory bulbs through the cribriform plate.

The optic nerve (II) is really portion of the brain since the retina is derived from an evagination of the diencephalon. The fibres of the optic nerve arise from a ganglionic layer on the surface of the retina.

The oculomotor (III), the trochlear (IV) and the abducent (VI) are true nerves in the sense that they arise from neurons in portions of the brain that conform to a segmental arrangement.

The trigeminal (V), VIIth, IXth, and X + XIth nerves are also segmentally arranged and are sometimes referred to as branchial nerves since during ontogeny they are related with embryonic visceral clefts or with structures connected with these.

The auditory (VIII) is a special somatic sensory nerve; it has vestibular and acoustic (cochlear) divisions.

The XIIth nerve (hypoglossal) is an entity but it is derived from a number of roots of spinal origin.

The motor nerves of the brain

The hypoglossal nerve arises dorsally in the myelencephalon from a nucleus which is broad and flattened dorso-ventrally as it is in the marsupial *Didelphys*. Its constituent cells are very large and are of the motor type; the axons of these motor cells innervate the hypoglossal muscles which are concerned with the movements of the tongue (p. 35)—a motor function of paramount importance to *Tachyglossus* and, significantly, the hypoglossal nucleus is under cortical influence via the pyramidal fibres.

The glossopharyngeal (IX), vagus (X), and accessory (XI) nerves. The motor nuclei of these nerves form a group—the nucleus ambiguus. The vagal part consists of a column of cells on each side of the medulla oblongata at its caudal end but posteriorly the columns approach one another and are continuous in the commissural nucleus of Cajal. The anterior portions of the columns were called the nuclei glossopharyngei by Kölliker (1901) but Abbie feels that they are part of the vagal columns. The motor component of the IXth nerve serves musculature derived from the third (hyoid) arch and the parotid salivary gland. The vagus nucleus gives rise to fibres that innervate the larynx, and to preganglionic fibres of the parasympathetic nervous system. As far as I know nothing has been published on the autonomic system of the Prototheria.

The accessory nerve, associated closely with the vagus is composed primarily of motor fibres distributed to the muscles of the pharynx.

The facialis (VII) nerve. Abbie finds, contrary to other workers, that the facialis nucleus is an entity and is not divided into dorsal and ventral parts as is the case in reptiles; in echidnas it is V-shaped so that in section in some planes it could give the appearance of division into dorsal and ventral nuclei. Although it is a single entity as in other mammals it does not have the ventral position of the facial nucleus found in most marsupial and eutherian brains, but it lies dorsal to the superior olive. In *Didelphys* it occupies an intermediate position, i.e. on a level with, and posterior to, the superior olive.

The VIIth nucleus is very large, a fact that has been correlated by Huber (1930) with the development of the superficial fascialis musculature. The beginnings of this can be seen in reptiles and birds where a sphincter colli, associated with a deep facialis muscle, the m. depressor mandibulae, is restricted to the neck region; the face, therefore, is a "rigid mask devoid of expression". Schulman (1906) and Huber have described the superficial facialis musculature in

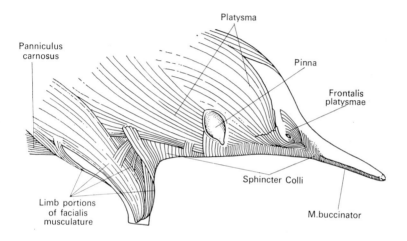

FIG. 33. Dissection of facialis musculature of *Tachyglossus*. After Huber (1930).

Tachyglossus, Ornithorhynchus and other mammals. Here the musculature is no longer restricted to the neck region and it has expanded into the face and become differentiated into muscle groups around the ear, eye, and the snout (Fig. 33). In *Tachyglossus* one layer has developed caudally as well as rostrally; this is the platysma muscle, which has expanded over the anterior part of the back; a major part of this platysma also extends forwards and downwards onto the forelimb; this limb musculature as well as the superficial fascialis musculature, *sensu stricto*, are all under the motor influence of the VIIth nerve. Huber points out that although the sphincter colli in the monotremes is well developed, there is no sphincter colli profundus which is "So characteristic of the marsupio-placentalian ground plan."

The abducens (VI) and accessory VIth nerve. The nucleus of the VIth is small and its fibres innervate the external rectus muscle of the eye. The nucleus consists of scattered small motor cells and the nerve itself is small, a fact that Abbie considers is correlated with the putative poor vision of echidnas, but, as he points out, that argument does not apply to the large IIIrd (oculomotor) nucleus.

About midway between the VIth and VIIth nuclei is a small group of cells which may be considered to be the accessory VIth nucleus since its position corresponds to that of the accessory VIth in other mammals; its function is unknown in echidnas.

The trigeminal (Vth) nerve. The motor nucleus lies slightly dorsal to the chief sensory nucleus of the Vth at about the antero-lateral border of the pons. It is relatively small and its fibres innervate the atrophied masseter and temporal muscles of the jaws.

The oculomotor (III) and trochlear (IV) nerves. These two nuclei are separated completely in echidnas—a relation reminiscent of the condition in some reptiles and different from that in other mammals. The anatomy and motor functions of these nerves are discussed in the section on the mesencephalon.

The pyramidal tracts

In eutherian mammals these are important tracts that constitute a direct motor connection between the cerebral cortex and the spinal cord. That cortico-spinal tracts exist in *Tachyglossus* is indisputable since Abbie (1938), Goldby (1939), and Lende (1964) have shown that certain regions of the cerebral cortex (see p. 101) are excitable and that various somatic motor responses follow stimulation of those areas. The identity of the fibre bundles that carry those motor impulses is a matter of debate. According to Abbie (1934) the pyramidal tracts are small and situated on the ventral surface of the medulla oblongata (Fig. 30); they decussate at the extreme posterior end of the bulb so that fibres pass to the opposite side to the VIIth and XIIth nuclei and to the ventral horn cells of the 1st cervical segment, but they do not descend any lower. According to Abbie this short course of the fibres may be interpreted as a primitive mammalian character and the fibres may be compared with the direct pyramids of other mammals. If all the cortico-spinal fibres did terminate at this level of the spinal cord, it would be difficult to reconcile this with the fact that stimulation of the cortex elicits movements of the hind limbs and tail region. As a matter of fact Goldby (1939) has demonstrated by degeneration experiments that cortico-spinal fibres arise in an area of the cortex, near the mid-line between sulci α and β, and pass caudally in the cerebral peduncles. At the level of the pons Varolii they decussate and pass caudally in the Zonalbündel of Kölliker (1901) to the dorsal part of the lateral column of the cord where they can be traced as far as the 24th spinal root. Now Kölliker's Zonalbündel is Abbie's tractus temporo-trigeminalis which he describes as arising in the cerebral cortex at area 4 of Schuster (1910), and running caudally in the lateral border of the cerebral peduncles; Abbie's pyramidal tracts, however, are stated to arise in area 3 of Schuster and to pass caudally in the medial border of the cerebral peduncles. The exact nature of the fibres of the tractus temporo-trigeminalis is not apparent from Abbie's description; he says "they serve to relate the forebrain with the hindbrain and cerebellum but are much more intimately associated with the trigeminal apparatus than with the vestibular". Kölliker thought it was a sensory tract; however, it appears from Goldby's experiments that the fibres are pyramidal. This, then, raises the question of the identity of Abbie's pyramidal tracts; Yamada (1938) (quoted by Goldby) says they do not exist but Goldby concedes their existence and suggests that they are cortico-bulbar fibres.

The fact that the cortico-spinal fibres decussate high up in the medulla of *Tachyglossus* is not unique; Fuse (1926) has described a decussation of pyramidal fibres just caudal to the pons in bats and edentates and there is a tendency for the fibres caudal to the decussation to take up a lateral position in the medulla.

THE SENSORY AND CO-ORDINATION
SYSTEMS OF THE BRAIN

The ascending tracts of sensory fibres occupy the posterior columns of the spinal cord. Some of the fibres of these tracts form synapses in the reticular nuclei in the medulla oblongata which pass the impulses to various effectory centres, but many other fibres of the ascending tracts pass to centres of co-ordination of a different type. These function by discharging the impulses which they have brought together not into effectory centres but into higher centres. Two of the most important of these are the gracile and cuneate nuclei which receive impulses of two-point discrimination and various proprioceptive impulses. Such impulses are sent via secondary arcuate fibres from these nuclei to the cerebellum. These nuclei are non-segmental in character, and one other very important co-ordination centre of this nature is the inferior olive. Indications of an inferior olivary nucleus can be detected in the medulla oblongata in lower vertebrates, but it attains its highest development in homoiotherms and is particularly well developed in the mammals. It is concerned with carrying proprioceptive impulses by way of spino-olivary and olivocerebellar paths.

The nuclei of five of the cranial nerves, numbers V, VII, VIII, IX, and X, are also concerned with the co-ordination of sensory impulses in the central nervous system. Visceral sensory fibres enter the medulla oblongata by way of the vagal, glossopharyngeal, and facial nerves. By analogy with what happens in other higher vertebrates it may be concluded that these fibres terminate in the grey matter at the level of entrance of the nerves, and that secondary fibres from here pass caudally in the fasciculus solitarius; this decussates and its constituent fibres terminate in the commissural nucleus of Cajal (Kappers, Huber, and Crosby, 1960) which, as has been seen, is also the posterior end of the nucleus ambiguus.

The gracile and cuneate nuclei

Separate in other mammals, these in echidnas are fused into a mass which forms a marked swelling on either side of the dorso-lateral surface of the medulla oblongata. As one might expect, the ascending fibre tracts in the posterior funiculi which terminate in the nuclear mass constitute a large proportion of the white matter of the cord. Abbie quotes a suggestion of J. T. Wilson to the effect that this great sensory development may be due to muscle sensibility associated with the highly developed control over the panniculus carnosus muscle by *Tachyglossus*.

From the gracile and cuneate nuclei some secondary axons pass out in a decussation to the opposite medial lemniscus, a tract of fibres that leads to the thalamus. Others form synapses in the inferior olive; and still others pass as external and internal arcuate, and as dorsal external arcuate, fibres to the corpus restiforme (p. 81).

The trigeminal system

The number of foramina on the skull for the peripheral distribution of the trigeminal nerve is fantastic—fourteen in all; the branches passing to the snout which has important tactile, pain, and temperature sensibilities.[1] The Vth is a mixed nerve with four nuclei of origin —the chief sensory, the dorsal root nucleus, the mesencephalic in the tectum of the mid-brain, and the motor which has already been described. The chief sensory nucleus is large and its caudal part is the nucleus of the descending root. The secondary fibres from the chief sensory nucleus are, for the most part, passed via a massive decussation to the opposite medial lemniscus. At this level, therefore, the medial lemniscus consists of a large tract of trigeminal and gracile-cuneate fibres ascending to the thalamus. The chief sensory nucleus also sends fibres to the pons and cerebellum.

Fibres from the descending root and its nucleus pass to various structures in the medulla oblongata—the pons, corpus trapezoideum and the external arcuate fibre system. Thus trigeminal impulses reach the cerebellum by two paths. The descending root is also connected to the nucleus arcuatus trigemini, the superior olive, the inferior olive, and the lateral reticular nucleus.

The mesencephalic nucleus of the Vth nerve is in the superior colliculus of the mid-brain roof. It has been postulated that the mesencephalic part of this nerve is concerned with conduction of proprioceptive impulses from the jaw muscles to this mid-brain nucleus and, from here, by connections with the motor nucleus of the Vth, a reflex path is set up which makes possible co-ordinated jaw movements (Kappers, Huber, and Crosby, 1960).

From this account it is plain that very little of the brain escapes an all-pervasive trigeminal aura.

The VIIIth nerve

The vestibular division, which accounts for two-thirds of the fibres of the whole nerve, enters the medulla oblongata at the posterior border of the pons just anterior to the cochlear division; most of the vestibular fibres pass into ascending and descending roots. These and their nuclei form a sort of continuous system reaching from the anterior limit of the pons to the caudal border of the medulla

[1] It may have auditory sensibilities also, see p. 115.

E—G

oblongata. Throughout their courses the roots give off fibres and are thus gradually dissipated. These fibres, leaving the roots, form up into two sets of unequal size, the smaller of which comprise the dorsal internal arcuate fibres, many of which end in the medial longitudinal fasciculi of the spinal cord; a few pass beyond and reach the opposite nucleus arcuatus trigemini. The larger group constitutes the ventral group of internal arcuate fibres. Some of these pass ventrally to the nucleus arcuatus trigemini of the same side, but the rest terminate in the opposite inferior olive and thus come to be connected with the opposite internal and external arcuate systems. At the level of the entrance of the vestibular nerve a similar tripartite decussation takes place; this time the fibres pass to the lateral and medial parts of the superior olive and to a rudimentary corpus trapezoideum. The fibres in these two tripartite decussations eventually reach the cerebellum via the corpora restiformes.

The incoming cochlear division of the VIIIth bifurcates into ascending and descending branches. The fibres of the former end up in a small dorsal cochlear nucleus and from here secondary fibres pass to the cerebellum and to the auditory decussations. Some fibres of the descending branch pass directly to the corpus restiforme and cerebellum, others go to the relatively large ventral cochlear nucleus and from here secondary fibres make connections to the restiform body, cerebellum and auditory decussations. These fibres also constitute a tripartite decussation associated with decussating vestibular fibres. Fibres from the dorsal and ventral cochlear nuclei pass to the opposite side and the majority unite to form a bundle— the lateral lemniscus, but a few terminate at some small cells—this is the rudimentary corpus trapezoideum from which secondary fibres pass to the superior olive. The presence of a corpus trapezoideum seems to be associated with the echidna's near-mammalian cochlea since in Metatheria and Eutheria the spiral cochlea goes hand in hand with a conspicuous corpus trapezoideum and the majority of cochlear fibres employ this route of decussation.

The lateral lemniscus, with its complement of auditory fibres, turns forward in the pons region and passes to the mesencephalon. On its way it comes into contact with the medial lemniscus, the two forming a great ascending sensory system. On entering the mesencephalon the lateral lemniscus turns dorsalward to send branches to the inferior colliculus—the mid-brain auditory centre—and to the medial geniculate nucleus; this is a metathalamic auditory centre—a relay to the auditory cortex.

The medial lemniscus with its large trigeminal component passes forwards and dorsally to give off many fibres to the superior colliculus where they end in the stratum griseum intermedium (see p. 91). The rest of the lemniscus ends in the ventral nucleus of the thalamus.

THE PONS VAROLII

This differs from the pons in other mammals in that it lies wholly posterior to the trigeminal nerve and that there are no fronto-pontine tracts. In transverse section it is found to consist of a large nuclear mass encapsulated by a thin shell of fibres. Cortico-pontine and cortico-arcuate fibres enter from the cerebral peduncles. The cortico-pontine fibres end around the pontine cells which give rise to secondary fibres passing to the cerebellum in the brachium pontis.

THE CEREBELLUM

The cerebellum, like the cerebral hemispheres, is a non-segmental appendage of the brain; it is an outgrowth of the dorsal lip of the fourth ventricle in the metencephalon and is a most important centre for sensory correlations. According to Kappers, Huber, and Crosby (1960) "It is a region of correlation of various somatic impulses predominantly, if not exclusively, proprioceptive in character, that is, impulses concerned with equilibration and orientation of the body in space."

In *Tachyglossus* the cerebellum is relatively large and in sagittal section it is seen to be divided into lobes (Fig. 29). It is attached to the brain stem by three peduncles on each side, the corpus restiforme, the brachium pontis, and the brachium conjunctivum. The lobes are separated into two main sets by a deep cleft—the fissura prima. The posterior part is further divided into two smaller parts called the pyramis and the pars auricularis by another cleft, the fissura secunda. The auricular region is the base of the cerebellum and it consists of transverse thickenings; one of these, the nodulus, is extended laterally on each side. The extensions are called flocculi and the corresponding parts of the pyramis are the paraflocculi. Compared with the

cerebellum of lower vertebrates that of *Tachyglossus* is characterized
by the great development of the transverse diameter and this development together with the flocculus and paraflocculus on each side
constitute the essentially mammalian structures of the cerebellum—
the cerebellar hemispheres; the portion lying between the hemispheres
is the vermis (Fig. 31).

Dillon (1962) agrees with de Lange (1918) and Abbie (1934) as to
the identity and position of the fissura prima in the echidna cerebellum but disagrees on the position of the fissura secunda which he
claims was confused with the fissura postero-lateralis by Abbie. If
one accepts Dillon's identification of the fissura prima and fissura
secunda, six of the conventional mammalian lobes of the cerebellum
can be identified in *Tachyglossus* and in *Ornithorhynchus* and a
seventh, peculiar to monotremes, can also be distinguished. Dillon
proposed the name lobus ventralis for this structure which is situated
between the lingula and the nodulus. Thus in the monotremes the
anterior part of the cerebellum consists of the lobus centralis and
the culmen; posterior to the fissura prima is the pyramis which
is separated by the fissura secunda from the pars auricularis;
the latter consists of the lingula, lobus ventralis, nodulus, and
uvula.

The white matter of the cerebellum forms a branching system
penetrating into the various lobes; the grey matter covers the stems
of white forming a cerebellar cortex. This contains the usual molecular, Purkinje, and granular layers and the efferent fibres arriving
via the restiform body and brachium pontis form synaptic connections here. Most of the efferent fibres from the grey matter must pass
to the two cerebellar nuclei of each side (the medial and the lateral
nuclei) since the main efferent tracts of the cerebellum, the brachium
conjunctivum of each side, arises in those nuclei. The fibres of the
brachium conjunctivum pass forward and ventrally where they are
joined by trigeminal and ventral spino-cerebellar fibres which run
to the cerebellum and thus form a small afferent component in the
predominantly efferent brachium conjunctivum. Anteriorly the
efferent fibres come to lie between the mesencephalic root of the Vth
nerve and the lateral lemnicus where they decussate and form
synaptic junctions in the red nucleus.

THE MID-BRAIN

The mesencephalon consists of a dorsal part, the tectum, and a ventral part, the cerebral peduncles. The tectal portions of the mid-brain are formed by the superior and inferior colliculi. The superior colliculi are comparable to the optic lobes of lower vertebrates and are regarded as visual centres. The inferior colliculi are auditory reflex centres.

The nucleus of the mesencephalic root of the trigeminal has a position, as has been described, near the ventral wall in the roof of the mid-brain.

The oculomotor and the trochlear nuclei (IIIrd and IVth cranial nerves) are situated in the floor of the ventricle in close association with the medial longitudinal fasciculus. This latter can be traced to the ventral part of the diencephalon but it is not known exactly where it terminates; posteriorly it passes through the pars intercalis diencephali and in the mid-brain fibres from it form synapses in the IIIrd and IVth cranial nerve nuclei. As explained above, in the medulla oblongata it receives fibres from the cochlear division of the VIIIth nerve. Also secondary reflex fibres from the trigeminal nerve pass in this tract and they appear to form a reflex path linking the Vth nerve with the oculomotor nuclei.

In the tegmental portion of the mid-brain the most prominent structure is the red nucleus in which large—and small—celled portions can be distinguished. In the tegmentum is also found the interpeduncular nucleus.

Superior colliculi

These are large and well developed, but in view of the putative poor eyesight of echidnas their functions are apparently not chiefly visual. It is possible to distinguish seven layers in each colliculus but most of the afferent fibres to it appear to end in one layer, the stratum griseum intermedium. Afferent fibres arrive from the optic chiasma (a very poor contribution) via the brachium superior; others come from the Vth nerve, the medial lemniscus, the lateral lemniscus, and from the cerebral cortex; there is also a superior collicular commissure. The efferent fibres arise mainly from the stratum griseum profundum and they are widely distributed in various fibre tracts. The most important of these are the fountains of Meynert.

These give rise to two tracts, the tecto-bulbar (medulla oblongata) and the tecto-spinal. Other efferent fibres from the stratum griseum profundum connect with the 3rd and 4th nuclei, most of the thalamic nuclei, the nucleus reuniens, the hypothalamus, the nucleus pretectalis, the pons, and with the cerebellum.

Inferior colliculi

The path of the auditory fibres from the lateral lemniscus to the inferior colliculus was described on p. 88. The nucleus in the posterior colliculus is lenticular in shape and it is surrounded by fibres of the lateral lemniscus. Efferent fibres from this nucleus pass to the medial geniculate nucleus (in the thalamus) via the brachium inferior. However, some fibres of the lateral lemnicus pass straight through the mid-brain without interruption in the inferior colliculi to form synapses in the medial geniculate body. Some of these are auditory fibres, and the echidna is here exhibiting in a minor way that cortical recognition of hearing, which is characteristic of higher mammals, since the impulses relayed to the dorsal nucleus of the medial geniculate body are in turn relayed to the posterior region of the cerebral hemispheres.

The cerebral peduncles

Posteriorly these are fused into a single structure, the tegmentum, which contains on each side an ovoid mass of grey matter—the red nucleus. This consists of large and small celled moieties; it receives fibres from the ventral thalamus and from the cerebellum via the brachium conjunctivum and gives rise to a large group of fibres—the rubro-spinal tracts. These, on issuing from the lower part of the nucleus, cross in the ventral part of the tegmentum to form the decussation of Forel. Their function in echidnas is unknown but they appear to be concerned with the execution of skilled muscular movements in man.

The ganglion interpedunculare, or interpeduncular nucleus, forms a very large mass on the ventral surface of the mid-brain between the cerebral peduncles. It receives from the habenular (olfactory) ganglia, fibres which enter and decussate before they form synapses at the cells of the nucleus. Efferent fibres from the interpeduncular nucleus then pass to visceral motor centres in the medulla oblongata; this, then, is the anatomical basis of the olfacto-visceral activities of the habenular ganglia. The tractus habenulo-peduncularis forms part of an important bundle of fibres, the fasciculus retroflexus, which also conveys fibres from the thalamus to the habenular ganglia. The fasciculus retroflexus thus contains ascending and descending fibres.

The connections of the medial longitudinal fasciculus with the oculomotor and trochlear nuclei have been mentioned. These nuclei lying in the central grey matter of the mesencephalon between the ventricle and the medial longitudinal fasciculus are separate entities unlike their counterparts in the rest of the mammalia. The 4th or trochlear nucleus is composed of scattered small cells the root fibres of which pass downwards through the mesencephalic grey matter to decussate and emerge. It innervates the superior oblique muscle of the eyeball. The nucleus of the oculomotor nerve is very large and reaches almost to the diencephalon. Its fibres innervate the extrinsic eye muscles except the superior oblique and the external rectus which is innervated by the abducent (VIth nerve). Between the two nuclei is a mass of very small cells which may be the Edinger–Westphal nucleus. This in other vertebrates provides the preganglionic fibres of the ciliary ganglion the cells of which in turn innervate the circular muscle of the iris and the ciliary muscle. There is no ciliary muscle, however, in the tachyglossid eye (p. 110).

The cerebral peduncles in the anterior region of the mesencephalun are widely separated and consist of Goldby's cortico-spinal (tractos temporo-trigeminalis), cortico-pontine, Abbie's pyramidal, and arcuate fibres. The substantia nigra, of unknown significance, consists of pigmented cells in close relation to the pyramidal tract.

PARS INTERCALIS ENCEPHALI

Between the mesencephalon and the diencephalon lies an indeterminate region in the brains of echidnas. In some accounts they are described as part of the diencephalon but Abbie considers them as representing a higher mesencephalic level rather than as diencephalic. The structures in question are the nucleus pretectalis, the posterior nucleus of the thalamus, the large-celled nucleus of the optic tract, the posterior commissure, and the fasciculus retroflexus. The latter is of especial importance since it contains fibres which arise from the pars medialis of the ventral nucleus of the thalamus, which, *inter alia*, is the end-station for trigeminal impulses, and which pass to the habenular region and the stria medullaris, both of which are concerned with the reception of olfactory impulses. This band of fibres thus connects the trigeminal end-station in the thalamus with the olfactory apparatus, linking tactile sensibility of the head and mouth with smell. Abbie points out that Jones' (1923) observations of echidnas fossicking support the operation of such a tract; he wrote:

> . . . on this testing it is not only the sensitive skin (of the snout) which is called into play; for judging by the frequent inspiratory sniffs which form the accompaniment of most of Echidna's activities the sense of smell is an important guiding factor.

The pretectal nucleus, which is phylogenetically ancient, and the posterior nucleus of the thalamus receive lemniscal fibres and fibres from the posterior commissure which unites the two pretectal nuclei; the pretectal nuclei probably also have connections with the lateral geniculate nuclei and with the habenular ganglion.

Both the nucleus pretectalis and the nucleus posterius of the thalamus are found within the superior collicular region in higher mammals, thus becoming entirely mesencephalic; the pars intercalis encephali is then no longer an entity.

THE DIENCEPHALON

The interbrain consists of a ventral hypothalamus, a middle thalamus (in two parts, sub- and dorsal thalamus) and a dorsal epithalamus. The hypothalamus contains the hypophysis, the mamillary body, and the tuber cinereum. The hypothalamus is concerned in the integration of functions carried out by the autonomic system.

The epithalamus contains the pineal gland and the paired habenular ganglia concerned with olfaction.

The dorsal thalamus consists of medial and lateral divisions, the medial containing anterior, medial, and mid-line groups of nuclei, while the lateral contains the ventral group of nuclei which receive the greater part of the lemnisci fibres. The group provides pathways to the cortex for the conscious recognition of pain, temperature, tactile, proprioceptive, and vestibular impulses. Also belonging to the lateral division of the dorsal thalamus are the medial and lateral geniculate bodies. The medial geniculate is a way station for auditory and the lateral is a similar station for visual impulses passing to the posterior regions of the cortex (p. 103). A large massa intermedia connects the two thalami.

The Hypothalamus

This consists of an optic-commissural part, a glandular part, and olfactory–visceral correlation centres in the tuber cinereum and the mamillary body. These three entities will be described in that order.

(a) The optic chiasma is very small and the decussation is practically complete. Fibres from it pass in the optic tract to the lateral geniculate body and to the superior colliculi, via the brachium superior. Three other commissural systems connecting mid-brain and diencephalic nuclei are found in this region: the commissures of Ganser, Meynert, and of Gudden.

(b) The hypophysis is a large, roughly pear-shaped body lying appressed to the tuber cinereum. It consists of two endocrine glands, both of ectodermal origin, but from different tissues: the pars nervosa is the sacculate swollen termination of a ventral extension of the infundibulum which is hollow and contains an extension of the 3rd ventricle; the pars anterior is a derivative of the buccal cavity ectoderm known as Rathke's pouch. A detailed description of the hypophysis is given in Chapter 6. The pars nervosa contains an extraordinary number of nerve fibres and their terminations (Rasmussen, 1938). In eutherian mammals and birds these fibres are known to arise in the supraoptic and paraventricular nuclei of each side in the anterior hypothalamus. The cells of these nuclei contain neurosecretory granules which are also found in the axons all the way down into the pars nervosa. Barer, Heller, and Lederis (1963) have shown that these granules, isolated from the nerves, contain the pars nervosa hormones oxytocin and vaspressin, which have milk ejection and antidiuretic properties respectively. Thus the supraoptic and paraventricular nuclei along with their dependent unmyelinated axons constitute an endocrine gland.

(c) The olfacto-visceral correlation centres are in the tubercinerum. These are the medial hypothalamic and preoptic nuclei and a ventral hypothalamic nucleus. These are all virtually continuous and their combined efferent fibres give rise to the medial olfacto-habenular component of the stria medullaris. The lateral hypothalamic and preoptic nuclei also form a continuous cell mass which lies among the fibres of the medial fore-brain bundle and which gives rise to the lateral olfacto-habenular component of the stria medullaris. The origin of the fore-brain bundle is ill-defined, but the bulk of the fibres appear to arise in the medial olfactory region of the cerebral hemisphere. As the fibres pass posteriorly they are distributed to the above-mentioned nuclei, the corpus mamillare, and the tegmentum. In addition to these fibres many others reach the hypothalamus from various regions of the brain. A compact mass of fibres from the cerebral hemisphere terminating in the hypothalamus at the dorsal aspect of the medial fore-brain bundle is the olfactory projection tract of Cajal; others come from the red nucleus, the medial lemniscus, the tectum, and from the posterior and ventro-medial nuclei of the thalamus.

The corpus mamillare is very large but its connections are chiefly with the lower centres in the brain stem and connections with the fore-brain are small. Those connections are: a rudimentary fasciculus mamillo-thalamicus and the tractus mamillo-tegmentalis which both arise from the medial nucleus. The fasciculus mamillo-thalamicus is ill-defined like that in the Sauropsida; the majority of these fibres terminate in the anterior poles of the ventro-medial and ventral-thalamic nuclei.

The largest tract is the peduncle of the corpus mamillare: it arises in the lateral nucleus and passes caudally where it is lost in the tegmentum.

The fornix, from the hippocampal cortex, is a poorly defined tract at this level and its fibres terminate in the lateral nucleus of the mamillary body.

The thalamus

The large size of the diencephalon is due chiefly to the hypertrophy of the ventral nucleus of the thalamus which projects caudally in a large "pulvinar" reminiscent of that found in higher primates (Fig. 31), but, unlike the primate pulvinar, its large size is due to hypertrophy of the ventral nucleus of the thalamus.

At the caudal border of the pulvinar and along the course of the optic tract in the brachium superior is a swelling, the lateral geniculate body. Medial to this and at the antero-lateral border of the cerebral peduncle is the medial geniculate body (Fig. 30).

The two divisions of the nuclei of the thalamus mentioned above are as follow:

(a) The lateral division which contains the ventral group of nuclei consisting of the nucleus ventralis and ventralis medius, and the dorsal nuclei of the medial and lateral geniculate bodies. The ventral nucleus itself, although enormous in *Tachyglossus*, is even bigger in *Ornithorhynchus*, whose trigeminal nerve is also much larger (Hines, 1929). Posteriorly the ventral nucleus projects as the pulvinar (Fig. 30) and anteriorly it reaches as far as the anterior end of the diencephalon and extends into the hemisphere compressing the internal capsule and the corpus striatum. The ventral nucleus is divided into lateral and medial parts; these receive spinal and trigeminal afferent fibres respectively from the medial lemniscus. Both parts of the ventral nucleus send fibres to the hemisphere through the lateral medullary lamina, and also to the habenular nuclei via the tractus thalamo-epithalamicus (tractus epithalamicus).

The nucleus ventralis medialis lies between the ventral nucleus and the periventricular grey matter and has connections with the habenular nuclei, the tectum, the hypothalamus, and the hemispheres; the fibres to the latter probably ending in the corpus striatum.

The dorsal nucleus of the medial geniculate body can only be identified by tracing the auditory fibres in the inferior brachium to their termination in a scarcely differentiated portion of the lateral part of the ventral nucleus. This termination represents the dorsal nucleus of the medial geniculate body in the higher mammals where a greater contribution of auditory fibres has led to an unequivocal differentiation of the nucleus from the ventral nucleus complex. The condition of the dorsal nucleus of the lateral geniculate body is much the same, it can only be identified by the termination there of optic fibres which have passed in the optic tract from the optic chiasma.

The combined auditory, optic, and posterior thalamus radiations pass to the posterior part of the cerebral hemisphere known as area 4 of Schuster (1910) (see p. 101).

As well as the ventral group of nuclei there are two ill-defined groups—the lateral and the anterior groups. These are associated with the ventral nuclei and carry out the same sort of functions, i.e. the receipt of various sensory impulses (with the exception of those carried by lemniscal fibres) and the radiation of those impulses to the posterior cortex and to the corpus striatum.

(b) The mid-line nuclei concerned with interdiencephalic correlations are anomalous compared with those in other primitive
mammals in that they are distorted and pushed into strange positions
by the hypertrophied ventral nucleus complex. This has made their
recognition difficult and their connections have not been traced.

The epithalamus

The habenular ganglion of the epithalamus exhibits the usual
medial and lateral nuclei which are connected by afferent fibres to the
pretectal nucleus, the medial part of the ventral nucleus of the
thalamus, the nucleus ventralis medialis, the opposite habenular
ganglion, and the interpeduncular ganglion. The habenular nuclei
are also connected to the medial and lateral hypothalamic and preoptic nuclei by substantial fibre tracts, the striae medullares. The
striae also carry contributions of cortico-habenular fibres via the
fornix (p. 99) while other fibres arrive on the stria from the medial
olfactory region independently of the fornix.

Efferent fibres pass from the habenula in the fasciculus retroflexus to the interpeduncular ganglion and from here impulses are
transmitted to the visceral motor nuclei of the medulla oblongata.

THE TELENCEPHALON

The olfactory bulbs are attached by short peduncles to the anterior
ends of the pyriform lobes of the hemispheres; each pyriform lobe
is a sinuously curved band which extends along the whole length
of the hemisphere. The paired olfactory tubercles on the floor of
the telencephalon are very large. In median longitudinal section the
telencephalon is roughly oval in shape, and at its anterior end is the
lamina terminalis in which is embedded the anterior commissure
linking the two halves of the corpus striatum together; dorsal to this
is the hippocampal commissure linking together the two cerebral
hemispheres. Dorsal to the hippocampal commissure is a prolongation of the fascia dentata which extends along the medial hemisphere
wall at its caudal end. At the anterior part of the fascia dentata, a
strand of fibres can be seen coming from the hippocampus. This
strand is the fimbria which passes caudally and is then known as the
fornix. The distribution of the fibres of the fornix is described below.

The olfactory nerves entering the telencephalon terminate in the anterior olfactory nucleus and from here efferent fibres leave in two sets, the lateral and the medial olfactory striae. Impulses from the former pass either directly to the hippocampus or indirectly via the lateral olfactory area. From the hippocampus the impulses pass via the fimbria-fornix to the stria medullaris (to the habenula), and to the lateral nucleus of the mamillary body which is connected by the poorly developed tractus mamillo-thalamicus to the ventral thalamic nuclei.

Medial olfactory strial fibres pass to: (a) the opposite anterior olfactory nucleus in the anterior commissure; (b) to the amygdaloid nucleus of the corpus striatum (via the stria terminalis), whence impulses pass to the stria medullaris, and to the olfacto-visceral centres in the tuber cinereum; and (c) to a medial olfactory area whence efferent fibres also pass to the habenula and via the medial fore-brain bundle, to the hypothalamus (probably the medial, preoptic and lateral hypothalamic nuclei) and the corpus mamillare.

From Ziehen's (1908) account it appears that the corpus striatum, which is situated in the lower half of the cerebral hemisphere is mammalian in character and consists of three nuclear groups: the nucleus caudatus, the n. lenticulostriatus, the n. amygdale, the n. accumbens, and Meynert's nucleus.

Very little is known of the connections of the caudate and lentiform complexes in *Tachyglossus*. A tractus striosubthalamicus arises in the medial part of the corpus striatum and passes to various nuclei in the subthalamus; it appears to be peculiar to monotremes (Hines, 1929; Abbie, 1934). The nucleus ventralis medialis sends forward fibres that probably end in the corpus striatum as they do in other mammals.

In *Ornithorhynchus* (Hines), and presumably in *Tachyglossus*, the lentiform nucleus is in two parts, the putamen and the globus pallidus; Meynert's nucleus is associated with the latter. The various nuclei are interconnected and the main efferent impulses of the corpus striatum pass via an entity called the ansa lenticularis, to subthalamic and mid-brain centres.

The functional properties of the corpus striatum and its relation to certain types of behaviour are discussed in the next section.

The cerebral hemispheres

In birds the corpus striatum is massive and is much more highly organized than that in mammals. Whereas the mammalian corpus striatum contains three nuclear centres, that in the sparrow, for example, exhibits ten such configurations. The cerebral cortex is relatively poorly developed and the corpus striatum carries out the correlation of the reactions and movements which form a part of instinctive behaviour. Instinct is highly developed in birds and its rather inflexible nature is due to the fact that the reflex areas and association neurons in the thalamus and corpus striatum conform to a pattern which is the result of ontogeny. This sort of behaviour, governed by the arrangement of neurons incorporated into a solid mass, is not easily modified to deal with unusual circumstances. In mammals the opposite is the case; a vast hypertrophy of the cerebral cortex dominates the corpus striatum which is organized into three nuclear centres only. The cerebral cortex is not a solid mass but is a layer of neurons the number of which in a phyletic sense is increased by increasing the area of the layer by folding. The layer formation allows of an arrangement of a great number of centres at the surface and this, coupled with the plasticity of synaptic activity (Eccles, 1953), is the anatomical and physiological basis of the versatility of mammals in making unusual correlations.

The architecture of the mammalian cerebral cortex is best understood by comparing it with the condition of the reptile hemisphere. Here there are two main longitudinal strips in the roof of the hemisphere; the laterally placed strip is the palaeocortex (= cortex pyriformis or olfactory cortex), and the median archaecortex (cortex hippocampi); in between is an indication of a third strip, the neocortex. In mammals the neocortex is large and overshadows the pyriform and hippocampal cortices; as a consequence the neocortex displaces the palaecortex to a ventral position and where the two meet a longitudinal fissure, the sulcus rhinalis, is formed. The neocortex also displaces the hippocampal cortex and since it has a median position it is squeezed or rolled to form another fissure, the sulcus hippocampi.

The consensus is that the neocortex is of dual origin, i.e. it is formed from parahippocampal and parapyriform portions. Abbie (1940), on morphological grounds, found that the neocortex of the monotremes conforms to the general mammalian pattern in that it is made up of the parapyriform and parahippocampal parts.

Although the neocortex in all mammals is very well developed the gyrencephalic cerebrums of *Tachyglossus* and of *Zaglossus* (Gervais,

1878; Kolmer, 1925) have been a source of astonishment to neuro-anatomists; Elliott Smith (1902) was constrained to write:

> The most obtrusive feature of this brain is the relatively enormous development of the cerebral hemispheres which are much larger, both actually and relatively, than those of the platypus. In addition the extent of the cortex is very considerably increased by numerous deep sulci. The meaning of this large neopallium is quite incomprehensible. The factors which the study of other mammalian brains has shown to be the determinants of the extent of the cortex fail completely to explain how it is that a small animal of the lowliest status in the mammalian series comes to possess this large cortical apparatus.

Smith was uneasy about the unfamiliar arrangement of the sulci and gyri in this cerebrum and rather than commit himself to terms that would imply homology with the sulci of other mammalian brains he labelled them with greek letters, and that system is still used. The cerebrum is compressed antero-caudally which gives it a rounded appearance. The neocortex is separated by a deep sulcus rhinalis from the pyriform lobe and beneath the frontal poles lie the two broad, flat, olfactory bulbs.

According to Brodman (1909) the cortex of *Tachyglossus* exhibits more or less the usual six layers found in those of other mammals. The layers are described thus: plexiform, small granular (referring to granules in small cells), medium to large-size pyramidal, large granular, inner large pyramidal, and the spindle cell layer. These are not immutable entities and some parts of the cortex may be "agranular". In the brain of *Tachyglossus* Schuster (1910) found that the sulcus alpha separates a posterior granular cortical formation (area 4) from an agranular formation which covered most of the lateral surface of the hemisphere. Abbie (1940), in a far more detailed study, confirmed that observation. This is particularly interesting in view of some fascinating results that have come from the experiments of Richard Lende (1964) on motor and sensory representation in the cortex of *Tachyglossus*.

The sensory areas were defined by the evoked-potential procedure, i.e. potentials developed in response to various stimuli were recorded by steel wire electrodes inserted in various parts of the cortex—the responses being amplified and displayed on a cathode-ray oscilloscope. The stimuli employed were as follow: tactile by a tap with a camel's hair brush, auditory by the click of a loudspeaker, and visual by an electronic flash. In the experiments on motor activities of the cortex, the anaesthetized animal was suspended from a rod by wires

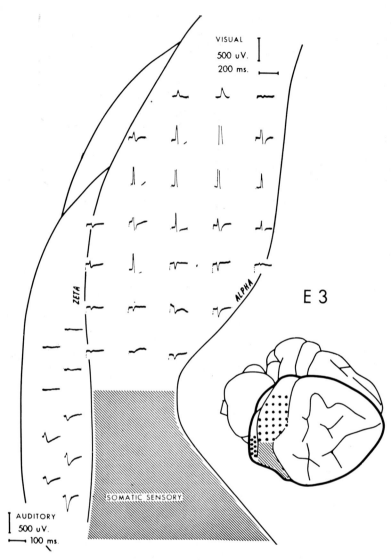

FIG. 34. Lateral view of right hemisphere in *Tachyglossus* showing auditory and visual fields. Frontal pole to the right, cerebellum to the left. The somatic sensory field is indicated by diagonal stripes. (Lende, 1964.) (Reproduced from *J. Neurophys.*)

which passed through the spines of the vertebrae so that the limbs hung freely; the exposed cortex was stimulated by the passage of current through bipolar electrodes with poles 1·5 mm apart.

It was found that auditory, visual, and somatic sensory areas were located as shown in Fig. 34. This shows the right hemisphere outlined in a heavy line; the shaded portion responded to tactile stimulation, the closely arranged dots represent the area which responded to auditory stimulation, and the sparsely arranged dots to visual stimulation. Drawings from photographs of the cathode-ray oscilloscope display are mounted in the area where the response was obtained. From this it is seen that the visual cortex is in an area sharply defined by sulci zeta and alpha and that the auditory area is at the posterior pole of the hemisphere equally sharply separated from the visual and somatic sensory areas by the sulcus zeta which lies immediately anterior to it.

The full extent of the somatic sensory area is shown in a lateral view of the right hemisphere (Fig. 35); the parts of the echidna which were stimulated, giving rise to the electrical charges in the cortex, are indicated by the small figures drawn on the appropriate part of the cortex. From this it can be seen that representation of the tongue was found to extend rostral to the lower end of the sulcus alpha; weak responses from stimulation of the limbs were also obtained in front of sulcus alpha but Lende is of the opinion that these are in the category of "fringe responses" which are known to be recorded electrically from regions adjacent to foci of maximal responses.

The location of the motor area as judged by movements obtained on stimulation of the cortex are shown in Fig. 36. From this it is seen that the motor region includes the whole of the sensory area behind alpha and an area of about the same size in the gyrus between sulci α and β. A remarkable feature of the overlapping sensory and motor area is that there is a correspondence of sensory and motor representation at each point (Fig. 37); where strong motor effects are elicited, in the neck and shoulder musculature, for example, equally well defined somatic sensory representation of those structures is found at the same locus in the cortex.

The echidna cortex is quite unlike that in other mammals: firstly, the grouping of the visual, auditory, and somatic sensory areas over the occipital pole of the cortex has not been observed in another mammal, and secondly, the relations of the three entities one to the other are different from those in other mammals; in echidnas the

E—H

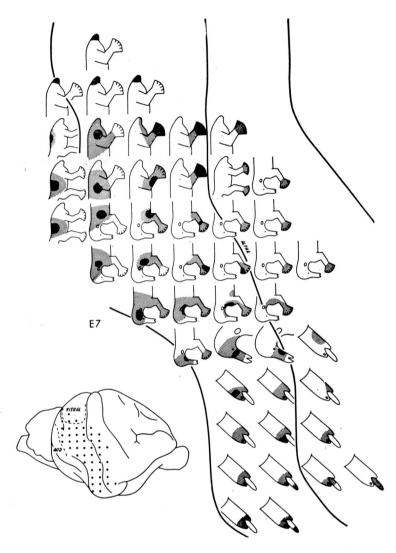

FIG. 35. Lateral view of right hemisphere, frontal pole to the left showing somatic sensory field. Dots indicate where responses are recorded. Shaded areas on figurines indicate areas stimulated and black areas denote where maximal response was elicited. Echidna E7. (Lende, 1964.) (Reproduced from *J. Neurophys.*)

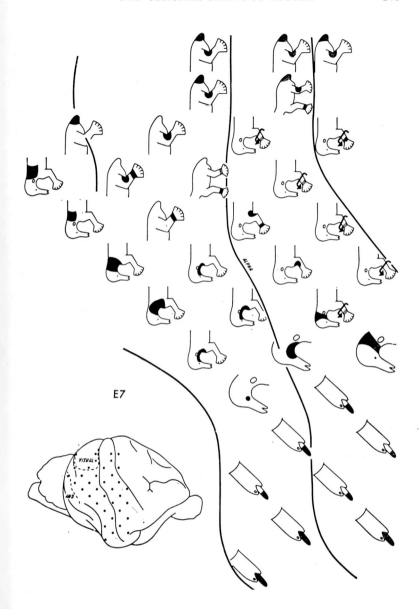

FIG. 36. Somatic motor field in echidna E7. (Lende, 1964.) (Reproduced from *J. Neurophys.*)

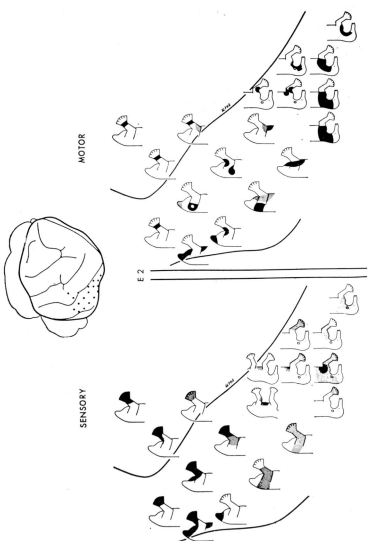

Fig. 37. Somatic sensory and motor data from one echidna E2. Dots on the right hemisphere indicate points of cortical recording on tactile stimulation which give the sensory results shown on the left. These same cortical points were then stimulated and the motor responses are shown on the right. (Lende, 1964.) (Reproduced from *J. Neurophys.*)

somatic sensory area is located at the ventro-lateral aspect of the occipital pole, the visual area is dorsal to this and the auditory area is posterior to these two. In marsupials the arrangement is quite different (Lende, 1963); however, the marsupial cortex and that of *Tachyglossus* are similar in the sense that a sensorimotor amalgam is found in both, but in the marsupial there is complete and coincident overlap of sensory and motor representation of the body; there is no separate motor area divorced from sensory representation as there is in the *Tachyglossus* cortex lying anterior to the sensorimotor amalgam. Thus the cortex of *Tachyglossus* bears a resemblance to the cortex of eutherians where only separate motor and sensory areas are encountered, but in totally different areas of the cortex from those in *Tachyglossus*; there the resemblance ends since there is no sensorimotor amalgam in the eutherian cortex, at least not in those studied so far.

Lende's observations are in agreement with Goldby's (1939) in that a tract of motor fibres, as shown by degeneration experiments, arises in an area which has somatic motor properties as demonstrated by delicate stimulation techniques. These results are also in harmony with the findings of Schuster (1910) and of Abbie (1940) on the difference of the cytology of the cortex anterior to sulcus alpha from that lying posterior to that sulcus, and they also substantiate Abbie's (1934) statement that the thalamic radiations terminate in the posterior region of the echidna cortex. However, they offer no support for his suggestions that the pyramidal tracts arise in the anterior pole of the cortex and that there is no frontal cortex as such. As Lende remarks "Ahead of the posteriorly situated sensory and motor areas established in this study there is relatively more frontal cortex than in any other mammal, including man, the function of which remains unexplored." When the functions of that region are known perhaps the reasons for the absence of fronto-pontine tracts in the monotreme cerebral peduncles will also be apparent.

CONCLUSIONS

Although the brains of echidnas for the most part are mammalian in character they do exhibit certain structures and arrangements that are also found in the brains of Sauropsida and for that reason they are called primitive. The motor system is in that category since the nucleus ambiguus and the hypoglossal nucleus are dorsally situated in the medulla oblongata, whereas they are ventrally situated in the eutherian myelencephalon; the facial nucleus occupies an intermediary position, nevertheless the presence of pyramidal tracts stamps the motor system as mammalian. Other differences from eutherian brains and likeness to sauropsidan are the retention of a pars intercalis encephali and the rudimentary condition of the fornix–mamillare–thalamic system; as a consequence of the latter condition discrete anterior nuclei in the thalamus have not differentiated from the main thalamic nuclei.

In other ways the brain shows specializations and developments not found in other primitive mammals: the organization of the cerebellum and the vast hypertrophy of the trigeminal sensory system with the consequent hypertrophy of the ventral nucleus of the thalamus.

The epithalamus is particularly well developed by virtue of its receipt of fibres from the pars medialis of the ventral nucleus of the thalamus and from the interpeduncular ganglion via the fasciculus retroflexus.

The location of the somatic sensory, visual, and auditory fields at the occipital pole of the cortex makes it unique among the brains of mammals so far studied and the presence of a sensorimotor amalgam, as well as a distinct motor area, the former a characteristic of marsupials, the latter of eutherians, in the one cortex, makes it even more so.

Finally it must be mentioned that the structure of the brain stem of *Ornithorhynchus* is very much like that of echidnas (Hines, 1929); where the one is specialized the other is likewise specialized, where it is primitive the other exhibits a like structure or arrangement, but it remains to be seen whether or not the lissencephalic cortex of *Ornithorhynchus* exhibits the type of sensory and motor representation found in echidnas.

CHAPTER 5

SPECIAL SENSES

THE EYES

According to Walls (1942) the published descriptions, with the exception of O'Day's (1938), of the eyes of echidnas are erroneous. The bulk of O'Day's observations, however, have not been published but have been made available to Walls who also had access to O'Day's preparations. The following descriptions are based on Walls' interpretations of O'Day's work.

In fresh specimens the eyeball is spherical and convex but fixation tends to produce collapse which confers an avian appearance on the eye. There are no nictitating membranes and the lower lids only are equipped with tarsal plates (plates of connective tissue shaped to fit the outer convexity of the cornea). On the other hand, *Ornithorhynchus* has nictitating membranes and tarsi in the upper and lower lids; it is appropriate to point out here that in the sauropsidan reptiles the lower lids only possess tarsi, and in the Metatheria and Eutheria the upper lids only are equipped with them.

Lacrimal (serous) and Harderian (sebaceous) glands are present in the eyes of *Tachyglossus* but Kolmer (1925) found only serous glands in the eye of *Zaglossus*. As an extra precaution against damage the corneal epithelium in the eye of *Tachyglossus* is keratinized as it is in those of ant-eating armadillos and aard-varks.

The relations of the extrinsic eye muscles are like those in mammals, that is to say the four "recti": superior, inferior, medial, and lateral take their origins at the rear of the bony orbit and become tendinous before they fuse with the tissue of the sclera. The two other muscles are attached obliquely to the eyeball and pass to the nasal side of the anterior part of the orbit. One of these, the inferior oblique, takes its origin there but the other, the superior oblique, passes through that fantastic pulley which is characteristic of the mammalian orbit, and passes to the back of the orbit where it takes its origin slightly anterior to those of the rectus muscles. There is also associated with the superior oblique a slip of muscle which has its origin at the anterior nasal orbital wall and its insertion emerging on the sclera with that of the superior oblique. This extra slip of muscle sometimes occurs in the adnexa of the human eye.

As mentioned in Chapter 3, the sclera contains the cartilaginous cup which is so characteristic of the sauropsidan eye. In *Tachyglossus* the cartilage is 27 μ thick in the region of the optic nerve but in *Zaglossus* it is 160 μ thick. This cup is surrounded by an outer

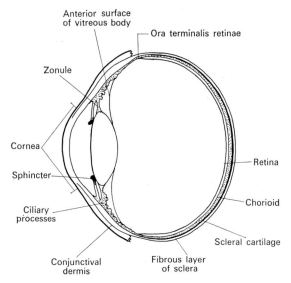

FIG. 38. Section of the eye of *Tachyglossus*. After Walls (1942). (Reproduced by permission of the Cranbrook Institute of Science.)

layer of fibrous scleral tissue which provides the insertions of the extrinsic muscles.

Internal to the cartilaginous cup is the thin chorioidal layer which naturally is pigmented and has a highly vascular choriocapillaris whose vessels have unusually large diameters and are connected to large veins. Since there are no blood vessels in the retina its nutrition is wholly dependent on the blood supply of the chorioid. The chorioid is continued anteriorly to form the uveal portion of the ciliary body; there is no ciliary muscle. These relations are best seen in a section of the eye (Fig. 38). The ciliary body which is covered by the ciliary portion of the retina, consists of about 60 processes whose anterior ends are interconnected by an annular shelf-like "sims". The iris is extremely simple and consists of little more than a prolongation of the retina with a few blood vessels attached to its anterior face. There is no dilator muscle, but there is a sphincter muscle bordering the iris.

The lens is small, and enjoys the distinction of being the "flattest of all lenses" (Walls), with a flatness index (diameter divided by thickness) of 2·75. It is suspended by numerous zonule fibres which arise in the ciliary body and the sims; the fibres are inserted compactly at the extreme periphery of the lens.

The retina is avascular and contains rods only, but that of *Ornithorhynchus* contains rods and cones of two kinds: single cones and double cones both of which kinds contains oil droplets. This type of retina is characteristic of that of marsupials but single cones only have been detected in Eutheria and none of those cones possess oil droplets.

The absence of cones from the retina of *Tachyglossus* (they are probably absent from those of *Zaglossus* also, but Kolmer's material was too poorly fixed to determine the matter) is not singular since many animals that shun the light such as edentates, bats, hedgehogs, and some prosimians have pure-rod retinas. If, as is believed, rods are responsive to weak light stimuli, such retinas represent an adaption for seeing in shady or dark places, and it follows that the sight of echidnas may not be as "defective" as one is led to think since echidnas spend a lot of their time in shady or dark places. However, the absence of any mechanism of accommodation coupled with the small size of the optic chiasma and optic tract do suggest that good eyesight is not one of the tachyglossid's strong points.

HEARING

The anatomy of the organs of hearing, with the exception of the organ of Corti, were described in Chapter 4. Corti's organ is the intermediary for conversion of sound waves in the perilymph into the electrical stimuli which are conveyed by the cochlear division of the VIIIth nerve to the dorsal and ventral cochlear nuclei.

The organ rests upon the basilar membrane and extends along its whole length from the proximal to the distal part of the scala media. From Alexander's (1904) and Kolmer's (1925) descriptions of a poorly fixed cochlea in adult *Tachyglossus* and *Zaglossus* and from well-fixed material in pouch young (Alexander) it appears that Corti's organ in echidnas is identical with that in eutherians, consisting essentially of long rows of exquisitely sensitive hair cells protected by, or attached to, a verandah-like roof, the tectorial membrane. The hair cells exhibit stiff cilia which project into the endolymph and may even be embedded in the overhanging tectorial membrane. The basal ends of the hair cells are in intimate relationship with the terminal fibres of the cochlear division of the VIIIth nerve.

Sound waves entering the cartilaginous ear trumpets set up, in the tympanic membrane, vibrations which are transferred by the long manubrium to the head of the hammer thence to the columelliform stapes via the incus. By analogy with what takes place in the eutherian cochlea it can be assumed that the movements of the expanded footplate of the stapes on the vestibular membrane are transmitted to the perilymph, and since the membrane in the round window can bulge into the middle-ear chamber in response to the movements of the stapes, corresponding movements can occur in the perilymph of the scala vestibuli. Thus each time the footplate of the stapes is pressed into the oval window the basilar membrane moves towards the scala tympani and bends the processes of the hair cells fixed to the tectorial membrane.

When the ear is stimulated by sounds, vibrations of the organ of Corti produce corresponding electric changes in the scala media. These minute potentials (less than 1 mV) can be detected by an electrode placed on the round window (Davis, 1957) and they are known as cochlear microphonics (CM). These microphonic potentials, which follow exactly sound pressure vibrations, are generated in the hair cells of the organ of Corti. Exact details of their generation are unknown but they appear to be dependent on the high potassium content of the endolymph in the scala media. The endolymphs of all vertebrates examined so far have high potassium and low sodium concentrations; mammals, for example, have about 150 mM K and 5 mM Na (Johnstone *et al.*, 1963).

In addition to CM there are other potentials in the scala media, the d.c. resting potential or endocochlear potential (EP) and sum-mating potential (SP) (see Konishi, Butler, and Fernandez, 1960, for review of literature). The d.c. potential in the mammalian cochlea is about + 80 mV with respect to plasma, about + 45 mV in birds and only + 2 to + 20 mV in reptiles (Schmidt, 1963). This d.c.

potential in the mammal cochlea is decreased by anoxia, but the reptilian d.c. potential is anoxia-insensitive (Schmidt, 1963; Schmidt and Fernandez, 1963). The summating potential (SP) is a steady potential in the scala media related to the average sound pressure. In addition to these potentials of the scala media, an action potential (AP) occurs, of course, in the cochlear division of the VIIIth nerve.

Thus the cochlea potentials give considerable insight into the nature of the physiology of the cochlea, i.e. whether or not it is

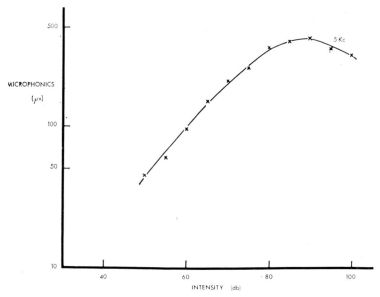

FIG. 39. Relationship of microphonic potential to applied sound pressure (db above 0·0002 dyne). The curve is reasonably linear up to 80 db. (Johnstone unpub.)

mammalian, avian, or reptilian in its characteristics. Recently Dr. Brian Johnstone and his colleagues at the University of Western Australia have studied these potentials in the echidna cochlea. Dr. Johnstone has very kindly sent me his results, which are about to be published, and they are as follow: the d.c. potential in the scala media of *Tachyglossus aculeatus aculeatus* and *ineptus* is approximately + 80 mV and it is anoxia-sensitive. CM, SP, and AP were 500 μV, 400 μV, and 100 μV, respectively and all very similar to those recorded in eutherian mammals (Fernandez and Schmidt,

1963; Schmidt, 1963; Schmidt and Fernandez, 1963). These values are very different from those recorded in reptiles (CM 10 μV, SP 100 μV, AP 20 μV) by Johnstone and Johnstone (1965). Furthermore, the CM in echidnas are smooth functions of sound pressure (Fig. 39) whereas in lizards there are several peaks and troughs (Wever *et al.*, 1963).

The cochlear microphonics audiogram, i.e. the sound pressure required to elicit a constant level of microphonics, was also recorded

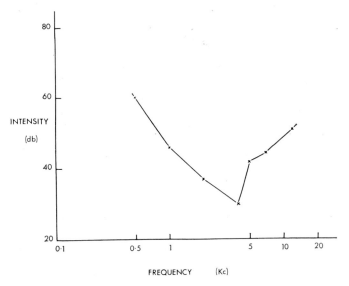

Fig. 40. Cochlear microphonic frequency responses. The ordinate is the sound pressure (in db above 0·0002 dyne) required to elicit a constant microphonic voltage (10 μV). (Johnstone, unpubl.)

in echidnas. It is very similar to the eutherian CM audiogram; maximum sensitivity was observed at 2–3 kc and the responses at 15 kc and at 500 c/s was some 30 db less sensitive (Fig. 40).

The frequency at which the cochlea was most sensitive depended somewhat on the condition of the cartilaginous external auditory meatus and since the dissection necessary to expose the round window caused some drying of the meatus, the true maximum sensitivity is likely to be nearer 2 kc than 3 kc.

Since it is known that the microphonic audiogram is a reasonable approximation to the true audiogram it may be inferred from this that the hearing of echidnas is similar in frequency range but somewhat less sensitive than the eutherian (for example cats) hearing. Thus the lack of coiling in the cochlea and the marsupial-like ossicles do not appear to give rise to hearing different from that in eutherians in any major way.

Johnstone also made some tests to see if the ear was peculiarly sensitive to sounds conducted by the body. Tapping the body at various points elicited very small microphonics but when the snout was tapped a large microphonic potential was observed. It is entirely possible then that echidnas get some sound information when its snout is resting on, or buried in, the ground.

Johnstone concludes that the echidna ear appears to be every bit as efficient as that in the Eutheria.

CHAPTER 6

ENDOCRINE GLANDS AND THE GLANDS OF THE IMMUNE SYSTEM

ADRENALS

Some nine separate studies of the prototherian adrenal have been made, but only on three occasions (Basir, 1932; Bourne, 1949; Wright, Jones, and Phillips, 1957) have the descriptions been based on observations of properly fixed fresh material. According to Basir and to Wright, Jones, and Phillips the adrenals, both left and right, are pear-shaped in *Tachyglossus aculeatus* (probably the subspecies *ineptus* was studied by Wright *et al.*, since these echidnas came from Western Australia) and in a typical specimen measured $1 \cdot 2 \times 0 \cdot 7$ cm and $0 \cdot 5$ cm deep. The anatomical relations with the kidneys are shown in Fig. 49. The whole gland is surrounded by a thick capsule of connective tissue embedded in which at the caudal pole is a mass of nervous tissue—Basir's ganglion. The caudal pole also contains the chromaffin tissue (Fig. 41), which is arranged as solid convoluted cords of tissue. The cells in the medulla appear to be of two tinctorially and structurally distinct kinds when stained with Heidenhain's iron haematoxylin: the cells at the periphery of the cords are elongated, arranged radially, and contain many darkly-staining granules (Fig. 42) and those at the core of the cords are polygonal, are not oriented in any particular way, and contain less granular matter than the peripheral cells. Possibly this is an anatomical expression of the elaboration of two active amines, epinephrine and norepinephrine. Bourne (1949) found that the relationships of medulla and cortex were highly variable and he claims that some adrenals had no chromaffin tissue whatever; whether or not those glands were serially sectioned is not stated.

The cortical tissue is made up of two types of cells and both types occur as irregularly arranged anastomosing cords, one or two cells in thickness (Wright, Jones, and Phillips, 1957). The cords are in many instances separated by sinusoids. Blood drains from all regions of the gland by these sinusoids which are interconnected. A large sinusoid passes from the capsule on the dorsal-lateral part of the gland, through the cortex, to join a smaller sinusoid. Here a large vein is formed by the junction of the two sinusoids and that

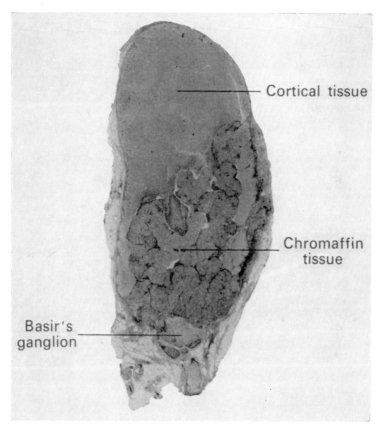

Cortical tissue

Chromaffin tissue

Basir's ganglion

FIG. 41. Median longitudinal section of right adrenal of *Tachyglossus a. aculeatus.* Heidenhain's iron haematoxylin. ×13.

vein passes through the chromaffin tissue. It is joined by more sinusoids before leaving the gland at the caudal pole.

One of the two types of cell found in the cortex occurs in the cords arranged around the periphery of the gland, lying immediately below the capsule. These are relatively large cells and when Mallory's triple stain is used to stain them, they take up the orange G com-

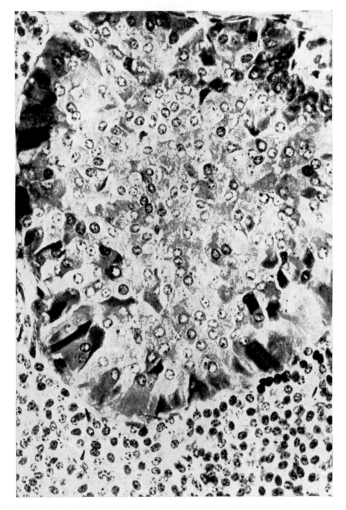

Fig. 42. Section through portion of chromaffin and cortical tissues of adrenal of *Tachyglossus a. aculeatus.* The cortical cells visible are of the small basophilic type. Heidenhain's iron haematoxylin. ×431.

ponent. The second type of cell is found in the deeper regions of the cortex and is particularly noticeable where the cortical tissue abuts against the chromaffin tissue. This cell is relatively small and, unlike the type at the periphery, is basophilic and does not stain with orange G.

In formalin-fixed glands Wright *et al.* found that Sudan black stain gave but a faint indication of lipid granules in the cortex. We have had much the same experience with the adrenal of *T. a. aculeatus*; a mixture of Sudans III and IV gave very little evidence of lipid droplets in formalin-fixed tissue. This is not to say that the echidna adrenal is incapable of laying down a store of lipid granules as eutherian adrenals do; many factors are known to influence the amount of lipid granules in the cortex and among these can be listed emotional stress and shock. In eutherians non-specific stressors can lead to the discharge of lipid from the adrenals and very likely this can happen in echidna adrenals. The adrenals that we studied were taken from an echidna killed a few days after it had been captured so that it is more than possible that it was terrified, a condition that would lead to discharge of lipids in eutherian adrenals. Until the adrenals in echidnas are studied under specified conditions the question whether or not lipid granules are stored in the cortex, remains open.

The arrangement of the cords in the cortex of the echidna adrenal is very like that found in bird and reptile adrenals (Wright and Jones, 1957; Sturkie, 1965), but in those animals the chromaffin tissue is scattered throughout the cortical tissue in the form of separate islets. The concentration of chromaffin tissue into a more or less well-defined mass is mammal-like so that the echidna adrenal exhibits that blend of mammalian and reptilian structures found in other organs. There is no real evidence that the cortical tissue is arranged into definite zones completely surrounding a discrete medulla as in the metatherian and eutherian adrenals, but Wright, Jones, and Phillips can detect a differentiation of cortical tissue into three layers which they designate, non-committally, zones 1, 2, and 3. This arrangement, they say "Demonstrates the potentiality of form finally achieved in the Metatheria and Eutheria in which the compact chromaffin tissue reaches its central position."

Corticosteroid secretion by the adrenals of Tachyglossus aculeatus

Weiss and McDonald (1965) have shown that free corticosteroids could be detected in only one instance out of five in peripheral whole blood. The steroids were cortisol (hydro-cortisone) and corticosterone in the minute concentrations of $0 \cdot 1$–$0 \cdot 2$ μg per 100 ml. Similarly corticosterone and cortisol were secreted into adrenal venous blood at very low rates; the maximum rate for corticosterone, for example, was only 2·6 μg per 100 mg adrenal per hr, which is minute compared with the rates of secretion found with rat, rabbit, guinea pig, and wombat adrenals (Weiss and McDonald, 1966).

Free or conjugated corticosterone, cortisol, or their tetrahydro derivatives could not be detected in measurable quantities in the urine of echidnas kept in metabolism cages—a finding in agreement with the observations of low secretion rates of corticosterone and cortisol. The significance of this is unknown at present and probably only adrenalectomy will give an estimate of the importance of the adrenals in echidna mineral and carbohydrate metabolic processes.

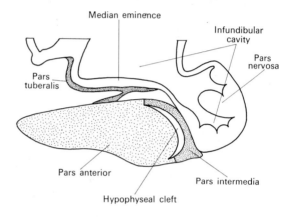

Fig. 43. Median longitudinal section of the pituitary gland of *Tachyglossus aculeatus*. After Hanström and Wingstrand (1951).

It is noteworthy, however, that echidnas are refractory to injections of large doses of cortisone as far as their blood sugar level is concerned (Griffiths, 1965a), suggesting that the minute amounts of gluco-corticoid secreted by its adrenals would be of little physiological significance to the echidna.

THE PITUITARY GLAND

As we have seen this is a large pear-shaped body dependent from the ventral surface of the infundibulum. Hanström and Wingstrand (1951) have described the arrangements of the various partes and their relationships to one another in the pituitary glands of one specimen of *T. a. setosus* and one of *T. a. aculeatus*. In both these pituitaries in median longitudinal section the pars anterior is seen to be pear-shaped with the narrow end anterior. At its dorsal surface the pars anterior comes into contact with a downward projection of the pars tuberalis, which is plastered along the whole length of the median eminence (Fig. 43). At the posterior end of the pars anterior is a hypophyseal cleft (a rest of the cavity of Rathke's pouch), which separates the pars anterior from the pars intermedia. The latter is closely applied to the antero-ventral face of the infundibular process or pars nervosa. In *T. a. setosus* Hanström and Wingstrand found that the pars intermedia was separated from the pars nervosa by a thin lamina of connective tissue which was not apparent in the *T. a. aculeatus* pituitary.

As far as the histology is concerned the pars tuberalis consists of chromophobe cells among which are scattered a few basophils. When stained with the Heidenhain azan technique the pars anterior is found to consist of two distinct regions: one, the anterior, exhibits many acidophils stained with carmine while the posterior region contains acidophils that stain for the most part with orange G. Both regions exhibit the usual sprinkling of basophil and chromophobe cells. The pars intermedia, unlike that in other vertebrates, is not a basophilic tissue but consists of acidophils and chromophobes.

The pars nervosa is noteworthy: in the eutherians and meta-therians the neural lobe arises as a hollow outgrowth from the floor of the diencephalon and its distal end grows into a solid swollen lobe which contains many characteristic cells called pituicytes which are related to the astrocytes of the central nervous system (Griffiths, 1940; Shanklin, 1944); among those pituicytes the terminations of the axons of the supraoptic nuclei of the hypothalamus are found (p. 95). In *Tachyglossus*, however, the infundibular cavity extends right down into the pars nervosa which is sacculated rather than knob-like, a condition like that found in the partes nervosae of the Sauropsida. In *Tachyglossus* the infundibular cavity is lined by ependymal cells whose processes intermingle with those of the pituicytes as they do in the pars nervosa of the chicken (Griffiths, 1940), but for some unknown reason the del Rio-Hortega (1921) silver carbonate technique that stains avian pituicytes so well stains only microglia, the representatives of the reticulo-endothelial system in the brain (cf. Vasquez-Lopez, 1940).

In the Eutheria the derivatives of Rathke's pouch elaborate protein and polypeptide hormones of high molecular weight but nothing is known of these in the Prototheria. On the other hand, Sawyer, Munsick, and Van Dyke (1960) have identified pharmacologically, the active principles in the pars nervosa of *Tachyglossus*. These are the two peptides oxytocin and 8-arginine vasopressin (antidiuretic factor) which are characteristic of all mammal pituitaries with the exception of those of the Suiformes which elaborate oxytocin and 8-lysine vasopressin (Ferguson and Heller, 1965). The

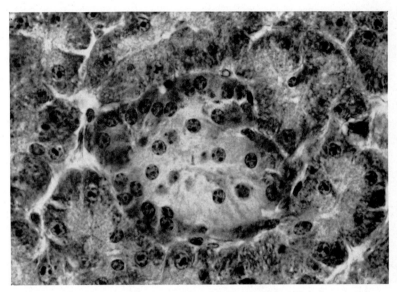

FIG. 44. Islet of Langerhans of *Tachyglossus a. aculeatus*. Showing central core of beta cells surrounded by a darkiy-staining ring of alpha cells. Gomori stain. (Griffiths, 1965a.) ×679. (Reproduced from *Comp. Biochem. Physiol.*)

Sauropsida, however, secrete an entirely different vasopressor–antidiuretic substance, 8-arginine oxytocin. This has equal pressor and oxytocic activity in the one molecule but in addition the sauropsidan pars nervosa elaborates oxytocin, so that the oxytocic activity here is the sum of the 8-arginine oxytocin + oxytocin (Follett, 1963), thus the partes nervosae of *Tachyglossus* and the Sauropsida are similar anatomically but different biochemically since the gland in *Tachyglossus* secretes hormones of the mammalian type.

Oxytocin is of peculiar importance to mammals since it brings about contraction of the myoepithelium which invests the alveolae of the mammary glands and thus brings about milk ejection (p. 190).

THE ISLETS OF LANGERHANS

The islets of Langerhans are distributed throughout the pancreas, which is a discrete organ, and they take the form of compact spheroidal groups of cells. The islets exhibit the usual alpha and beta cells,

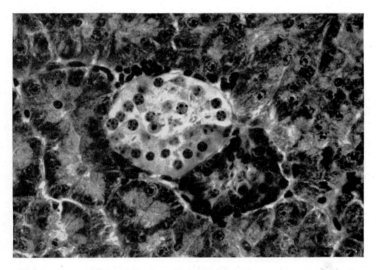

FIG. 45. An islet of Langerhans equipped with alpha, beta, and indifferent cells. The alpha cells form a discrete darkly-stained group peripheral to the others. Gomori stain. (Griffiths, 1965a.) ×453. (Reproduced from *Comp. Biochem. Physiol.*)

which secrete glucagon and insulin respectively, as well as C or indifferent cells. Many of the islets consist of alpha cells alone, or of indifferent cells alone, but the majority consist of a core of beta cells surrounded by a ring of alpha cells (Fig. 44), reminiscent of those in the rat pancreas. A few islets may possess all three classes of cells but where this happens the trend is, again, towards a discrete group of alpha cells peripheral to the rest of the cells (Fig. 45).

The quick fall of the blood sugar to a normal level after injection of glucose (Fig. 20) argues that an active secretion of stored insulin takes place in response to the hyperglycemia. However, crude insulin preparations of echidna pancreas, unlike similar preparations of rat pancreas (Griffiths, 1940), have no hypoglycemic activity when injected into rabbits (Griffiths, 1965a); on the contrary, they had marked hyperglycemic activity—a glucagon effect. This suggests that the echidna islets store more glucagon than insulin. The blood sugar of the echidna, however, responds in a normal way to injection of regular insulin but insulin has no anabolic effects in normal echidnas (Griffiths, 1965a). This is not novel since many normal Eutheria fail to exhibit enhanced growth or other anabolic effects in response to injected insulin, but insulin consistently induces growth and a positive nitrogen balance in diabetic animals. An attempt, therefore, was made to induce diabetes mellitus in echidnas with the idea of testing the effect of insulin in them. Injections of alloxan were found to be useless since the kidneys were more susceptible to the necrotic effects of alloxan than the islets of Langerhans were (Griffiths, 1965a); furthermore, injections of cortisone and of cortisone + porcine hypophyseal growth hormone failed to induce diabetes, contrary to their effects in many eutherians. The question, then, whether or not insulin has anabolic effects such as improved N_2 retention in echidnas, remains open.

THE THYROID GLAND AND OTHER DERIVATIVES OF THE PHARYNGEAL POUCHES

The development of the thyroids, thymus, parathyroids, carotid glands, and the post-branchial bodies have been described by Maurer (1899) in embryonic stages 40 to 47 and in a pouch young 12 cm long. The anatomy of the glands in one adult animal have also been described.

In the youngest stage the usual four pairs of pharyngeal pouches are found (Fig. 46). The first pair extending between the mandibular and hyoid arches come into relation at their distal ends with the auditory capsules and give rise to the tympanic cavity of either side and to the eustachian tubes. The second pair give rise to a pair of outgrowths that come into contact with the wall of the 3rd arterial arch; each of these outgrowths is nipped off and is transformed into a ganglion, which, along with other cellular elements forms a carotid body.

On the ventral surface of the pharynx between the 1st and 2nd sets of pouches an unpaired diverticulum appears which, when freed from the pharynx, will form the thyroid gland. The 3rd pair of pouches produces two sets of outgrowths which will disengage themselves from the pouches and migrate into the neck there to form the paired thymus and parathyroid glands. Another pair of parathyroids is formed from derivatives of the 4th pair of pharyngeal pouches which also give rise to the paired post-branchial bodies. In some mammals the 4th set of pouches forms a minor contribution

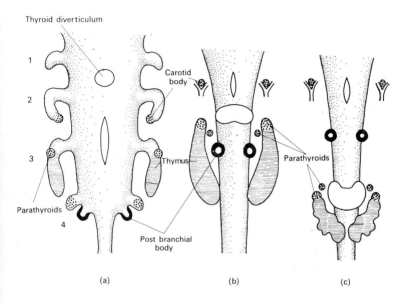

FIG. 46. Stages in the development of derivatives of the pharynx in *Tachyglossus*. (a) stage 40; (b), stage 47; (c) half grown echidna. 1, 2, 3, 4 = pharyngeal pouches. After Maurer (1899).

to the thymus, but in general the 3rd set of pouches is the major source of thymus tissue and the *Tachyglossus* thymus conforms to this pattern.

During the ensuing stages of development the analagen of the thyroid gland, the thymus glands, and of the parathyroids migrate caudally down the neck and come to lie in the thoracic cavity posterior to the diaphragm, attached to the trachea and in contact with the pericardium. In the half-grown echidna (Fig. 46 (c)) the thymus glands are relatively enormous but in the full-grown echidna they are tiny relative to the thyroid (Maurer, 1899). This process of atrophy is similar to that which takes place in birds, eutherian mammals, and in man.

In contrast to the three glands described, the post-branchial bodies retain a position anterior to the diaphragm and are attached laterally to the trachea.

Nothing has been published on the structure of the adult thyroid gland in *Tachyglossus* but Kolmer (1925) described a badly fixed, cytolysed gland of *Zaglossus bruijni*. However, Mr. M. Augee of Monash University has kindly sent me two of his slides of sections of the thyroid in *T. aculeatus aculeatus* and from this material it is apparent that the thyroid consists of the usual close aggregation of follicles or vesicles of variable size, the microscopial appearance of which gives no cause to disagree with Marine's (1932) statement that the gland is "Similar in all animals from fish to man." Each follicle consists of a single layer of epithelial cells which encloses a mass of colloid. However, in this specimen the epithelium is tall and resembles that of the normal rat thyroid and is quite unlike the flattened epithelium found in the guinea-pig thyroid; the colloid is lightly stained which is indicative of an actively secreting gland—dark-staining colloid is characteristic of sluggish inactive thyroids. Doubtless the tachyglossid thyroid will prove to exhibit vastly different cytological pictures at different times of the year much as the thyroids do in other mammals that hibernate (see Kayser, 1961).

The structure of the paired thymus glands in adult *T. a. aculeatus* has been described by Diener and Ealey (1965). Each gland consists of numerous highly vascular lobules each of which is divided into cortical and medullary zones as they are in those of eutherian mammals. The medulla contains many Hassall's corpuscles; Diener and Ealey state that there is no significant difference between the thymuses of *Tachyglossus* and of Eutheria so presumably the cortex consists of densely packed small lymphocytes among which are interspersed relatively few reticular cells. In the medulla this relationship is reversed and here one sees few lymphocytes and many reticulocytes. The Hassall bodies, rounded acidophil structures, consist of concentrically arranged cells which show signs of degeneration and hyalinization.

The glands of the immune system

These are the lymph nodules, spleen, thymus glands, and the appendix.

The lymph nodules occur in the chest, neck, pelvic region, and in the mesenteries. Lymph nodules in the form of tonsillar tissue also occur in the pharyngeal region associated with the submaxillary glands (Diener and Ealey, 1965). Peyer's patches were later found in the gut by these authors (Diener and Ealey, 1966). Each nodule consists of a single follicle of lymphoid tissue consisting of a peripheral cortical region of small lymphocytes enclosing a medullary zone composed of primitive cells; this medullary zone is equivalent to the germinal centre of the eutherian lymph node follicle. The nodules in *Tachyglossus*, however, consist of one follicle each, a condition unlike that found in the lymph nodes of those Eutheria that have been studied; here the nodes consist of a series of follicles grouped together.

Some lymph nodules in *Tachyglossus* are suspended in the lumina of large lymphatic vessels (Fig. 47), but the contents of the nodules varies; some are empty or contain only a few lymphocytes, others are filled with lymphocytes and red blood cells.

In the appendix the lymphoid follicles in general resemble the nodules found in subcutaneous tissue but they differ in that there is a central core of epithelial cells. Diener and Ealey suggest that each follicle in the appendix may have arisen as an accumulation of lymphocytes around an epithelial crypt and that as it developed the structure of the crypt was lost. The appendix of echidnas is very like that in rabbits and the bursa of Fabricius in birds.

The spleen consists of two lobes, and where they unite a third shorter appendage is found giving the organ a triradiate shape (Cuvier, quoted by Owen, 1847) and at the end of the short appendage is a pear-shaped enlargement. Basir (1932) has described the microscopial anatomy of the spleen and he finds that it is invested with a well-developed fibrous capsule which contains a considerable amount of smooth muscle and which sends trabeculae into the splenic pulp. These trabeculae form an anastomosing network in the interior of the organ. In between the network is the splenic pulp the stroma of which consists of a branching syncytium formed by reticular cells in which run reticular fibres. This loose stroma is filled with red blood cells. The arteries and veins enter and leave the spleen at the hilum. The arteries pass along the trabeculae into the splenic pulp enclosed in a connective tissue sheath. In the pulp these sheaths become invaded with small lymphocytes forming the white pulp or malpighian corpuscles. The venous capillaries and sinuses are lined

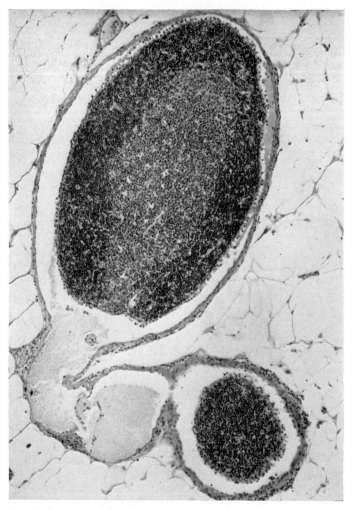

FIG. 47. Lymph nodules of *Tachyglossus* within the lumen of a lymphatic
vessel. Haematoxylin and eosin (Diener and Ealey, 1965). ×95.

by an incomplete layer of reticular cells forming numerous openings
in their walls through which red blood cells can pass directly into
their lumina. Diener and Ealey (1965) find that some red cells also
occur in the white pulp. The cellular elements of the red pulp consist
of, according to Basir, reticular cells, macrophages, and the blood

cells, but in the pear-shaped enlargement he found, in addition to these, special large cells whose cytoplasm is filled with coarse acidophil granules which are so numerous that the nucleus is displaced to one side of the cell; Basir hazarded no opinion as to the nature of these cells but it is possible that they are degenerate plasma cells, the acidophil crystals of which are set free and are known as Russell's bodies.

As far as the microscopical anatomy of the malpighian corpuscles (white pulp) is concerned Basir found that each corpuscle is surrounded by a large blood sinus, that they are formed entirely of small lymphocytes, and that no germinal centres are present. Diener and Ealey (1965), on the other hand, speak of marginal zones and of germinal centres which contain primitive pyroninophil cells, in the white pulp.

The immunological responses of the lymphoid tissue to injections of bovine serum albumin, sheep red cells, colloidal carbon, and to I^{125}-labelled flagellar antigen from *Salmonella adelaide* have been studied by Diener and Ealey. Following its subcutaneous injection, colloidal carbon was found to accumulate in the peripheral zones of the lymph nodules and a fine web of phagocytic processes retaining the carbon particles was evident, as it is in the lymph nodes of rats injected with carbon. In echidnas, however, the carbon particles spread into the medullary zone of the follicle; this does not happen in the rat follicles. Furthermore, when I^{125}-labelled flagellar antigen is injected nothing comparable to the selective retention of antigen at the periphery of primary lymphoid follicles in the rat is found in the echidna lymphoid follicle. However, evidence of an immune response is seen in the form of clusters of pyroninophil cells detectable among the small lymphocytes. Other evidence of an immune response to flagellar antigen was forthcoming from study of humoral antibody formation. No antibody was detectable following injections of bovine serum albumin or of sheep red cells, but antibody was found in blood after injection of 1 mg of flagellar antigen; the peak titres, however, were considerably less than those found in the blood of mice and rats following injection of flagellar antigen. Furthermore, there is no clear-cut memory response after challenge injection of antigen in echidnas (Diener, pers. comm.) but the response does appear to be more pronounced than that found in amphibia. Subsequent work on a large number of echidnas confirms this finding, in substance, in that some echidnas show no anamnesty response whatever while others exhibited some response which was, however, much less than that exhibited by eutherian mammals (Diener and Ealey, 1966, Plenary session of XIth International Congress of Haematology, Sydney, Aust.). These authors suggest that the erratic memory response of the echidna immune system may be due to the diffuse distribution of single lymphoid follicles so that there is less chance that the same follicle reacts to antigen after a primary as well as a secondary antigen injection; on the other hand, the multifollicular lymph nodes of the Eutheria would have a better chance of receiving primary and secondary doses of antigen since several follicles in a node would be exposed to the antigen.

CHAPTER 7

THE REPRODUCTIVE ORGANS

THE MALE SEXUAL ORGANS

These consist of paired testes and vasa deferentia, Cowper's glands, and a penis. There is no scrotum, the testes being situated internally just posterior to the kidneys and attached to them by a fold of peritoneum. This fold continues to the neck of the bladder and encloses the vas deferens which is highly convoluted. The epididymis passes from the anterior end of the testis to its connection with the vas deferens which leads to the urogenital sinus. Here each vas enters the sinus at its dorso-lateral aspect on a level with the emergence of the neck of the bladder from the ventral surface of the sinus.

The urogenital sinus is a long tube passing posteriorly through the pelvis where it communicates with a cloaca into which the rectum also opens. The cloaca is furnished with a sphincter at its posterior end. This arrangement of a simple tubular urogenital sinus carrying urine and sperms is found in many marsupials.

At a short distance anterior to its opening into the cloaca, the urogenital sinus communicates by means of a separate opening with the central canal of the muscular penis which is housed in a diverticulum of the ventral surface of the cloaca—the preputial sac. Thus urine does not enter the penis but passes straight through the urogenital sinus into the cloaca (Home, 1802). These relationships are best understood by reference to a drawing by Keibel (1904) of the urogenital system in a stage 53 pouch young (Fig. 48). In the adult the preputial sac is thin and fibrous and the erect penis can only escape from this sac by passing through a small sphincter-like hole in the ventral wall of the cloaca and then out through the cloacal sphincter to the exterior (Fig. 49).

The penis in a large adult is about 7 cm long, somewhat compressed dorso-ventrally and about 1·25 cm wide. The glans is grooved giving the impression of being bifid and each portion bears a pair of bulbous processes each of which bears a rosette of epidermal rays so that the whole glans gives the appearance of bearing four flower-like prominences. The seminal urethra divides into two, each division subdivides and passes to the exterior through the centre of each foliated papilla.

Presumably during copulation the swollen proximal end of the

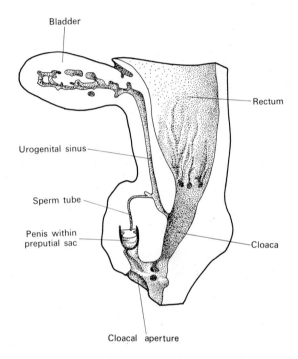

FIG. 48. Section, diagrammatic, through the urogenital system of stage 53 pouch young of *Tachyglossus*. After Keibel (1904a).

penis occludes the lower end of the urogenital sinus so that sperm are forced to enter the seminal urethra rather than pass straight through to the cloaca. The penis of the marsupial bandicoot, *Perameles nasuta*, is like that of *Tachyglossus* in that there is a separate seminal urethra used solely for the passage of sperm, while a urinary passage opens separately into a cloaca (van den Broek, 1910).

The corpus cavernosum within the penis of *Tachyglossus* is divided into two moieties but both are enclosed by a common fibrous sheath.

The paired Cowper's glands (Home, 1802; Voit, 1906) are very well developed and consist of an outer mantle of striated muscle enclosing a system of convoluted tubular glands which lead into a secretion reservoir from which an efferent duct emerges. The muscular mantle is connected to the sphincter muscle of the cloaca. The tubules of the gland, which are lined by a cuboidal epithelium, are separated one from another by a layer of connective tissue; the

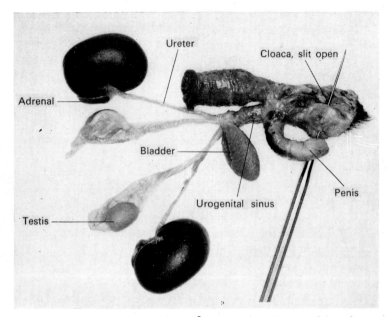

FIG. 49. Male reproductive organs. $\frac{7}{10}$ natural size. The preputial sac has been removed to show the penis and a probe has been passed through the aperture leading from the preputial sac into the cloaca.

collecting ducts are lined by a columnar epithelium. The efferent duct of each side enters the sperm urethra near its connection with the urogenital sinus.

The fully developed testes are large ovoid bodies consisting of an outer tunic of connective tissue immediately below which is a collection of seminiferous tubules. The size of the testes seems to vary with the time of the year, e.g. two echidnas whose body weights were 5·5 kg and 4·5 kg and which were taken in early April and early September, respectively, both had sets of testes weighing

50 g/set, but another large echidna, weighing 5·5 kg, taken in early November, had a set of testes weighing only 6 g. In a progress report Johnstone and Ealey (1965) state that testes regress in spring and summer and enlarge in autumn and that spermatogenesis is at a maximum during June and July. Their observations apparently were made on domesticated echidnas and on wild echidnas kept in captivity for 2 months. It is not known if spermatogenesis ceases in the regressed testes; spermatogenesis could not be detected in the testis of a domesticated echidna that I have examined; there were no lumina in the tubules and only a solid mass of identical cells could be observed.

At present, then, the situation is vague, due to lack of published information; what is very much needed is a study of testis size and condition in wild adult echidnas of reasonably uniform body weight throughout a whole year. However, the information available is in agreement with what is known of the breeding season of *Tachyglossus* in Australia (p. 154).

Spermatogenesis

The tubules of the ripe testes are invested with a layer of connective tissue and the tubules for the most part are closely appressed to one another so that there is very little interstitial tissue (Benda, 1906). This author has described the processes of spermatogenesis and spermiogenesis in detail: the ripe tubules have an average diameter of 375 μ and that of the lumina is 150 μ. At the periphery of the tubule, cemented to a basement membrane, is a layer of spermatogonia among which Sertoli cells are interspersed; these are very well developed in *Tachyglossus* and stretch from the basement membrane to the lumen of the tubule. They reveal no definite cell membranes and in keeping with the large amount of cytoplasm the nuclei are enormous oval bodies situated well away from the basement membrane. The spermatogonia are rounded cells and are confined to the basement membrane region but they divide and produce a number of cells which are pushed towards the lumen. After an unknown number of divisions a generation of spermatocytes is produced. This transformation of a spermatogonium to a primary spermatocyte involves the condensation of several spheres of chromatin in the nucleus into a single structureless ball of chromatin from which achromatic threads pass out to the nuclear membrane. This is followed by a stage in which fine threads of chromatin can be seen at the periphery of the chromatin ball, and in the cytoplasm a mass of mitochondria accumulates at one pole of the nucleus. The mitochondria later become dispersed and the whole of the chromatin in the nucleus is organized into a mass of threads; this cell is now a primary spermatocyte and is in a condition ready to undergo meiosis. At the first stages of this process the whole spermatocyte increases in size and the chromatin threads of the nucleus conjugate side by side and then they segment to form recognizable chromosomes. The nuclear membrane disintegrates and these paired chromosomes arrange themselves into an equatorial ring and make contact with fibres which converge distally to form the achromatic spindle. The meiotic division then takes place and two secondary spermatocytes are formed. The diploid number of chromosomes in *Tachyglossus* (see p. 141) is $62 + 2X$ chromosomes in the female and $62 + 1X$ in the male; there is no Y chromosome. Thus the secondary spermatocytes must contain 32 and 31 chromosomes respectively. According to Benda the secondary spermatocytes form separate daughter cells but electron microscope studies may show that cytokinesis is incomplete and that the cytoplasmic bridges that exist between spermatocytes of other mammals may also exist in monotremes.

Another "Reifungsteilung" takes place and the products of that division are the spherical spermatids. These are more numerous than any other type of cell found in the tubule and they are characterized by their small size, well-marked cellular membrane and a small spherical nucleus which contains a nucleolus. At the beginning of its transformation into a spermatozoon, the cytoplasm of the spermatid exhibits a small sphere of archiplasm and an associated body, the idiosome or Golgi apparatus. A vacuole soon appears in the centre of the archiplasm—in other mammals it has an excentric position. No acrosomal thickening is apparent in the wall of the archiplasma vacuole, but Benda feels that this is due to the deficiencies of fixation in his preparations. Next, a pad of mitochondria appears around the archiplasm and just below the cell membrane are found the centrosomes. Usually these are two entities but Benda found only a single rod-like form which had a central constriction. At this stage of development a flagellum is present and it appears to arise from the distal part of the rod (see p. 136). The cytoplasm at this stage of development contains another well-defined granule, the chromatoid body, which is about the size of the archiplasmasphere and which takes up dyes that stain the nuclei.

E—K

The spermatids now become polarized so that the archiplasma vacuole migrates to one end of the nucleus and the centrosome rod + flagellum migrate to the other end of the cell. The archiplasma vacuole enlarges and its anterior border fuses with the cell membrane; this defines the anterior end of the spermatid. Also at this time the nucleus commences to elongate rapidly, becomes cylindrical in form and exhibits aggregation of the chromatin.

The archiplasma vacuole now assumes a cup shape and is plastered over the curved anterior end of the nucleus which apparently protrudes into the vacuole forming a cone-shaped plug; acrosomal material is still not visible.

The centrosome meanwhile has become segmented and it is now apparent that it consists of a ring-shaped body placed near the posterior pole of the nucleus and of two grana situated between the nucleus and the ring. The flagellum arises from the most posterior of the granules and passes through the centre of the ring-shaped body to the exterior. With the further elongation of the nucleus this centriole complex is displaced to the posterior end of the cell until it comes to lie just beneath the cell membrane.

During the process of elongation of the nucleus an ephemeral structure, the manchette, appears at the hind end of the nucleus. This is a tubular structure which arises at the hind end of the nuclear membrane and passes backwards so that it surrounds the centriole complex and the origin of the flagellum. Shortly after it achieves its definitive form, the manchette is squashed into a rudiment by the elongating nucleus.

During this development of the spermatids they become cemented to the cytoplasm of the Sertoli cells at their distal ends so that clusters of spermatids project into the lumen of the tubule. Benda noted that two separate generations of spermatids could be present in the cytoplasm of the one Sertoli cell.

Further development of the spermatid involves the transformation of the archiplasma portion into an elongated spear-like structure. The chromatin condenses into a homogeneous mass that stains intensely and the whole nucleus acquires a vermiform appearance since it is thrown into 2–3 coil-like undulations. The bulk of the cytoplasm is confined to the posterior end of the cell and it gradually decreases in amount until the cell membrane approaches the nuclear membrane.

In the definitive spermatozoon a mitochondrial sheath is found

around the anterior part of the flagellum as it is in other spermatozoa (Retzius, 1906; Benda, 1906); Benda could not follow its
genesis but he suspects that its development is different from that in
other mammals. A neck region free of mitochondrial sheath was not
found in monotreme sperms and this finding has been confirmed by
electron microscopy carried out by Mr. Leon Hughes, who has
kindly allowed me to publish his results; these follow in the next
subsection.

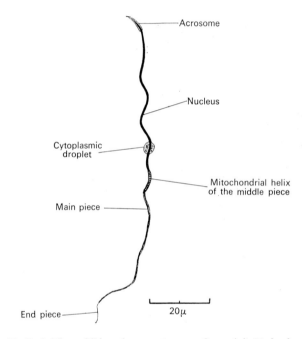

FIG. 50. Definitive epididymal spermatozoon of an adult *Tachyglossus a.
aculeatus*, weight 4500 g, taken 4.4.66. (Hughes, unpubl.)

Structure of the epididymal spermatozoon

This is filiform in shape and, in smear preparations from the
epididymis, it measures 121 μ in total length; the morphology is
illustrated in Fig. 50 and the dimensions of the various parts of the
spermatozoon are given in Table 10. The nucleus, which measures
50·4 μ, has the form of an elongated filamentous spiral of about three
coils and is composed of a dense homogeneous material giving a

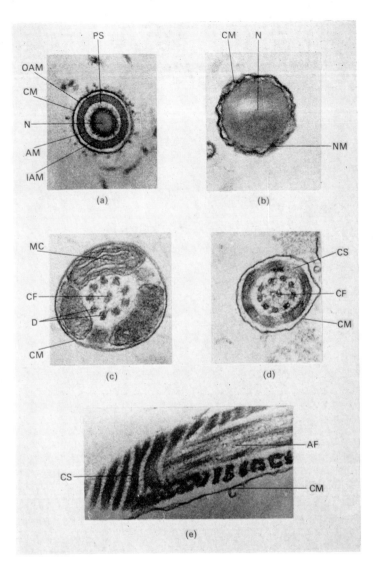

FIG. 51

(*for caption see p.* 139)

positive reaction for deoxyribonucleic acid with the Feulgen re-agents. The nucleus tapers to a point rostrally and it is circular in cross-section throughout the entire length of the head (Fig. 51 (a)).

During epididymal maturation of the sperm the scanty cytoplasm of the spermatid has become a cytoplasmic bead, which undergoes a rostral migration along the nucleus as it does in the sperm of various marsupial species.

Although its development could not be traced by Benda, an acrosome is present in the definitive spermatozoon; it takes the form

TABLE 10

Echidna spermatozoon dimensions[a]

Mean length $\mu \pm$ standard error

Acrosome	Nucleus	Middle-piece and neck	Main-piece	End-piece	Total flagellum
$6\cdot7\pm0\cdot17$	$50\cdot4\pm0\cdot48$	$6\cdot0\pm0\cdot15$	$59\cdot9\pm1\cdot82$	$4\cdot9\pm0\cdot15$	$70\cdot7\pm1\cdot88$

[a] Smear preparations of sperm were made as described by Hughes (1965). The images of 30 sperm from a Heidenhain's iron haematoxylin preparation were projected by Xenon arc at a magnification of 1674 times. The spermatozoon outlines were traced and measured to the nearest $0\cdot2$ mm, using a curvimetre.

FIG. 51. Electron micrographs of sections taken at various levels in epididymal spermatozoa of *Tachyglossus a. aculeatus*. (a) Transverse section of the head in the acrosomal region showing, from the centre outwards, the nucleus (N), perinuclear space (PN), inner acrosomal membrane (IAM), acrosomal material (AM), outer acrosomal membrane (OAM), and the cell membrane (CM). (Hughes unpubl.) ×60,000. (b) Transverse section of post-acrosomal region of the head of the sperm showing nucleus (N), nuclear membrane (NM), and the cell membrane (CM). (Hughes unpubl.) ×60,000. (c) Transverse section of sperm at the level of the middle piece showing the mitochondrial sheath (mitochondrial cristae) MC, axial filament complex consisting of central pair of fibrils (CF), and circle of nine doublets (D) near each of which is a peripheral fibril, cell membrane (CM). (Hughes, unpubl.) ×60,000. (d) Transverse section of main piece of spermatozoon, showing central fibrils of axial filament complex (CF), cortical sheath (CS), and cell membrane (CM). Axial filament doublets are not accompanied by peripheral fibrils in this region. (Hughes, unpubl.) ×60,000. (e) Oblique section of main-piece of sperm showing axial filament complex (AF), spiral bands of the cortical sheath connected by anastomoses (CS), and the cell membrane. (Hughes, unpubl.) ×60,000.

of a cap which in cross-section appears as a ring of uniform thickness surrounding the nucleus. The acrosome covers the anterior 6–7 μ of the length of the nucleus. The acrosomal material is homogeneous and stains with fast-green in Feulgen fast-green preparations; it is bounded by an inner and outer membrane. A perinuclear space between the nucleus and the acrosome is evident but a nuclear membrane in the acrosomal region is not detectable (Fig. 51 (b)).

The posterior end of the head bears a notch into which is inserted the flagellum. Not enough material was available to make out the ultrastructure of this region, which is called the neck, but it is apparent that mitochondra are applied to the base of the nucleus and that they surround the neck, the rostral portion of which contains centriole derivatives while the posterior part gives rise to the axial filament complex. Posterior to the neck is the middle-piece, the mitochondrial sheath of which has a spiral configuration; the structure of the mitochondria is the same as that in other mammalian spermatozoa (Fig. 51 (c)). The posterior limit of the middle-piece is marked by the ring centriole. The axial filament complex passes through the centre of the middle-piece and is made up of a central pair of microtubules surrounded by nine pairs of microtubules, the latter being equidistant from the central pair of fibrils and from each other (Fig. 51 (c)). Each of the nine pairs of microtubules has at its peripheral, radial, aspect a small fibril, which are all of the same size. The mitochondrial sheath of the middle-piece is surrounded by the cell membrane which is the limiting membrane of the whole spermatozoon.

The main-piece of the sperm is circular in cross-section, measures $59 \cdot 9 \mu$ in length, and tapers posterially. The axial filament complex in this region is like that in the middle-piece with the exception that the peripheral fibril, associated with each pair of microtubules, was not detected here (Fig. 51 (d)). The axial filament complex of the main-piece is surrounded by a spirally wound cortical sheath. These spirally wound bands branch and form anastomoses at frequent intervals (Fig. 51 (e)). Lateral thickenings of the tail sheath were not evident.

The filiform structure of the echidna and platypus spermatozoon resembles that of many sauropsid species and for that reason it might be said that the monotreme sperm is reptilian in character, but Franzen (1956) points out that the filiform sperm is found in individuals of many invertebrate phyla while other members of the same phyla possess considerably less differentiated sperm. Apart from the elongations of the head and from the presence of mitochondria overlying the neck region, the structure of the echidna sperm bears a greater resemblance to eutherian sperm than it does, for example, to the marsupial spermatozoa described by Hughes (1965).

The number and structure of the spermatogonial and somatic chromosomes

Van Brink (1959) has compared the morphology of the chromosomes in reptiles and birds with that in one specimen of *Tachyglossus aculeatus aculeatus*. This was a male and spermatogonial chromosomes at mitosis were studied. In four mitotic figures the numbers of chromosomes counted were 62, 64, 63, and 63 respectively. From these observations it was tentatively advanced that the male sex is heterogametic, one of the larger chromosomes being nominated as an X chromosome. It could not be decided from the material available whether the heterogamety was of the XO or XY type. The morphology of the autosomes is extremely interesting since there are all gradations from macrosomal down to microsomal chromosomes without clear demarcation of where "macro" becomes "micro". Microchromosomes have not yet been detected in other mammals but the chromosome complements of Sauropsida contain many such elements.

Bick and Jackson (1967) have carried out a detailed study of the chromosomes in both sexes of *T. a. setosus*, using the techniques of tissue culture of leucocytes and of testis squash; their results substantiate van Brink's tentative claim that the male sex is heterogametic. Their idiograms (Fig. 52(a) and (b)) show unequivocally that the heterogamety is of the XO type; a condition that is unique among mammals studied so far. Bick and Jackson, however, found that the chromosome nominated by van Brink as the X chromosome is one of a pair of large autosomes which are all acrocentric in *Tachyglossus*. In the females, however, there is a pair of large metacentric chromosomes and in the males one such metacentric chromosome; these they designate the X chromosome.

Echidnas exhibit again that admixture of reptilian and mammalian characters (with an individual *Tachyglossus* flavour) even in their chromosomes: microsomal chromosomes like those in Sauropsida, but unlike the reptilian complement, differentiated X chromosomes are detectable; heterogamety of the male as in other mammals and

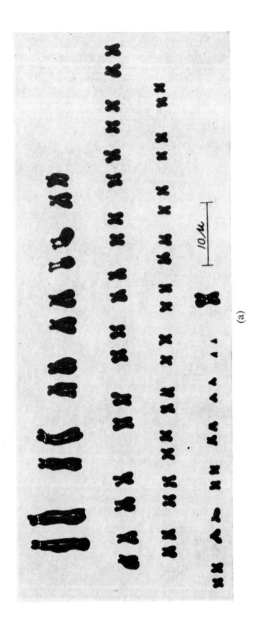

(a)

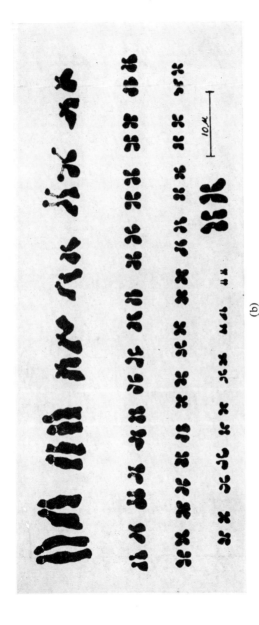

(b)

FIG. 52. Idiograms of the chromosomes of *Tachyglossus a. setosus*. (a) Male. (b) Female. The X chromosomes are the large chromosomes situated at the right-hand end of the lower row. (Bick and Jackson, 1967.)

not in the female as in Sauropsida Aves; unique heterogamety of the
XO type as against the XY type found in other mammals.

THE FEMALE SEXUAL ORGANS

These consist of two large thin-walled infundibular funnels which
enclose the paired ovaries attached to the antero-ventral faces of the
kidneys by a fold of peritoneum. The funnels are the distally ex-

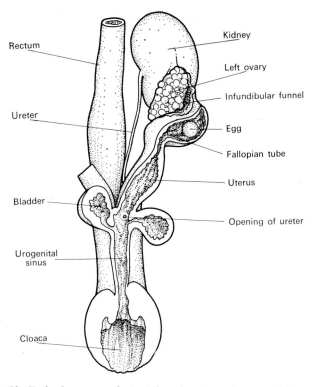

FIG. 53. *Tachyglossus a. aculeatus.* Dissection of female urogenital organs.
After Jones (1923).

panded ends of the oviducts each of which consist of a relatively
thin-walled anterior part, the Fallopian tube, often described as
convoluted, but a drawing of a mature urogenital system by Wood
Jones (Fig. 53) shows no sign of this. Possibly after a series of preg-
nancies the oviduct becomes convoluted. The lower or posterior ends

of the oviducts are differentiated to form uteri; these communicate with a long median unpaired urogenital sinus at the level of the entrance of the ureters and of the neck of the bladder which depends from the ventral surface of the urogenital sinus. The latter opens into the cloaca, thus eggs, urine, and faeces pass out through the one cloacal sphincter. This urogenital system is fundamentally the same as that in marsupials save that during ontogeny the lower ends of the Mullerian ducts, at a point anterior to their union with the urogenital sinus, develop two ingrowths which ultimately unite in the mid-line to form that marsupial oddity, the median vagina (Buchanan and Fraser, 1918).

Oogenesis

Prior to the publication of Flynn and Hill's paper (1939), information about oogenesis in monotremes was fragmentary. Poulton (1884) had described the existence of a vitelline membrane around the oocyte and Caldwell (1887) made observations of fundamental importance concerning the follicular epithelium surrounding the mature oocyte. Caldwell, of course, shares the honour with Haacke (1885) of the discovery that monotremes are oviparous; Caldwell informing by telegram a meeting of the British Association on September 2, 1884, that *Ornithorhynchus* and *Tachyglossus* are oviparous and Haacke demonstrated the pouch egg of *Tachyglossus aculeatus multiaculeatus* to the Royal Society of South Australia, also on September 2, 1884.

As far as Zaglossus is concerned, one study only of the ovary was published after it was known that monotremes were oviparous; this was Kolmer's (1925) on the ovary of *Zaglossus bruijni*: both ovaries were of the same size but the largest follicles did not exceed $1 \cdot 5$ mm in diameter and oogonia were not detectable. He noted the presence, in the cytoplasm of the oocytes, of fat-containing globules and protein granules and that the arrangement of the yolk spheres resembled those of reptilian eggs. This animal was not ovulating and had been separated from males for at least 10 years, nevertheless it was lactating (p. 184).

Only the left ovary is functional in *Ornithorhynchus* but both ovaries in *Tachyglossus* are capable of producing eggs, as they are in *Zaglossus*, presumably, but generally only one follicle ripens at a time (Flynn and Hill, 1939). These authors have given a comprehensive account of oogenesis in *Tachyglossus* and I have drawn on that work for the following description of oogenesis and fertilization.

The ovary is roughly oval in shape and is covered on its outer surface by spherical swellings of different sizes—the developing follicles. The average dimensions of the ovaries are $13 \cdot 6 \times 9 \cdot 1$ mm. The germinal epithelium may be quite thin in places being made up of flattened cells but the structure varies from this condition, through cuboidal, to a high columnar epithelium, which may be thrown into folds. Clear spherical cells $0 \cdot 02$–$0 \cdot 023$ mm in diameter are found in the cuboidal epithelium. These are apparently oogonia but Flynn and Hill could detect no transitory stages between these and small oocytes $0 \cdot 042$–$0 \cdot 06$ mm in diameter already enclosed by a thin flattened follicular epithelium. Gatenby (1922) failed to find oogonia in the adult and adolescent ovary of the platypus, so he concluded that the maturation prophase stages must have taken place before adolescence. Flynn and Hill are inclined to think that something of this nature occurs in *Tachyglossus*.

Flynn and Hill recognize three stages in the development of oocytes; these are as follow: at the first phase of development the oocytes range in diameter from $0 \cdot 06$ to $0 \cdot 15$ mm in diameter and they are found in the cortical zones of the ovary just below the germinal epithelium. The nucleus is eccentric in position and lies close below what will become the upper pole of the egg. Within the nuclear membrane is a loose reticulum in the strands of which are dispersed many fine granules; a large body, presumably a nucleolus, is found associated with numbers of smaller nucleoli. The zona pellucida at this stage takes the form of a homogeneous membrane, lying just below the follicular epithelium, which consists of a single layer of cuboidal cells with large spherical oval nuclei. Immediately below the zona is a thin striate layer of material and beneath this striate layer and separating it from the cytoplasm below is the egg membrane.

At the second phase of the growth of the oocytes they achieve a size of $0 \cdot 2$–$0 \cdot 5$ mm in diameter. In this cell the fat droplets are organized into a definite cortical fatty zone; yolk-sphere primordia appear among these fatty droplets and their subsequent multiplication is at the expense of the fat globules. The zona pellucida has greatly increased in thickness.

The third phase of oogenesis embraces the growth of the oocyte of $0 \cdot 6$ mm diameter to the full grown oocyte $3 \cdot 9$ mm in diameter. At the early phases of this stage of development the oocyte exhibits a peripheral layer of cytoplasm which is thickened in the region immediately above the nucleus. The latter has by now achieved its definitive position at the upper pole of the oocyte and the thicker layer of cytoplasm is the primordium of the germinal disc. Beneath the peripheral layer of cytoplasm is a yolk-sphere layer and central to this is a medullary zone which contains finely alveolar cytoplasm and yolk-sphere primordia. This medullary zone has a peripheral layer of vacuolated cytoplasm—the primordium of the latebral yolk zone and from this a column of cytoplasm of similar structure rises up towards the nucleus. This tract is the primordium of the neck of the latebra. As Semon (1894c) recognized, the latebra has much the same form and relations as that in the sauropsidan egg. In its completed form it has a club-shaped body, centrally situated, and a thin stalk which runs up in the egg axis to terminate in a saucer-shaped plug of yolk which underlies the germinal disc (Fig. 54).

By the time the oocyte is about 1 mm in diameter the cuboidal cells of the follicular epithelium have changed into columnar cells and the zona pellucida appears as a homogeneous layer below which is the striate zone and the egg membrane which is by now a detachable entity.

In the final phases of oogenesis the body of the latebra exhibits a central core of vacuolated cytoplasm which contains many eosinophil granular spheres which later become basophil. According to Flynn and Hill these granular spheres are the main source of supply of fine yolk spheres in the lateral yolk zone.

The latebra persists in the uterine egg up to the short primitive-streak stage but it is not certain that there is any transference of fine-grained yolk up to the lateral neck to the yolk bed at that stage.

The nucleus during the third stage of oogenesis appears in section as a plano-convex body, the upper surface of which is flat and is in contact with the disc cytoplasm (which is circular and has radial symmetry) while the convex surface rests on the yolk bed. Internally the nucleus exhibits a meshwork of linin threads bearing minute granules of chromatin, and a large number of nucleoli.

The zona pellucida and the egg membrane of the full-grown oocyte are extremely thin.

The follicular epithelium surrounding the full-grown oocyte of 3·96 mm average diameter is better developed at this stage than at any of the preceding stages; it now consists of an epithelium two cells deep throughout. Its constituent cells contain secretion granules,

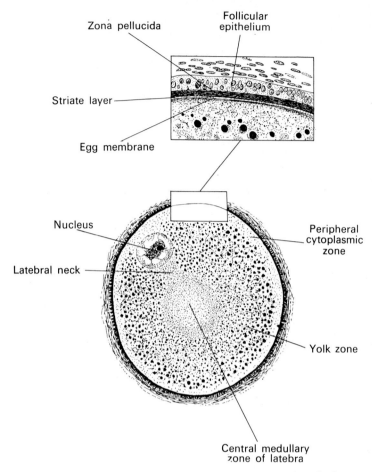

Zona pellucida

Follicular epithelium

Striate layer

Egg membrane

Nucleus

Peripheral cytoplasmic zone

Latebral neck

Yolk zone

Central medullary zone of latebra

FIG. 54. Section of oocyte 0·65 × 0·60 mm in diameter, of *Tachyglossus a. setosus*. After Flynn and Hill (1939). Reproduced by permission of the Zoological Society of London.

the precursors of the follicular fluid, which forms a continuous layer surrounding the oocyte at the time of maturation. Caldwell (1887), who discovered this secretion, thought that it was associated with the formation of albumen when the egg had passed into the Fallopian tube. However, C. J. Hill (1933) concluded that the albumen layer around the egg is formed by the granular secretion of the cells lining the upper two-thirds of the Fallopian tube. Flynn and Hill, however, regard Caldwell's discovery of singular importance since in their opinion the secretion is the homologue of the liquor folliculi of the Graafian follicle of other mammals and that the monotreme follicle is fundamentally different from that of Sauropsida which lack follicular fluid.

After growth of the oocyte is complete maturation takes place. This involves the formation of the first maturation spindle at the centre of the germinal disc; the spindles taking up a position perpendicular to the disc surface. After division the first polar body, one of the products of that division, is given off in the ovary. After this division a second maturation spindle is formed and the germinal disc begins to acquire its definitive elongated form. The ovum is now shed into the funnel (infundibulum) which completely envelopes the ovary. The funnel contains a viscid fluid which facilitates the passage of the egg into the Fallopian tube; here the egg is fertilized, coated with a layer of albumen outside which a very thin shell membrane forms. Whether fertilization takes place before or after the albumen is laid down is not known, but Flynn and Hill commonly found sperms embedded in that layer. C. J. Hill (1933, 1941) has described in detail the formation of the infundibular secretion and of the albumen layers and she finds that the infundibulum is lined by a single layer of columnar epithelium containing cells of two types: ciliated non-secretory and non-ciliated secretory cells. The latter form a clear fluid which is shed into the funnel just before ovulation. The funnel leads into the Fallopian tube proper which is lined by a tall columnar epithelium; the cells of that epithelium elaborate the albumen coat of the egg. The albumen is laid down in two layers formed at different levels in the Fallopian tube. In the upper two-thirds of the tube the epithelium secretes a dense layer of albumen onto the egg while in the lower third a fluid type of albumen is secreted and laid down over the dense layer. In addition to the fluid albumen, another secretion is elaborated by the convoluted glands that occur in this region of the Fallopian tube. C. J. Hill believes that this secretion is concerned with the formation of the basal layer of the shell.

Between the lower portion of the Fallopian tube and the uterus is a junctional region where tubal glands are numerous and intermixed with uterine glands. In the uterine segment proper, tubal glands are no longer detectable and uterine glands lined by a tall columnar epithelium of ciliated and non-ciliated cells take their place. The non-ciliated cells are secretory and their activities will be discussed later.

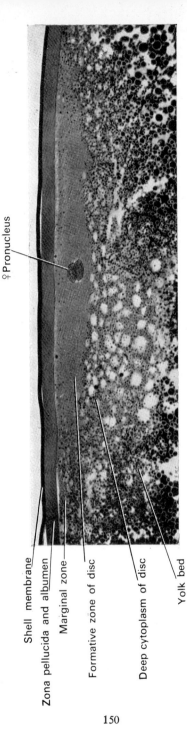

♀ Pronucleus

Shell membrane
Zona pellucida and albumen
Marginal zone
Formative zone of disc
Deep cytoplasm of disc
Yolk bed

Fig. 55. Section of uterine ovum, 4·5 mm in diameter, through the germinal disc region, showing the male and female pronuclei overlapping one another (Flynn and Hill, 1939). Reproduced by permission of the Zoological Society of London. × 290.

It is commonly believed that the processes of oogenesis, described above, are found only in Sauropsida and the Prototheria; this is not so since the formation of the egg in *Didelphys virginiana* (McCrady, 1938) exhibits some remarkable similarities to that of *Tachyglossus*. McCrady finds that fertilization of the egg of *Didelphys* takes place at the extreme upper end of the oviduct and the egg then commences to pass down the Fallopian tube. During this passage, concentric layers of albumen are deposited on the zona pellucida; the albumen sometimes trapping spermatozoa as it does in the *Tachyglossus* egg. The albumen finally forms a layer some 0·25 mm thick before it passes to the uterus. Just before it does so, a shell membrane is secreted upon the surface of the albumen by the shell glands found in the lower part of the oviduct. In the uterus the diameter of the egg including ovum, albumen, and shell, is about 0·6 mm. As in the case with the uterine egg of *Tachyglossus* the shell is flexible and it grows with the growth of the embryo. The shell persists throughout development and during a major part of that time the vesicles or eggs float freely in a nutritive fluid secreted by uterine glands which become prominent at the sixth day of pregnancy.

Shell membranes and albumen layers are also found around the eggs of Australian marsupials but in no instance does the albumen layer approach the thickness of that in the egg of *Didelphys* (see Caldwell, 1887; Hill, 1910; Sharman, 1961). According to C. J. Hill (1933) the shell of the marsupial egg is equivalent to the basal layer of the monotreme egg shell.

To return to the fertilization of the egg in *Tachyglossus*: the second polar body has been formed as a result of the second maturation division and both polar bodies appear near the centre of the germinal disc which, of course, contains the ♀ pronucleus. After penetration by a sperm the ♂ pronucleus comes to lie in the disc about 1 mm away from the ♀ pronucleus and the two polar bodies migrate and take up a position at the margin of the disc. The first polar body remains undivided. The egg has by now descended to the uterus.

The two pronuclei now approach one another (Fig. 55) and become applied forming an almost spherical body divided at the equator (Fig. 56) by the limiting membrane; a short time later, however, it is not possible to detect the membrane between the two pronuclei. This is the process of conjugation which precedes formation of the first cleavage spindle.

E—L

After fertilization has taken place and the two layers of albumen have been deposited, the basal layer of the shell membrane is formed when the egg is in the tubal gland region of the Fallopian tube. C. J. Hill (1941) found that the tubal glands showed signs of maximal secretory activity at this time and she concludes that the tubal gland

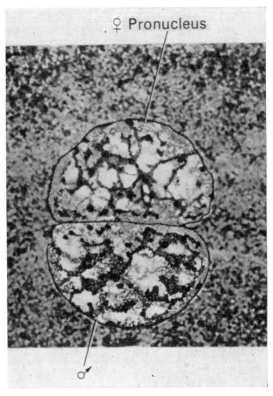

F<small>IG</small>. 56. The two pronuclei superimposed on one another. Conjugation is now almost complete. (Flynn and Hill, 1939.) (Reproduced by permission of the Zoological Society of London.) ×1921.

secretion is responsible for the formation of the basal membrane of the shell. As the egg passes through the junctional region a second layer is formed, probably from the secretions of the tubal and uterine glands of this region, and at the same time the egg grows and increases in diameter. The second layer exhibits a differentiation into a matrix substance in which radially arranged rod-like bodies are formed. By the time the egg is 10 mm in diameter the rodlets have increased greatly in length at the expense of the secretion in the tubal and uterine gland cells. The egg passes to the body of the uterus where uterine glands only are found. These give rise to a nutritive fluid, which the egg absorbs and as a result it grows and attains the full size of 14–15 mm diameter. As the egg grows the basal layer expands, the rodlets become separated, and the spaces between them become filled with a clear matrix.

The processes of secretion of the nutritive fluid are not known in echidnas, but they have been described in the platypus by C. J. Hill (1933, 1941). The secretion formed in the superficial and middle parts of the uterine glands is finely granular and as it is formed it is passed to the apices of the cells, forcing them to project into the lumina of the glands.

These projections and their contained secretion are cut off as small vesicles. Eventually the granules in these vesicles liquify and the fluid passes through the enclosing cytoplasmic covering into the lumen of the uterus where it is absorbed by the growing egg.

After the shedding of the two secretions—the first concerned with the formation of the rodlet layer, the second with the nutritive fluid—a third secretion is produced by cells in the uterine glands when the glandular precursors of the nutritive fluid are in process of being shed. This third secretion is coarsely granular and the glands reach the height of activity when the egg has attained its full size. This secretion is the precursor of the massive protective layer of the shell, the laying down of which is completed only when the egg has reached its full size.

The structure of the shell of the newly laid egg of *Tachyglossus* has been described by Caldwell (1887), Semon (1894c), and J. P. Hill (1933). The latter description is the more detailed of the three and the facts are as follow: the shell of the pouch egg resembles the intrauterine egg of *Ornithorhynchus* which lays its eggs into a nest. In *Tachyglossus* the basal layer is $0 \cdot 0016$ mm thick and peripheral to this is the rodlet layer $0 \cdot 01$–$0 \cdot 012$ mm thick. Outside both these layers is a third which forms the greater part of the thickness of the shell. Two zones can be detected in this layer: the inner immediately outside the rodlet layer consists of coarse granules of irregular form and size between which numerous spaces are found, and an outer formed of still larger and more irregular granules. Pore canals in the form of irregular cleft-like passages are found stretching from the inner zone to open on the surface. These surface pores are small and are not very numerous.

The processes of cleavage, following fusion of the pronuclei, and their relation to the growth of the egg and to the formation of the shell, will be described in Chapter 8.

THE BREEDING SEASON

Semon (1894a) records that *T. a. aculeatus* or perhaps *acanthion* begins to breed, in the Burnett River district of Queensland, at the end of July—no intra-uterine eggs being found before the 23rd July, and Caldwell (1887) found intra-uterine stages during July and August. Before this, however, Haacke (1885) found an egg on August 25, 1894, in the pouch of a Kangaroo Island echidna (*T. a. multiaculeatus*) which had been taken to Adelaide on August 3. As far as *T. a. aculeatus* is concerned, Broom (1895) observed an egg in the pouch of one specimen laid about October 2 and Griffiths (1965b) obtained a pouch young about 200 g in weight on November 11. However, the most detailed information on the breeding season of echidnas has been published by Flynn and Hill (1939) who worked on *T. a. setosus*. This breeding season lasts from June 29 (one record only of a fertilized egg *in utero*) to September 4 (the latest date of the year of which they had any record of an intra-uterine egg). They found that most of the females caught in August contained uterine eggs. Flynn and Hill appear to hold the world's record for echidna-egg collecting; they insouciantly remark:

> It is of some interest to note that there is no very great agreement between eggs collected on the same day as regards their degree of development. On August 15th, 1930, for example, 14 eggs were obtained ranging from an egg with an unsegmented disc, just fertilized, to two eggs measuring $14 \cdot 80 \times 14 \cdot 00$ and $15 \cdot 00 \times 14 \cdot 10$ mm respectively, the former containing a flat embryo with 11 pairs of somites and the latter an abnormal embryo.

From all these observations it appears that the breeding season of *T. aculeatus* in the eastern and south-eastern parts of Australia lasts from the end of June to early September. S. J. J. Davies (pers. comm.) mentions that he found an echidna with a pouch young (5 cm in length) in August at Mileura, Western Australia, which suggests that the breeding season may be at the same time of the year as that of the eastern subspecies.

Collett (1885) took an echidna with an engorged udder, but no pouch, in March and from this he infers that the breeding season commences in March; however, in all probability (see p. 203) Colett's echidna had just weaned and abandoned its young one.

Copulation in wild echidnas has been recorded twice in the literature: Broom (1895) received a pair of echidnas taken in copulation on September 4. He kept the pair together in a box; he states, however, that the male refused to eat, took no interest in the female, and died on the 14th day of confinement. The female, however, developed a pouch which was evident 26 days after copulation, and on the 28th day after, an egg was found in the pouch. From this equivocal evidence it is surmised that the gestation period is about 27 days. The other copulation observed was described by Burrell (1927) on hearsay evidence, but the date of occurrence is not given.

Dobroruka (1960) has described copulation in echidnas kept in Prague Zoo. Apparently it takes place venter to venter with head to head or with heads pointing in opposite directions and only the cloacal apertures in contact. Unfortunately no egg was laid following that copulation.

CHAPTER 8

EMBRYOLOGY

EARLY CLEAVAGE STAGES

When the egg arrives in the uterus, conjugation of the nuclei occurs and the egg is now ready to undergo cleavage.

Caldwell (1884, 1887) showed that this process in the egg of *Tachyglossus* is meroblastic, the first cleavage furrow dividing the germinal disc into a larger and a smaller area. The second furrow is laid down at right-angles to the first so that the 4-celled stage is made up of two large and two small blastomeres lying on top of the yolk. Flynn and Hill (1939) failed to find a 2-cell stage but they found the 4-cell stage to be as Caldwell described it (Fig. 57). These prospective blastomeres are not yet separate cells since they are not delimited from the cytoplasm of the egg lying below (Fig. 58). The blastodisc forms an area which is roughly circular in outline with a diameter of about 0·45 mm.

This 4-celled stage passes through an 8- to 16-blastomere stage containing 32 nuclei since division of the original 16 nuclei has taken place while the blastomeres have not yet divided. The dimensions of the blastodisc are now 0·72 × 0·62 mm and it consists of two sets of blastomeres—a peripheral set of large marginal blastomeres open to the surrounding yolk and to that lying below the disc, and an inner group of smaller central blastomeres delimited on all sides except below where they are open to the yolk. This differentiation persists in the 32-blastomere stage and it is similar to the differentiation of the blastomeres found in the eggs of Sauropsida (Fig. 59).

As cleavage proceeds the marginal blastomeres lose their distinctive character and the blastodiscs of successive stages, as a result of active mitotic divisions in various planes, become more than one cell thick and eventually a circular biconvex blastodisc is formed. At this stage of its development the blastodisc is about 4 cells deep centrally and thins out peripherally to one cell. The constituent cells now have limiting membranes and are separated from the yolk, in fact the whole blastodisc is marked off from the yolk bed by a thin yolk membrane. Meanwhile, in the marginal zone of the yolk bed around the periphery of the biconvex blastodisc a large number of free cells have appeared; these have the ability to migrate through the cytoplasm of the egg and are called vitellocytes by Flynn and Hill

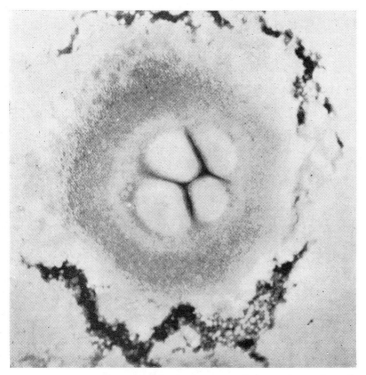

Fig. 57. Early cleavage, 4-celled stage looking down on the surface of the blastodisc (Flynn and Hill, 1939). (Reproduced by permission of the Zoological Society of London.) ×74.

(1947). They are formed by the division of the marginal cells of the disc and it is here at the margin of the disc that most of the vitellocytes are found, situated superficially close below the shell membrane. However, some are found just below the margin of the blastodisc while others take up positions below the yolk membrane outside the disc periphery. All the vitellocytes multiply and undergo a transformation into active cells with long pseudopodia-like processes.

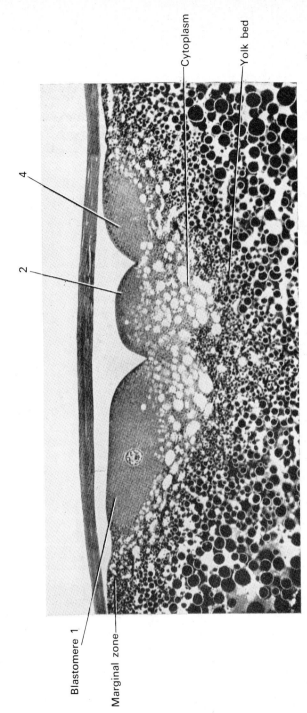

FIG. 58. Section through the blastodisc at the 4-celled stage; the blastomeres are not yet separated from the cytoplasm below the disc (Flynn and Hill, 1939). (Reproduced by permission of the Zoological Society of London.) ×209.

Blastomere 1

Marginal zone

4

2

Cytoplasm

Yolk bed

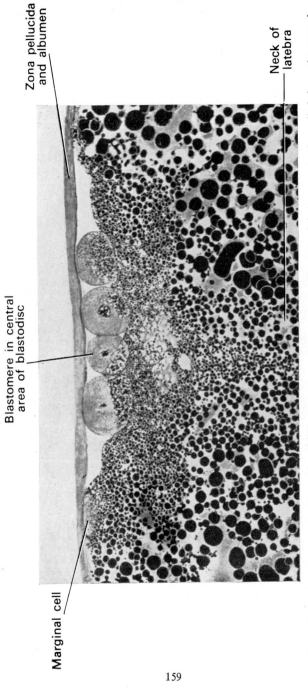

Zona pellucida
and albumen

Blastomere in central
area of blastodisc

Marginal cell

Neck of
latebra

FIG. 59. Section through the blastodisc at 32-celled stage. The marginal cell at the left is open to the yolk below; the central blastomeres are delimited from the yolk but they contain yolk spheres. (Flynn and Hill, 1947.) (Reproduced by permission of the Zoological Society of London.) ×184.

159

The cells of the blastodisc continue to multiply and form a body that has a ragged irregular contour owing to the presence of outgrowths of groups of cells (Fig. 60). This figure shows a surface view of an ovum 4·7 mm in diameter in which the number of superficial cells present in the disc is about 220. The cells in the central region are closely arranged, uniform in size, and form a layer 5–6 cells deep.

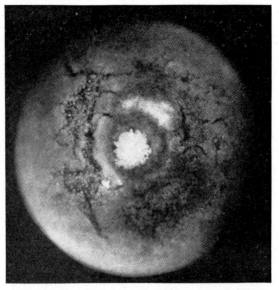

FIG. 60. Surface view of blastodisc of ovum 4·7 mm in diameter. The ragged edge is formed of vitellocytes. (Flynn and Hill, 1947.) (Reproduced by permission of the Zoological Society of London.) ×14·6.

FORMATION OF THE UNILAMINAR BLASTODERM

The stage just described precedes a very important development in the conversion of the blastodisc into a blastoderm surrounded by an entity called the germ ring. This is formed by the linking together of the vitellocytes, both peripheral and submarginal, to form a smooth syncytial ring around the blastodisc. In Fig. 61 about half the circumference of the blastodisc is seen to have a smooth outline formed by the fusing vitellocytes, while the other half is still ragged in outline.

The blastodisc is about 6 cells deep (Fig. 62) and in section submarginal vitellocytes can be seen. These will migrate to the periphery and fuse with the marginal vitellocytes forming the germinal ring. In this way the germ ring either abuts onto the outer ends of the blastomeres at the periphery of the disc or it may extend inwards below them for a short distance.

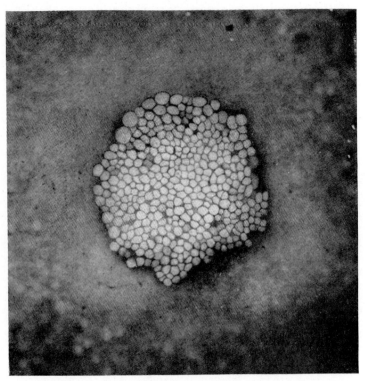

FIG. 61. Surface view of blastodisc of ovum 4·4 mm in diameter. The periphery is becoming regular in outline since the vitellocytes are fusing to form the germinal ring. (Flynn and Hill, 1947.) (Reproduced by permission of the Zoological Society of London.) ×90.

From this time onwards the germ ring commences to grow outwards over the surface of the ovum and at the same time the blastodisc does likewise, the thickness of the disc decreasing so that it passes through a 4–3- and a 2–3-celled phase. The outcome of this is the metamorphosis of a thick disc into a thin blastoderm consisting of a superficial layer and a deeper central layer 2–3 cells thick, these cells being loosely dispersed. The latter finally crowd into the

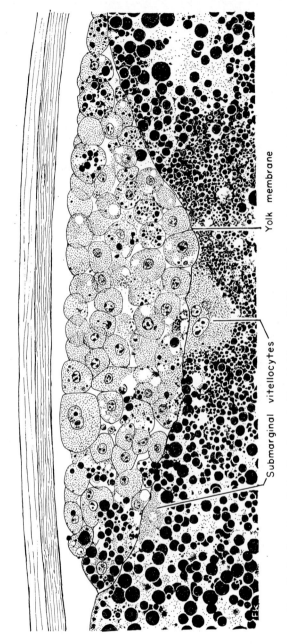

Yolk membrane

Submarginal vitellocytes

Fig. 62. Section through the disc shown in Fig. 61 (Flynn and Hill, 1947). (Reproduced by permission of the Zoological Society of London.) ×362.

superficial layer which continues to follow the growth of the germ ring around the spherical ovum.

Quite early in the development of the blastoderm, before it is truly unilaminar, prospective ectoderm and endoderm cells can be detected. Of the two the prospective ectoderm cells are the more numerous. They are relatively large and their cytoplasm is vacuolated while the prospective endoderm cells are small with small deeply staining nuclei and non-vacuolated cytoplasm.

The unilaminar-blastoderm stage of monotreme development was discovered by Semon (1894c), but his obsession with the notion that the primary germ layers must be laid down by activity at a blastopore led to erroneous interpretations. Some of those misconceptions were

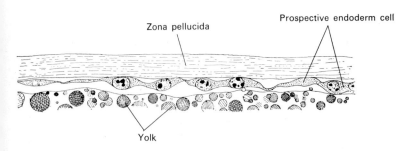

Fig. 63. Unilaminar blastodermic membrane, diameter of ovum 4·4 × 4·26 mm, diameter of blastoderm about 3 mm. After Flynn and Hill (1947). (Reproduced by permission of the Zoological Society of London.) ×447.

corrected by Wilson and Hill (1907), but they in turn clouded the issue by mistaking the yolk navel (see p. 164) for the primitive knot. This error in interpretation was admitted and corrected (Wilson and Hill, 1915) and Flynn and Hill (1947) with a magnificent supply of embryos at their disposal have confirmed Semon's original findings and given a definitive account of the formation of the germ layers. The first step in the differentiation of those layers is the formation of the unilaminar blastoderm, an arrangement that ensures that all the prospective ectoderm cells are in their positions at the surface of the blastocyst (Fig. 63).

The germ ring and the unilaminar blastoderm continue to grow over the yolk. By the time the circumferential measurement of the blastoderm is 7·0 mm and that of the uncovered lower pole is about

3·0 mm, many of the prospective endoderm cells exhibit pseudo-podial processes whereas the prospective ectoderm cells are spindle-shaped and thin.

FORMATION OF THE BILAMINAR BLASTODERM

When the circumferential diameter of the blastoderm is 9·5 mm and that of the lower pole is about 2·0 mm, the prospective endoderm cells begin to form anastomotic connections with one another and to show signs of amoeboid movement. Soon after they start to migrate inwards from the superficial layer of the blastoderm and by the time it has almost completely covered the yolk leaving a small area 0·56 × 0·43 mm uncovered, the endoderm cells have formed a network the interstices of which become filled in with cells derived by mitotic division of the cells of the network. In this way a complete layer of endoderm cells is formed beneath the ectoderm and the unilaminar blastoderm is converted to a bilaminar vesicle.

With establishment of the endoderm its constituent cells commence to ingest yolk granules and are thus converted into genuine yolk endoderm. The ectoderm is composed of large flattened spindle-shaped cells with oval, flattened, nuclei.

The remaining small area of the yolk is covered by blastoderm and at the point of closure a scar-like thickening of the yolk navel is formed. This structure is very like the yolk navels of the eggs of sauropsidan reptiles. The structure of the bilaminar vesicle and the yolk navel are shown in Fig. 64.

The complete enclosure of the yolk converts the egg into a potential vesicle or blastocyst which is capable of increasing in size by cellular division. In this way the necessary space for the development of the embryo and for storing the nutritive fluid secreted by uterine glands is achieved. The fluid provides the nutrition of the embryo during the remainder of the intra-uterine period since the yolk gradually liquefies and is used up. This stored uterine fluid also provides the nutriment for the incubatory period.

The whole egg is 5·7 mm in diameter when the yolk navel is established. Up to this stage there has been no sign of formation of an embryo, but now, at the opposite pole to the yolk navel, a longitudinal thickening in the ectoderm appears; this is the primitive streak which at this stage is 0·6–1·26 mm long.

Information on the embryology of echidnas past this level of development is fragmentary and consists of occasional remarks here and there by C. J. Hill (1933) and Flynn and Hill (1939, 1947) on the presence of primitive streaks and somites. When the egg is 7–8 mm in diameter the primitive streak is 4 mm long, and by the time the egg is 11·5 mm in diameter an embryo with 3–4 pairs of somites has been achieved.

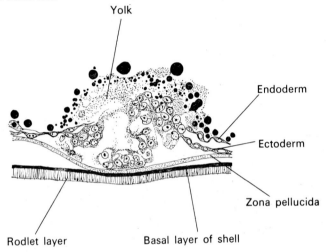

FIG. 64. Section through the bilaminar blastocyst at the yolk navel. Note basal and rodlet layers of the shell membrane. The ovum from which this section was made was 5·7 mm in diameter and a primitive streak primordium 0·6 mm long was present. After Flynn and Hill (1947). (Reproduced by permission of the Zoological Society of London.) ×174.

The egg shell stays at a 2-layer level of organization (basal + rodlet) from the 4-cell stage until the egg is 10–11·8 mm in diameter. The rate of infiltration of uterine fluid and the rate of growth from the 5·7 mm to the 11·8 mm diameter stage are assumed to be very rapid since Flynn and Hill found very few eggs between 6 and 14 mm in diameter. During this period of rapid growth the blastocyst comes into intimate association with the uterine wall, as it does in *Didelphys virginiana* (McCrady, 1938), a circumstance that no doubt facilitates the passage of nutritive fluid from the uterus to the interior of the blastocyst.

When the egg has achieved a diameter of 11·8 mm the third layer (granular) of the shell is laid down but the egg increases in size until it is 14–15 mm in diameter; it acquires an ellipsoidal shape, representative measurements being $14\cdot8 \times 14\cdot0$, $15\cdot0 \times 13\cdot8$, and $14\cdot6 \times 13\cdot0$ mm. The egg is now ready for laying and Hill and Gatenby (1926) state that the embryo within has 19 pairs of somites.

No one knows how the egg gets into the pouch but once it is in place it is retained by hairs plastered across it (Broom, 1895). I have recently had an opportunity to confirm Broom's observations: a female echidna brought to the laboratory on October 4, 1966, and from which a biopsy sample of mammary gland was taken on October 18, 1966, laid an egg *circa* the 22nd October. This was unexpected since the pouch could scarcely be termed such, it was simply a shallow depression with thick tumescent borders. The pouch area was wet and sweaty 2 days before the egg was laid. When discovered the egg was found to be retained in the posterior end of the depression by hairs lying across it. Unfortunately the handling must have upset the mother since the egg was found squashed the day after discovery;[1] Broom had the same sad experience.

After ovulation a corpus luteum forms in the ruptured follicle. Hill and Gatenby (1926) present a description of that gland found in an echidna that had laid an egg 1–2 days previously. The corpus luteum was pear-shaped measuring $4\cdot5 \times 3\cdot5$ mm. Cytological examination showed it to be "In a fairly advanced stage of regression", the luteal cells exhibiting colloidal and granular degeneration of the cytoplasm and vacuolization of the nuclei. Leucocytic infiltration and the presence of much connective tissue were also apparent. From this evidence and from studies of the corpora lutea of the platypus and of another echidna, Hill and Gatenby conclude that regression of the corpus luteum sets in long before the egg is laid.

Comparison of early development of Tachyglossus *with that in Metatheria*

It is appropriate to digress here and comment on the similarity of the development of the primary germ layers in echidnas to that in marsupials. In *Dasyurus* (Hill, 1910) and *Didelphys* (McCrady, 1938) cleavage is preceded by extrusion of yolk from the ovum in the form of a single body of yolk in the case of *Dasyurus*, and as yolk bodies in that of *Didelphys*. The blastomeres formed as a result of cleavage lose

[1] See Appendix V.

contact with one another and migrate radially to flatten themselves
against the zona pellucida. During this migration the albumen layer
becomes thinner and finally disappears from the egg of *Dasyurus* so
that the zona pellucida comes into contact with the shell membrane.
In *Didelphys* the albumen persists longer, but in both cases the shell
is strong and resilient so that the cells flattened against it form a
unilaminar blastocyst with the extruded yolk occupying the interior
of the cyst. At no stage is a morula formed as is the case in eutherian
development. The blastocyst cavity then becomes filled with a
coagulable fluid derived from that poured into the uterine lumen
through the secretory activity of the uterine glands. After a period
of growth the cells of the unilaminar blastocyst differentiate into
prospective ectoderm and endoderm cells. In *Dasyurus* the latter
acquire pseudopodia and migrate in from the outer layer to form a
cell network which is filled in by mitotic division of the cells to form
a complete new vesicle inside the outer. In *Didelphys* virtually the
same process takes place save that the endoderm cells are large and
rounded at first but as they migrate inwards they acquire pseudopodia and later become flattened to form a sheet of endoderm inside
the outer vesicle. In this way the bilaminar blastocyst is formed very
much in the way it is formed in *Tachyglossus* and *Ornithorhynchus*.

The endodermal sac with its outer layer of ectoderm was called
the bilaminar omphalopleure by Hill (1900) who regarded it as the
first of the extra embryonic membranes to be formed. As in the
monotremes the formation of an embryo has been inhibited up to
this stage, but a primitive streak soon appears in the ectoderm and
development proceeds along lines similar to those found in the
monotremes. The resemblance becomes closer when the uterine
fluid absorbed by the monotreme egg through the bilaminar omphalopleure brings about the disintegration of the yolk mass and the
constituent spherules become disseminated in the fluid contents of
the yolk sac cavity (Semon, 1894c; Hill, 1910) as the yolk spherules
do in the yolk sac in marsupials.

EXTERNAL FEATURES AND EMBRYONIC
MEMBRANES OF EMBRYOS FROM POUCH EGGS

The remainder of our knowledge of the embryology of *Tachyglossus* is confined to Semon's (1894 b and c) descriptions of a series
of embryos designated stages 40–45, which were found in pouch

eggs, and stages 46–53 which were all pouch young. Semon dealt only with external features, which are beautifully illustrated, but his many colleagues have contributed descriptions to the *Zoologische Forschungsreisen in Australien* of the development of various organ systems, the more interesting of which are dealt with elsewhere in this book.

Stage 40 is an embryo about 7 mm long, with blunt lobate limb buds and remarkably prominent pharyngeal pouches. Somites number about 39 pairs and there is a well-developed tail. At stage 43 the gill pouches are by now incorporated into the neck; the limbs are still lobate but the anterior pair are larger than the hind pair and the tail is relatively larger than in stage 40. At stage 44 the forelimbs are pentadactyl, the tail is undergoing a reduction in size and the hind limbs are still in limb-bud condition. At stages 43 and 44, the anlage of that most interesting structure, the egg-tooth, appears (Seydel, 1899). At first it has the form of a median conical papilla which arises from the snout region of the head and projects downward over the oral opening. It consists of a downgrowth of the head mesoderm which carries the overlying epidermis before it to form its external covering. At stage 44 it is longer and portion of the epidermis shows differentiation of its cells to form an enamel organ. From the exterior inwards the tooth consists of the following layers: an external buccal epithelium, an enamel epithelium of columnar cells, a basement membrane, and a layer of odontoblasts—derivatives of the meso-dermal core which forms the dental pulp of the tooth. Above the egg-tooth a median mesenchymal condensation appears which is distinguishable into a middle portion and two lateral wings; these form the lateral portions of the premaxillae. The basal portion of the mesenchyme of the tooth likewise forms bone which unites with that of the median part of the premaxilla, thus the tooth acquires a solid foundation. By stage 45, according to Seydel (1899) and Hill and de Beer (1949), the tooth has a sharp point and is invested with solid enamel while the dental pulp, rich in capillaries, is enclosed by the bone forming the attachment to the premaxilla. This stage just precedes hatching.

Semon (1894c) had the good fortune to take an echidna carrying a newly hatched pouch young; it was considered to be just born because the drying remnants of the foetal membranes were still adherent to the navel. This little animal (stage 46) was about 1·5 cm long, the forelimbs were well developed, the hind limbs, however, were still at the bud stage, exhibiting slight indications of digits. The snout region was compressed and showed no sign of its capacity to develop into an elongated beak. According to Seydel, and Hill and de Beer, recently hatched echidnas still exhibit the egg-tooth but Semon's illustration of stage 46 shows no sign of it (Fig. 65a).

Semon (1894b) has described the foetal membranes of echidna embryos in pouch eggs at stages 42, 43, and 45. The embryo lies between the large vascular yolk sac which occupies the whole of the space inside the egg on the left side of the embryo while the space to the right of the embryo is occupied by the equally large allantois.

The extra embryonic mesoderm and the coelomic cavity associated with it is found between the ectoderm and endoderm of the bilaminar blastocyst so that the embryo, amnion, allantois, and yolk sac come to be completely surrounded by the upwards as well as downwards growth of a layer composed of somatic mesoderm and ectoderm— the serosa. At the same time the yolk sac comes to be covered in its entirety by a mesodermal layer in the form of splanchnopleure and, where the mesoderm + endoderm of the sac comes into contact with the serosal membrane, in the form of omphalopleure. Since the latter consists of endoderm, mesoderm, and ectoderm it is termed trilaminar omphalopleure. Similarly, the allantois during its growth outwards pushes the splanchnic mesodermal layer outwards until it meets the serosa. Here a fusion of the layers occurs to form the chorion.[1] Both the yolk sac and the allantois arise from stalks dependent from the underside of the embryo, as they generally do in amniotes. The arterial supply of the yolk sac, in its typical form, consists of two branches from the dorsal aorta; these break down into numerous smaller branches distributed in the mesoderm all over the surface of the sac. In a few echidna embryos Semon found that the artery from the aorta to the yolk sac was unpaired. In all cases, however, a *rete mirabile* of blood vessels on the surface of the sac is formed. The venous drainage of this *rete* forms up into two large veins which unite and pass as a single vein into the embryo via the yolk-sac stalk. The yolk sac is hollow and is replete with nourishment derived from the uterine secretions. The internal lining of the yolk

[1] In some amniotes the allantois fails to grow out far enough to meet the serosa, nevertheless that part of the serosa nearest the allantois is called a chorion by some authors; I prefer to use the term only if there is contact between allantois and serosa.

(a)

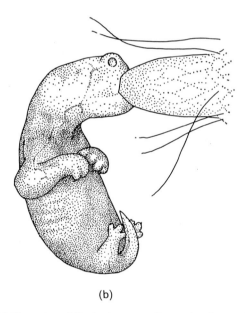

(b)

Fig. 65. (a) Neonatus of *Tachyglossus aculeatus* showing well-developed forelimbs, hind-limb buds, open external nares, and eyes covered with skin. The amorphous mass over the navel is dried foetal membranes. After Semon (1894c). ×2·8. (b) Neonatus of *Megaleia rufa* attached to the teat. The forelimbs show the same development relative to the hind-limb buds, the eyes are covered with skin and the nares are open. After Sharman and Calaby (1964). ×2·7.

sac consists of a columnar epithelium of endoderm cells loaded with yolk granules.

The allantois is also richly vascular over the whole of its surface, the arterial supply consisting of a pair of arteries arising from the posterior end of the dorsal aorta. The venous drainage is collected into two veins which enter the embryo through the allantoic stalk.

This arrangement of the foetal membranes of the *Tachyglossus* embryo within the egg is not unlike the arrangement of the foetal membrane associated with the embryo of the marsupial *Phascolarctos* (Semon, 1894b). There is an important difference, however, in that the extra-embryonic mesoderm penetrates only half to two-thirds of the way around the blastocyst between the ectoderm and endoderm, so that the yolk sac is only partially invested with mesoderm and the trilaminar omphalopleure is of limited extent; a great part of the yolk is invested with non-vascular bilaminar omphalopleure as in the early monotreme blastocyst. In the marsupials the limit of extension of the extra-embryonic mesoderm is marked by a large blood vessel— the sinus terminalis.

The allantois of *Phascolarctos* grows out and pushes the splanchnic mesoderm outwards until it fuses (*verwachsen*) with the serosa to form true chorion tissue.

The limited extent of vascular trilaminar omphalopleure found in *Phascolarctos* is characteristic of all marsupial blastocysts (Semon, 1894b; McCrady, 1938; Sharman, 1961; Hughes, Thomson, and Owen, 1965). The allamtois, however, does not make contact with the serosa to form chorion in *Didelphys virginiana* (McCrady, 1938), *Trichosurus vulpecula, Protemnodon rufogrisea, Potorous tridactylus, Setonix brachyurus* (Sharman, 1961) nor in *Pseudocheirus peregrinus* (Sharman, 1961; Hughes *et al.*, 1965). It does form a chorion, in addition to the instance of *Phascolarctos*, in at least three species of Peramelidae; here a chorio-allantoic placenta is formed consisting of a true syncytial fusion of maternal and foetal tissues (Hill, 1898, 1901; Flynn, 1923).

It has been demonstrated by Hill (1910), McCrady (1938), and by Sharman (1961) that in at least five species of marsupial the resilient shell membrane surrounding the blastocyst persists until near term. Thus a shell membrane is interposed between the embryonic membranes of the foetus and the maternal tissues for most of the gestation period; in the monotremes it is present all the gestation period and it may well be so in *Didelphys*. In fact McCrady

(1938) states that a placenta is not formed during the gestation of *Didelphys* since the vesicles can be removed from the uterus at any stage of development without interference with either the maternal or the embryonic circulations.[1] Sharman (1961), however, considers the vascular omphalopleure of these marsupial blastocysts to be a placenta even though a shell membrane is interposed between the embryonic membranes and maternal tissues most of the gestation period, the argument being that foetal membranes concerned with uptake of nourishment from the uterus are placentas. If one concedes this the omphalopleure of the monotreme blastocyst might be considered to be a placenta during the period it is in intimate contact with the wall of the uterus, especially since the yolk at that period is disintegrating and the blastocyst is filled with uterine secretions. This conclusion supports the contention of Hill (1910) that marsupial developmental processes are slightly modified monotreme developmental processes and that both kinds are basically different from those of Sauropsida. In the oviparous Sauropsida the egg contains enough yolk for the production of a young one complete in itself. On the other hand, the ova of the monotremes and the marsupials are smaller than those of reptiles and the amount of yolk is wholly inadequate for the production of the embryo, the nutrients required for complete development being supplied by the glands of the uterus. One might point out here that the developmental processes of the monotremes and many of the marsupials are also basically different from those of the viviparous Sauropsida since these exhibit early breakdown of the shell membrane *in utero* and the formation of a sophisticated chorio-allantoic placenta (Weekes, 1930) equal in complexity to that of many eutherians. At term, fully viable independent young are dropped.

Comparison of the neonatus of Tachyglossus *with those of marsupials*

The new-born pouch young of the marsupials *Trichosurus vulpecula* (Buchanan and Fraser, 1918), *Didelphys virginiana* (McCrady, 1938), and *Dasyurus viverrinus* (Hill and Hill, 1955) exhibit many modifications associated with living in a pouch and with a diet of

---

[1] Extension of this argument would lead to the absurd conclusion that pigs have no placentas since there is no intimate fusion of maternal and foetal tissues and the embryos can be removed without disruption of the circulation.

milk; similar modifications are found in the new-born pouch young of *Tachyglossus*; some of these caenogenetic specializations in the two groups are described as follow:

Body form and egg-tooth. The body form of the marsupial neonatus and that of the monotreme is similar (Fig. 65 (a) and (b)), the forelimbs showing the same enormous development relative to the lobate hind-limb buds. The marsupial neonatus has no egg-tooth but the uterine embryos of *Trichosurus vulpecula* and *Phascolarctos cinereus* exhibit a rudiment of the egg-tooth which has a structure similar to that of the *Tachyglossus* egg-tooth at stage 43 (Hill and de Beer, 1949). The pouch young of these two marsupials also exhibit anlagen of the caruncle as do those of *Didelphys aurita, Caluromys philander,* and *Perameles nasuta,* but the last three mentioned show no trace of an egg-tooth anlage (Broom, 1909; Hill and de Beer, 1949).

Excretory system. According to Fraser and Buchanan (1918) and Hill and Hill (1955) the mesonephroi of *Trichosurus* and of *Dasyurus* are well developed and functional at birth. In *Didelphys* McCrady (1938) found that it remained well developed and probably functional until the metanephros became functional about one week after birth. In all three of these marsupials the rests of the allantois are present as the urachus and as a swollen basal portion which gives rise to the bladder. These organs are at a similar stage of development in *Tachyglossus* (Keibel, 1904a); at stage 44 the pronephros (Vorniere) is a shrunken remnant, the mesonephros (Urniere) is well developed with apparently functional glomeruli but the anlagen of the metanephros are evident also. At stage 46 the latter show in the deeper regions of the cortex a few definitive glomeruli. At stage 47 the mesonephros is still an organ of impressive dimensions but the metanephros has achieved a marked increase in growth and in the central regions of the cortex fully differentiated glomeruli are found in large numbers, while at the periphery glomeruli in all stages of development are discovered. The urachus, as in the marsupial neonatus, is a solid rest of the allantoic stalk which is expanded at its base to form the bladder.

The mesonephros is still present at stage 51 but it now shows signs of atrophy.

Olfactory and other sense organs. In the new-born of the marsupials *Didelphys* (Selenka, 1887) and *Dasyurus* (Hill and Hill, 1955) the nasal septum is present in its definitive form, the external nares leading back into the large nasal cavities which communicate with the pharynx through the internal nares; turbinal ingrowths are not apparent. Similarly, the external nares in stage 46 *Tachyglossus* (Seydel, 1899) lead back into the nasal cavities which are extensive, the nasal septum is united to the false palate and the naso-palatine canals are well developed but the cartilages for the support of the maxillo-turbinals are immature. The naso-palatine canals lead backwards and communicate with the pharynx.

In *Dasyurus* olfactory sense cells are present in the olfactory portion of the nasal epithelium and olfactory nerve fibres pass from there into the olfactory bulbs. In *Tachyglossus* differentiated nasal epithelium is present in the dorso-medial wall of the nasal passage according to Seydel's (1899) illustrations but it is not known whether or not sense cells are present. It seems likely that they are since Seydel shows olfactory nerve fibres entering the bulbs. These are differentiated at stage 44; at stage 46 they are enormous relative to the telencephalon and contain extentions of the lateral ventricles (Ziehen, 1905). The olfactory organs appear to be the only sense organs capable of functioning since the eyes are covered with skin and they do not open until several weeks of pouch life have passed; likewise the organs of hearing in *Dasyurus*, *Didelphys* and *Tachyglossus* are rudiments at birth, the ear ossicles being still plastered onto the posterior end of Meckel's cartilage (Gaupp, 1908, see p. 60; McCrady, 1938; Hill and Hill, 1955). The membranous labyrinth in *Tachyglossus* at birth, however, exhibits all the structures found at stage 51 (Fig. 26) but differences in proportions of the parts are found; the ductus reuniens, for example, is thick and is not as well defined as at stage 51. A comparison of the reconstruction of the membranous labyrinth of *Didelphys* at birth (Larsell, McCrady, and Zimmerman, 1935) with that of *Tachyglossus* at the same stage (Alexander, 1904) shows them to be practically identical.

The lungs. Concerning the lungs of *Tachyglossus*, Narath (1896) wrote:

> Man denke nur an die höchst auffällige Thatsache dass zwar bis zur Geburt des Thiere all Seitenäste des Stammbronchus entwickelt sind, dass aber die weitere Verzweigung dieser noch nicht zum Abschluss gebracht wurde und dass endlich die Bildung von definitiven Alveolen noch gar nicht begonnen hat! Das Junge wird also im wahrsten Sinne des Wortes mit einer embryonalen, noch lange nicht fertig entwickelten Lunge geboren und ist gezwungen, mit dieser zu athmen.

Similarly, the young of *Didelphys* (Selenka, 1887; Bremer, 1904) and *Dasyurus* (Hill and Hill, 1955) are born with equally embryonic lungs which are nevertheless functional and in both the monotremes and the marsupials the caenogenetic modifications are of the same nature. True alveoli are not present but the bronchi end blindly in modified bronchioles which function as respiratory chambers ("geräumiger Luft-kammern") for some weeks after birth. These chambers are lined with true respiratory epithelium but later, when the definitive infundibuli and alveoli arise from them, they become ordinary respiratory bronchioles.[1] In *Tachyglossus* the ductus Botalli is

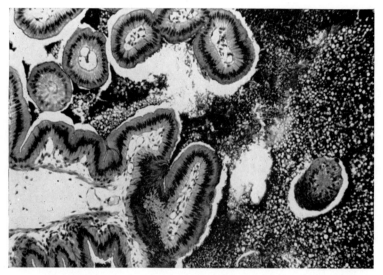

FIG. 66. Parasagittal section of portion of the stomach of a suckling echidna, weight 850 g, length 25·5 cm. Heidenhain's iron haematoxylin. (Griffiths, 1965b.) ×120. (Reproduced from *Comp. Biochem. Physiol.*)

obliterated at birth so that all blood from the right ventricle is passed solely to the lungs (p. 212). Apparently the same holds true in *Dasyurus* since Hill and Hill state that the pulmonary artery passes up to the ventral side of the trachea and turns back below it to reach the lungs.

The alimentary canal. Oppel (1896a) reported that the stomach of a "Beutelfötus" (size and weight unspecified) of *T. aculeatus* was not lined with stratified squamous epithelium as is the adult stomach (Fig. 12), but with an epithelium composed of columnar cells. This

[1] See Appendix IV.

was confirmed by Griffiths (1965b) who found that the columnar epithelium persisted until the pouch young was at least 850 g in weight and 25·5 cm long (Fig. 66). This type of epithelial lining is probably associated with a diet of milk since in a very young free-living echidna 29 cm long and 900 g in weight the stomach was lined by a thin layer of stratified epithelium. Although free-living this little echidna was probably not quite weaned since it would ingest milk and custard but not termites (see p. 203).

Heuser (1921) found that glands are not present in the stomach of *Didelphys* at birth, "nor can any of the elements be regarded as cells associated with the formation of acid as found in the functioning stomach of higher mammals". The stomach of the new-born red kangaroo, *Megaleia rufa*, is lined with a columnar epithelium

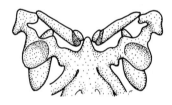

FIG. 67. Pectoral girdle of pouch young of *Trichosurus vulpecula*. Note union of scapulae to sternum by coracoid cartilages. After Gregory (1947), by courtesy of the American Museum of Natural History.

(Griffiths and Barton, 1966) which is very like that in the stomach of the pouch young of *Tachyglossus* and of *Didelphys*. Nevertheless, in the stomach of *Megaleia* at birth pepsin is present and low pH is encountered in the stomach contents at the 5th day of pouch life. No parietal cells are demonstrable until the 200th day of pouch life; however, the apparently simple epithelial cells of the stomach of the neonatus of *Megaleia* exhibit electron microscopically the characteristics of cells capable of producing pepsinogen granules and hydrochloric acid. It will be interesting to find out if the epithelial cells lining the stomach of the pouch young of *Tachyglossus* are of this nature.

From Keibel's (1904b) drawings of cross-sections of an echidna embryo at what he terms stage 45a (just before birth) the anatomy of the duodenum and small intestine, as far as the number and complexity of the villi are concerned, is identical with that of *M. rufa* at birth.

The skeleton. The chondrocranium of *Tachyglossus* at stage 46 is essentially the same as that found at stage 48 (Fig. 21) save that the tectum posterius is not as well developed and the whole skull has a more open dish-shaped appearance. Anlagen of the following membrane bones are discernible: parietals, frontals, squamosals, each with a zygomatic process, nasals, septomaxillae, premaxillae, maxillae and palatines.

The chondocranium of *Dasyurus* at birth, however, is relatively immature in structure. It is shallow and saucer-shaped but its chief constituent parts are joined to form a continuous casing for the support of the brain and olfactory organs (Hill and Hill, 1955). The anlagen of three membrane bones only can be detected, namely: premaxillae, maxillae, and palatines. Pilae antoticae, of course, do not appear.

The shoulder girdle of the new-born marsupial is remarkable for the fact that coracoid cartilages connect the scapulae with the sternum (Fig. 67). Broom (1897) who discovered this circumstance, pointed out the similarity to the monotreme shoulder girdle (Fig. 28 (a)). Later in development the coracoid cartilages atrophy in the marsupial pectoral girdle but they persist and become ossified in the monotremes. Hill and Hill (1955) noted that in addition to coracoids the pectoral girdle in the new-born *Dasyurus* exhibited the anlagen of a transitory interclavicle.

It would appear from the above descriptions that the larvae of the monotremes and the marsupials possess a number of caenogenetic modifications in common.

CHAPTER 9

THE MAMMARY GLANDS

ANATOMY

Since the possession of mammary glands is a criterion diagnostic of living mammals, one might expect that the morphology of those glands in the Prototheria would have been studied in great detail, but as far as *Tachyglossus* is concerned little is known and that little has been gleaned from observations of fixed tissues taken from a few non-lactating animals.

One learns from these descriptions (Owen, 1832, 1865; Gegenbaur, 1886; Klaatsch, 1895; Ruge, 1895; Eggeling, 1907; Bresslau, 1907, 1912a, and 1920) that the two mammary glands, located on either side of the abdomen and situated between the dermis and the abdominal muscles, consist of 100–150 separate lobules filled with tubular glands resembling sweat glands. Owen (1832) records that male echidnas have small mammary glands and Haacke (1885) gives the measurements of rudimentary mammary glands dissected out from two male specimens of *T. a. multiaculeatus* as about 8 mm long by 4 mm wide with lobules 2 mm long. These animals, moreover, were taken in September when the females are known to be suckling their young. Westling (1889), however, found that the mammary gland in a very big echidna (47 cm long) measured $2 \times 1 \cdot 5$ cm, a size not disproportionate to the large size of the animal. Nevertheless, one learns with astonishment that Bresslau (1920) inferred from this single observation:

> That the male *Echidna* as well as the male *Ornithornynchus* have their mammary glands just as strongly developed as the female . . . as regards the development of the mammary glands in the male it would be very desirable to know how they behave during ths suckling time of the young.

Griffiths and McIntosh (unpubl. data), however, are studying the seasonal development and regression of the mammary glands in *Tachyglossus* and their results, so far, are in agreement with those of Haacke. The glands were measured in excised specimens or *in situ*

in anaesthetized echidnas from which biopsy specimens were taken.
During the months in which egg-laying (July, August, and September)
and lactation in the females occurs (August to February or March,
see p. 203) the male glands were found to consist of collections of
tiny lobules directed dorsally into the dermis and at right-angles to
the surface of the areolae. The length of the lobules did not exceed
5 mm. The size of the glands in two females just coming into lactation in July and August were 40 × 23 mm and 50 × 30 mm respectively. Fully lactating glands in three females taken in November
measured at least 60 × 34 mm (Fig. 68). At their proximal ends the

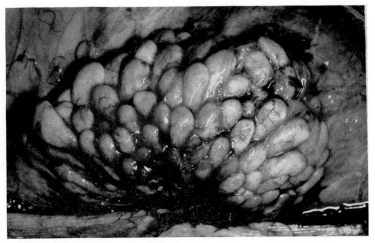

FIG. 68. Mammary gland of lactating *Tachyglossus a. aculeatus.* ×1·5.

lobules of the glands in both sexes are collected together so that they
open to the exterior on the ventral surface at two quite small areas,
the aforementioned areolae, which are about 6 mm long and 2–3 mm
in breadth. In echidnas carrying pouch young the areolae are situated
on each side of the mid-line of the dorsal-lateral surface of a pouch
or incubatorium discovered by Haacke (1885). The pouch (Fig. 69)
develops at the beginning of each breeding season,[1] and the areolae
are located about midway between its anterior and posterior ends
(Fig. 70). Owen and Gegenbaur were unaware of the existence of the
incubatorium and biologists of their time thought that the young

[1] Dobroruka (1961) mentions the curious circumstance of the periodic appearance and disappearance of a pouch in a male echidna kept at Prague Zoo.

echidna was carried in one of two slit-like pockets at the bottom of which were the areolae. The mistake arose from Owen's (1865) observations of a preserved female echidna whose abdominal wall had been cut longitudinally so that, no doubt, the curled-up edges of the cut gave the impression that there were two small pockets on either side of the mid-line. Unfortunately Owen did not draw the specimen as he saw it, but as he thought it ought to be. This one drawing had considerable influence for the next 40 years on biological theory concerned with the phylogeny of the marsupium in

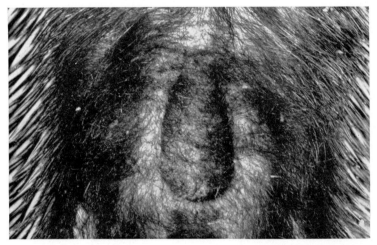

FIG. 69. Entrance to pouch of *Tachyglossus a. aculeatus*. The swollen appearance of the lips is due to the presence of the mammary glands beneath the skin. At the time the pouch was carrying the young one shown in Fig. 1. (Griffiths, 1965b.) (Reproduced from *Comp. Biochem. Physiol.*)

the Metatheria. This influence culminated in the publication of three ingenious interpretations of the nature of the "mammary pockets", with the help of which Gegenbaur, Klaatsch, and Ruge, respectively, tried to explain the phylogenetic development of mammary glands throughout the whole of the class Mammalia. After the publication of Haacke's paper, Bresslau discovered the true nature of mammary pockets by reading the text of Owen's paper as well as looking at his drawing.

To return to the structure of the mammary glands, Gegenbaur noted that the terminal duct of each lobule opened into the invagination of the skin surrounding a hair, whose follicle was situated in the

areola, and that sebaceous glands (Talgdrüsen) associated with the
follicle also opened into the same invagination. Thus milk and
the products of the sebaceous glands pass to the exterior through the
same channels. Gegenbaur also noted the presence of convoluted
sweat glands (Knäueldrusen) in a circumscribed area of skin peripheral to the areola. I am able to confirm all those findings (Fig.
71) but Kolmer (1925) could not find Talgdrüsen in the areola of
Zaglossus and he was not certain whether or not Knäueldrusen were
present in the skin around the areola; confirmation of the absence of

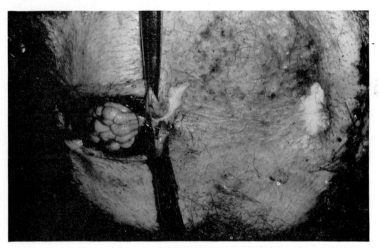

FIG. 70. Portion of mammary gland exposed. This echidna had been injected 7·75 min previously with oxytocin. Note milk welling up from
areolae, and the mammary hairs. ×0·8.

sebaceous glands will have to await further research into the histology
of the mammary gland of *Zaglossus*, but if it is shown that sebaceous
glands are absent, the areola of *Zaglossus* will be exactly like the milk
patch of *Ornithorhynchus* which lacks Talgdrüsen opening at the
bases of the mammary hairs (Gegenbaur). The presence of these
mammary hairs has led to the erroneous guess that milk is imbibed
by licking it off the hairs, and since no one has had occasion to
observe the suckling of pouch young, Linzell (1959) is constrained to
state "In the egg-laying monotremes . . . a fatty secretion is produced
shortly after the young are hatched and this is licked off as it exudes
from the base of the hairs." Marston (1926), however, showed that the

mysterious fatty exudate is milk since the principal protein present
was casein, the carbohydrate was lactose and the fat was milk fat.
Since the publication of Linzell's review it has been shown (Griffiths,
1965b) that the milk is imbibed by sucking and that there is an

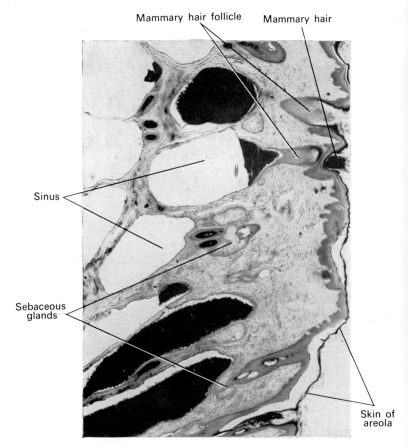

FIG. 71. Sagittal section through portion of milk areola of lactating *Tachy-glossus a. aculeatus.* ×35.

efficient "let down" mechanism for the ejection of milk; this will be
discussed later.

Gegenbaur found that the lobes in the glands of his echidnas
consisted of simple unbranched tubes which on the whole resembled
those of sweat glands. This resemblance was doubtless accentuated

by the fact that the glands were quiescent and were not secreting milk. The process of transition from the non-lactating condition to the actively secreting gland is not known in detail, but Griffiths and McIntosh have observed in biopsy material taken on July 13 from a female *T. a. multiaculeatus* (wt. 3325 g), that the lobules of the gland consisted of almost solid cords of cells in which a lumen was rarely detectable. Further samples taken on August 5 from the same

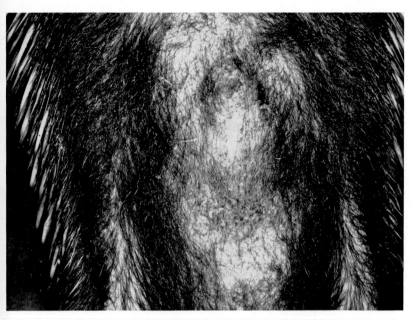

FIG. 72. Pouch, showing regression after the young one has been cast out. The two milk areolae are visible at the anterior end of the pouch area. (Griffiths, 1965b.) (Reproduced from *Comp. Biochem. Physiol.*)

animal showed that the lobules consisted wholly of hollow tubules identical with those described by Gegenbaur and by Bresslau. In another female echidna (wt. 4200 g) taken on July 22 the glands were actually secreting a turbid fluid, which contained solids to a concentration of 12% w/w and which flowed spontaneously following intramuscular injection of oxytocin. Both these echidnas had partially developed pouches which failed to achieve their definitive structure during the period of observation of 3–4 weeks and since eggs were not laid they were deemed to be non-pregnant. This suggests that the

E—N

mammary glands differentiate and grow at the start of the breeding season independently of pregnancy. This notion is supported by the observation that Kolmer's (1925) *Zaglossus bruijni*, which died in the Vienna Zoo, after being on its own for 10 years, had no eggs in its uterus but the mammary glands were engorged with milk which ran out of the gland when it was cut open; Kolmer likened the free-hand sectioning of the gland to the sectioning of a rabbit mammary gland at the height of lactation.

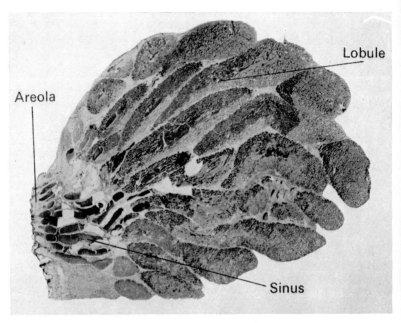

Fɪɢ. 73. Sagittal section of mammary gland of lactating *Tachyglossus a. aculeatus*. Heidenhain's iron haematoxylin. ×3·6.

The pouch young at birth is about 1·5 cm long (Semon, 1894c) but the size and degree of differentiation of the mammary glands at this time are unknown. However, by the time the pouch young is 10 cm long and weighs about 90 g the mammary glands are quite obvious beneath the skin and appear as two half-moon-shaped swellings at either side of the lips of the pouch. When the spines of the pouch young reach such a length and sharpness that the mother cannot stand it any more she refuses it entry to the pouch but she continues to

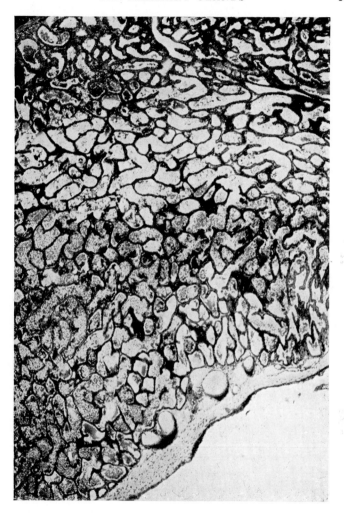

FIG. 74. Section of portion of lobule of the gland shown in Fig. 73. The central lightly staining area shows transition from alveoli to ductules. Heidenhain's iron haematoxylin. ×43.

suckle it (p. 198). The pouch quickly regresses (Fig. 72) and finally disappears (Griffiths, 1965b) only to reappear next breeding season, but the mammary glands continue to increase in size and to produce large quantities of milk for the young one. Such a gland taken from a female that had no recognizable pouch is shown in Fig. 68. The

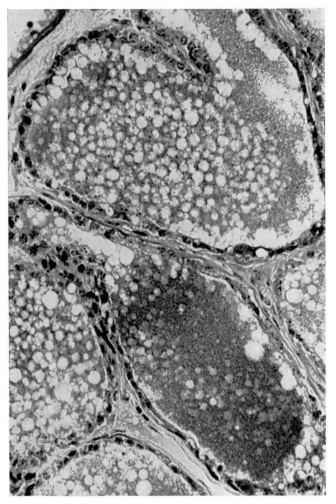

FIG. 75. Section through portion of resting alveolus showing epithelium of flattened cells. The cellular elements discernible in the septa between the alveoli are myoepithelial cells. Heidenhain's iron haematoxylin. ×434.

lobules are swollen club-shaped bodies (Fig. 73) which contain hundreds of conventional alveoli (Fig. 74). These communicate with centrally located ductules leading into larger ducts which terminate at large sinuses (Figs. 71 and 73) lined by a thin flattened epithelium. The milk ejected into these sinuses is then passed to the exterior

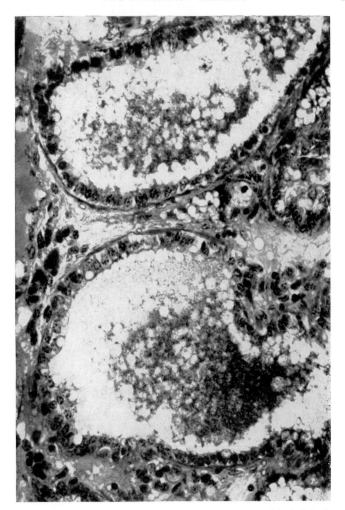

Fig. 76. Epithelium of actively secreting alveolus. Heidenhain's iron haematoxylin. ×434.

through ducts of relatively large calibre whose openings are in the invaginations of skin surrounding the mammary hairs at the surface of the areola.

The alveoli are lined by the epithelium which secretes the milk and, like the secretory cells in the mammary glands of eutherians, the cells in different parts of the echidna gland exhibit active and

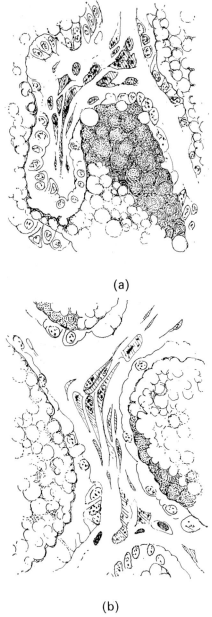

(a)

(b)

FIG. 77 (a) and (b). Septa between alveoli of mammary gland showing myo-epithelial cells. Heidenhain's iron haematoxylin. ×372.

non-active secretory phases. The cells of the non-secretory alveolus are flattened and have elongated nuclei (Fig. 75). Those in an actively secreting alveolus are cuboidal and vacuolated and in some instances the cells appear to be fragmented much as they appear to be in the eutherian alveolus (Fig. 76). The cells of the alveolus are cemented to a basement membrane and external to that membrane is a layer of myoepithelium. Gegenbaur demonstrated the presence of this type of smooth muscle in the quiescent gland where it forms an investment around the simple unbranched tubules. Kolmer also found that the

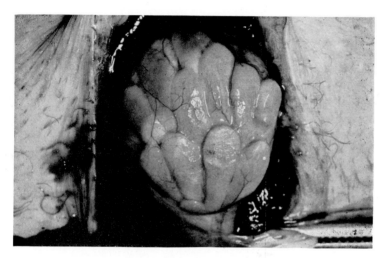

FIG. 78. Portion of mammary gland exposed. Three minutes after injection of oxytocin. Note flaccid flattened appearance of lobules. ×2.

alveoli in the gland of his *Zaglossus* were surrounded by smooth muscle cells arranged in parallel bundles very like, he thought, those around the tubules of sweat glands.

Attempts to stain myoepithelium in the mammary gland of *Tachyglossus* by the specific staining method of Richardson (1947) were not successful but cellular elements, well fitted by descriptions of myoepithelium in other mammals, could be demonstrated by staining with Heidenhain's iron haematoxylin without counterstain. This epithelium situated between the basement membranes of adjoining alveoli consists of fusiform bipolar and of branched cells with elongated thin nuclei (Fig. 77 (a) and (b)). This is a reasonably

satisfactory way of staining this tissue and some experiments about
to be described support the notion that it is myoepithelium.

As Linzell (1955) has shown myoepithelium is the target tissue for
the polypeptide oxytocin, the application of which to the cells brings
about their contraction with consequent deformation of the alveoli
and increase in intra-alveolar pressure thus leading to the expulsion
of the milk into the efferent ducts. In the lactating eutherian, oxytocin
is secreted into the bloodstream by the posterior lobe of the pituitary
gland in response to the stimulus of sucking at the nipple. That

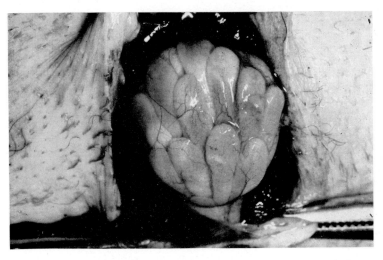

FIG. 79. Six minutes after injection of oxytocin. The lobules are beginning
to take on a rounded appearance. ×2.

hormone carried by the blood to the myoepithelium brings about
milk ejection. Injection of exogenous oxytocin will also bring about
milk ejection in eutherians and it was found to be effective in this
way in lactating echidnas. Three animals were used for the study
and each had a regressed pouch and well-developed mammary
glands. Each animal was anaesthetized with Bayer Avertin injected
intraperitoneally, and a portion of one mammary gland was exposed
by an incision extending from the areola, laterally for about 1·5 in
as shown in Fig. 70. Synthetic oxytocin (Sandoz) was then injected
intramuscularly at the rate of 9 international units/kg body weight;
thereafter photographs of the exposed lobules were taken at frequent

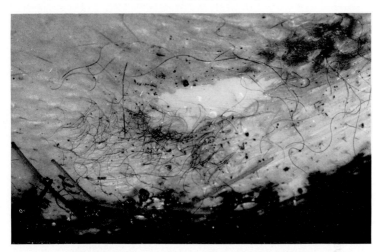

FIG. 80. Spontaneous flow of milk, 6 min after injection of oxytocin, at areola on side opposite to operation, note mammary hairs. ×2·5.

intervals during the next 10 min. A description of one experiment, which was typical of all three, follows.

Before and up to 3 min after injection of oxytocin the lobules had a flat, flaccid, appearance (Fig. 78), but at 6 min after injection they had changed their shape and exhibited a rounded swollen appearance (Fig. 79) while milk appeared spontaneously at the areola on the

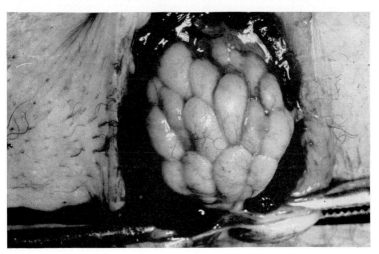

FIG. 81. 7·5 min after injection of oxytocin. ×2.

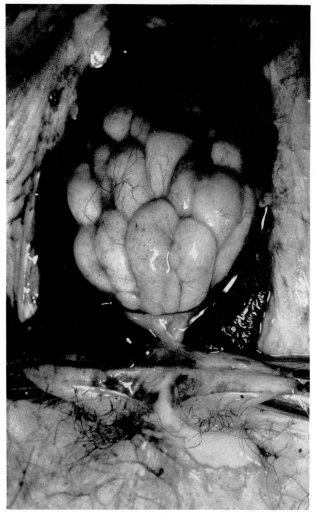

FIG. 82. 7·75 min after injection of oxytocin. The lobules have now assumed
a swollen, mottled appearance. ×2·7.

unoperated side (Fig. 80). At 7·5 min after injection the short
rounded form of the lobules was marked (Fig. 81) and the surface of
each had a mottled nodular appearance which might be ascribed to
the action of a contractile tissue around the alveoli; shortly after
this milk was flowing spontaneously at both areolae (Figs. 70 and 82).

These experiments show that oxytocin has a milk ejection effect in *Tachyglossus* which is consistent with the concept that the alveoli are invested with myoepithelium.

The processes of regression of the gland after weaning and of the transition to a quiescent state are unknown.

DEVELOPMENT

The anlagen of the mammary glands of all the Mammalia consist of a thickening of the skin located on each side on the ventro-lateral parts of the embryo, towards the posterior end. These are known as primary primordia (Bresslau, 1920), but in the Eutheria they have been given the name of milk streaks. The extent and location of the primary primordia are identical in the Prototheria and the Metatheria, but in some Eutheria they may extend over the length of the trunk but in others, where the nipple rows do not extend beyond the region of the navel, the condition is the same as in the monotremes and marsupials. During development the primary primordia shift towards each other in a medio-ventral direction and take up their definitive positions on the abdomen. From this it is clear, as Bresslau stated:

> That in all three orders [sic] of Mammalia, the first indifferent primordia of the mammary apparatus from which the later milk organs spring, are homologous—that is the primary-primordia of the Monotremes and the Marsupials and the milk streaks of the Placentals.

The primary primordia of the mammary glands in *Tachyglossus* are apparent in the stage 42 embryo (5 mm crown–rump length) as two small ectodermal thickenings on either flank a little above the place where the hind-limb buds emerge. The cutis beneath the thickenings is differentiated in that there is an accumulation of nuclei and blood vessels. The primary primordia shift from their lateral positions as development proceeds so that they come to lie, on either side, close to the line of origin of the amniotic folds (Fig. 83). At this stage the primary primordia are lens-shaped in form and they project above the level of the neighbouring skin. However, Bresslau claims that at later stages of development they become flat and inconspicuous and that this condition persists until the embryo hatches.

Soon after birth the skin closes over the navel opening but the muscle layer beneath the skin at that place does not grow and thicken as it does elsewhere, thus in the middle of the panniculus carnosus there remains an oval area relatively free of muscle tissue. This is the region which will give rise to the pouch, and at its antero-lateral portions the two primary primordia are situated. These are easily distinguishable again because in the course of development of the embryo, hairs have been developed and are uniformly distributed in the skin, except in the primary primordia, which are free of them. However, when the pouch young is 4–5 cm in length (stages 51 and 52), the development of hair follicles begins within the primary primordia with a vigour not seen elsewhere in the skin. When the follicles consist of a simple downgrowth invested by stratum germina-tivum, they begin to bud off outgrowths which become glands; those in the centre of the primary primordium becoming mammary glands, those at the periphery giving rise to sweat glands (Fig. 84). At first

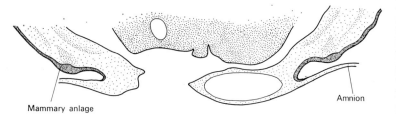

Mammary anlage

Amnion

FIG. 83. Transverse section of ventral portion of echidna embryo, stage 45. After Bresslau (1907). ×48.

both these derivatives look alike but as development proceeds they take very different courses. Within the area that will become the areola the outgrowths on the hair follicles become much larger and form elongated club-like structures while the sweat glands become convoluted (Knäueldrusen) as seen in Fig. 85. During the course of further development a hair and its associated sebaceous gland are produced by each follicle and the mammary tubules elongate and penetrate deep beneath the skin.

The embryology of the mammary glands in the Metatheria is very like this process in the Prototheria but there are differences associated with the development of nipples; the primary primordia break up into small nodules from which project downwards below the epidermis, knob-shaped structures, which are the nipple primordia. From these knobs primary epithelial sprouts grow out, each of which gives rise to a secondary bud, and to two tertiary buds. The primary

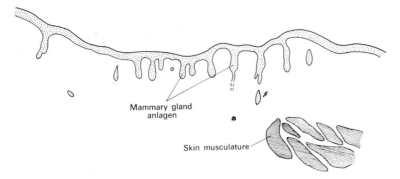

FIG. 84. Transverse section through pouch area of echidna young, stage 51. After Bresslau (1907). ×45.

buds form mammary hairs identical with those in *Tachyglossus*, the secondary the mammary glands, and the tertiary buds give rise to sebaceous glands associated with the mammary hairs (Bresslau, 1912b, 1920; O'Donoghue, 1911). In most of the marsupials the hairs and sebaceous glands regress early in ontogeny but in the koalas the hairs persist, even in the fully differentiated nipple, for a time before finally disappearing (Bresslau).

In spite of this evidence from the ontogeny of the mammary glands of the close affinity of Prototheria and Metatheria, there is no such evidence that the pouch or incubatorium of *Tachyglossus* is

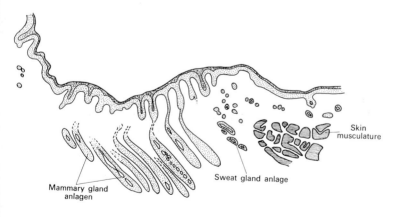

FIG. 85. Transverse section through pouch area, stage 53. After Bresslau (1907). ×18.

homologous with that in the Metatheria. In the first place some of the most primitive Metatheria, the Dasyuridae, have no pouch and exhibit no sign of a pouch during ontogeny; it is only in the more sophisticated marsupials that pouches are present and as Wood Jones (1923) remarks "The pouch was no birthright of the didelphian stock; the marsupium is a marsupial acquirement and a marsupial specialization." This does not mean that all pouchless marsupials never did have a pouch; in *Myrmecobius fasciatus*, the marsupial anteater, the pouch is secondarily lost early in its development, the primordia of the pouch can be observed but they quickly disappear. Moreover, in those forms with a well-defined marsupium it develops in an entirely different way from that of the echidna. The incubatorium is an unpaired single formation, the marsupium is a complex formed by the fusion of a series of epidermal invaginations called marsupial pockets by Bresslau (1920). These flatten at their inner margins and the lateral walls of the pockets fuse to form the wall of the marsupium. One last point of difference between the marsupium and the incubatorium is that the latter is evanescent; it appears at the beginning of the breeding season and it quickly regresses when the pouch young is cast out.

GROWTH OF THE POUCH YOUNG AND THE COMPOSITION OF THE MILK

In spite of many attempts echidnas have been bred twice only in captivity, once in Berlin in 1908 (Heck), and once in Basel in 1955. Consequently study of growth of pouch young and the lactation of their mothers is a matter of opportunism rather than of planned study; however, during the last 3 years we have had just that opportunity of observing the growth of echidna pouch young. Three lactating animals with pouch young have been obtained so far; one *Tachyglossus aculeatus aculeatus* from western New South Wales and two *T. a. multiaculeatus* from Kangaroo Island. The little we know of growth and milk intake in pouch young has come from study of these animals. A description of the work on the New South Wales echidna has been published (Griffiths, 1965b) and the results of that study will be compared with those on the Kangaroo Island animals. All three lactating mothers were fed a custard of milk and eggs containing a ration of *Nasutitermes exitiosus*.

The pouch young of the New South Wales echidna weighed 241 g at the start of the study and its length was 16 cm. At the end of 43 days of observation it was 25·5 cm in length and weighed 850 g. The increases in the total body length and the body weight were roughly linear with time (Fig. 86) at that stage of its development; the mean daily increase in body weight was about 14 g/day and the

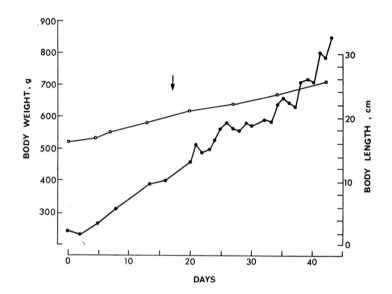

FIG. 86. Body weight and body length of the pouch young of *Tachyglossus a. aculeatus* as a function of time. Arrow shows when the young one was cast out of the pouch. (Griffiths, 1965b.) (Reproduced from *Comp. Biochem. Physiol.*)

rate of increase in body length was 0·23 cm/day. For the first 16 days of the study he was carried in his mother's pouch (Fig. 87) the entrance to which was pear-shaped and about 9 cm long (Fig. 69); it was large enough to accommodate the young one completely. When she was picked up, however, she contracted her abdominal muscles so that the young one was partly squeezed out of the pouch; the head, shoulders, and forelimbs remained enclosed. From that position a sharp wrench was necessary to break the grip of the strong forepaws on the hair inside the pouch and to pull the young one out completely. Inside the pouch the two milk areolae could be seen placed well apart on the dorso-lateral walls of the pouch.

At the 16th day of observation the weight of the young one was 400 g, the eyes which had been opened only partially were now completely open, the spines were sharp and projected from the skin, the total length of a spine taken from the flank was 10·7 mm; the rectal temperature was 29·4°C. On this day the young one was

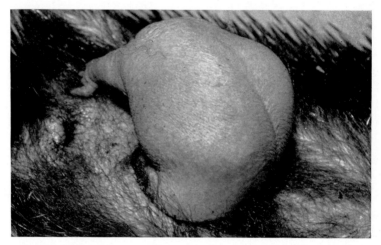

FIG. 87. *Tachyglossus a. aculeatus*, pouch young weight 307 g, entering pouch (Griffiths, 1965b). (Reproduced from *Comp. Biochem. Physiol.*)

dropped from the pouch for good and from then onwards the mother's pouch regressed quickly so that it was only a rudiment a week later (Fig. 72). The supply of milk, however, was undiminished and the mother made visits at irregular intervals of up to $1\frac{1}{2}$–2 days to feed the young one.

During the period of pouch life it was noted that the temperature of the pouch and rectal temperature of the pouch young were 30·6°C, while the rectal temperature of the mother was 30·5°C. Von Lendenfeld (1886), however, found that the temperature of the pouch could be about 2°C higher than "blood temperature" of the female. During the next 27 days the young one slept most of the time curled up; the lowest temperature observed in that period was 30·5°C and the highest was 31°C; the ambient temperature fluctuated between 21° and 31°C. During the period of pouch life we disturbed the mother as little as possible for fear that her milk production would fall off, but after the young one left the pouch it was easy to measure growth rates and the quantities of milk imbibed at a feeding, without the disturbance of wrenching out the young one. During a 4-day continuous watch four sucklings took place and by means of frequent determinations of body weight the milk intake at each suckling was measured. It was found that the day's ration is taken in about half an hour and that this amounted to 7–10% of the body weight. This process of suckling was a touching sight: the mother would carefully move up to the young one, raise the snout and gently nudge him with it until he lay between her forelimbs, one of these would be used to push him well under the body. She would then arch her back to keep the venter clear of the floor and the young one would then hang on upside down, clinging to the abdominal hair with his forepaws.

The young one takes the milk by sucking which is audible. From tape recordings of a suckling it was found that the rate was 1·27 sucks/sec; at this particular feed 35 g milk was imbibed in 19 min actual sucking time: sonagram sound spectra taken from the recording showed that the noise had a wide range of low frequencies (Fig. 88) and that it could attain the pitch of 6 kc. Even at that pitch there was considerable energy in the sound which may be ascribed to the vigour of the sucking process.

Plainly the young of *Tachyglossus* takes its milk by sucking and not by licking it off the mammary hairs, at this stage of its development at any rate; it is possible that newly hatched and early stages of pouch young get their milk by licking it up as it is ejected into the areolae.

The fact that the pouch young about 500 g in weight can imbibe between 40 and 50 g of milk in a matter of minutes, coupled with the observations that oxytocin can bring about a spontaneous flow of milk apparently by raising intra-alveolar pressure, argues that *Tachyglossus* has a milk ejection mechanism like that of the Eutheria; in connection with this argument it should be pointed out that although the pituitary gland of *Tachyglossus* elaborates oxytocin (p. 122), it has yet to be determined whether or not sucking at the areolae induces a reflex secretion of oxytocin into the bloodstream.

The pouch young that were studied in *T. a. multiacule atus* were

E—O

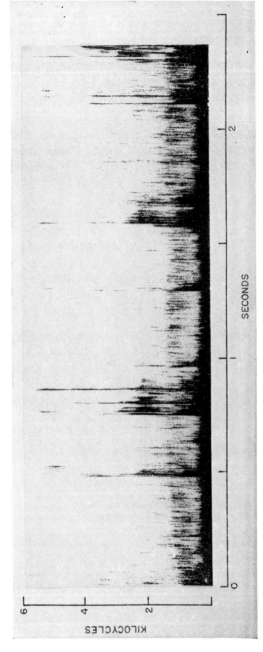

Fig. 88. Sonagram of sucking noise made by suckling echnida when imbibing milk (Griffiths, 1965b). (Reproduced from *Comp. Biochem. Physiol.*)

obtained at a much earlier stage of development than the one just described. Both were about 11 cm long and weighed about 100 g. This time we were prepared to take risks and remove them from the pouch daily to see how much and how often milk was imbibed and also to take milk samples frequently for analysis. However, our optimism was not justified since one of the echidnas, after two injections of oxytocin given a week apart, refused to suckle the young one and it died. The other echidna was phlegmatic and allowed us to take a series of milk samples after injection of oxytocin, during a period of 44 days observation. The changes of body weight and length of this pouch young are shown in Fig. 89. From this it is seen that the ratio of body weight to body length is much different from that in the *T. a. aculeatus* pouch young and that *T. a. multiaculeatus* left the pouch when it was 15·5 cm long and weighed about 170 g, whereas *T. a. aculeatus* was over 400 g in weight and 21 cm in length when it was dropped. The Kangaroo Islanders, moreover, were precocious in other ways: they could scramble around actively when only 100 g in weight and spines were evident as early as the 12 cm body-length stage, whereas *T. a. aculeatus* was not really capable of co-ordinated movements when it was 800 g in weight and 25 cm long. These differences are probably sub-specific differences, but they could also be related to the large differences in size of the mothers; the *T. a. multiaculeatus* echidnas were 2800 and 3000 g in weight respectively, whereas the *T. a. aculeatus* specimen varied from 4200 to 4500 g. However, this discrepancy in size between adult breeders may also be ascribed to sub-specific differentiation since echidnas of both sexes weighing more than 3000 g were not detected on Kangaroo Island with the exception of one female which weighed 4200 g, whereas 4–5 kg females are common in New South Wales and males come much larger.

It is also apparent from Fig. 89 that the young one in the pouch is fed as infrequently as when it is living on its own; from the daily body weight measurements it appears that it was fed about 30 times in 40 days.

Information on how long the pouch young stay in the pouch, and what happens to them in the bush when they are cast out, is meagre. Semon's aborigines found the first young ones outside the pouch in the middle of October, and the first egg in the uterus at the end of July, thus about 10 weeks would elapse between fertilization and casting out from the pouch. If one accepts the equivocal evidence of

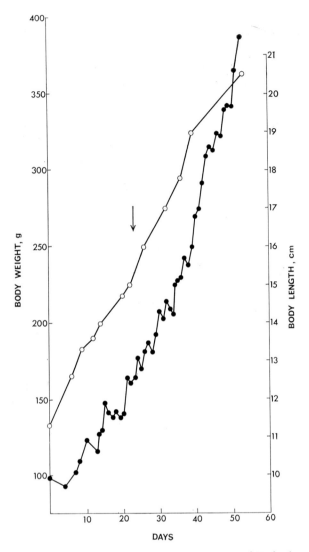

FIG. 89. Body weight and body length of pouch young of *Tachyglossus a. multiaculeatus* as a function of time. Arrow shows when the young one was cast out of the pouch.

Broom (p. 155) that the gestation period is about 27 days, this leaves about 8 weeks of life in the pouch as an egg and a suckling. Semon was told that the female returns often to the young one which is buried in a little burrow. Apparently Semon himself observed a suckling lying in such a burrow for he says: "I was able to substantiate this statement by finding fresh traces of the old echidna near the resting place of the young one, and the presence of milk in the stomach and intestine of the latter." Confirmatory evidence has been published by Barrett (1942) and Hodge and Wakefield (1959). Barrett found a spineless, smooth-skinned baby echidna on its own in a burrow dug in sandy soil; Hodge and Wakefield found a female echidna and a very small baby echidna, that had a pelage and short spines, at the end of a burrow 4 ft long. The burrow was observed occasionally over a period of 3 weeks and on those occasions it was found to be alone, but since "it remained fat and healthy for three weeks", it was assumed that the mother came back from time to time to suckle it. Just how long this keeps up no one knows but there is slight evidence that weaning in the Canberra district occurs in March since a very small echidna, about 29 cm long and 900 g in weight, walking about on its own, was taken on March 22, 1965. This little animal ingested milk and custard but it would not eat termites; it seems likely therefore that it had been on a milk diet and has just been separated from its mother. In support of that notion is an observation of another tiny echidna seen in the company of a very large echidna on March 3, 1966. Unfortunately both of these escaped down a drain so it could not be ascertained whether or not the young one was still suckling. Since these echidnas, in all probability, had been born in the September–October breeding period of 1964 and 1965 respectively, it suggests that the mothers look after their young for at least 3 months after dropping them from their pouches.

Composition of the milk

Marston (1926) published an account of some constituents of milk taken from a recently killed echidna whose pouch young (size and weight unspecified) had been removed 14 days before. With the methods available at that time he found that lactose and casein were present and that the fat was triolein; no short chain fatty acids were detectable either free or in triglycerides. The total solids were present in a concentration of 36·8 g per 100 g.

We have obtained milk samples by squeezing the milk glands after oxytocin (7 IU/kg body wt.) had been injected intramuscularly. The first 5–6 ml obtained in this way was used for analysis. This milk is

TABLE 11

Amounts of some major constituents of echidna milk

Subspecies and weight of young one (g)	Total solids (g per 100 g)	Total N₂ (g per 100 ml)	Total lipid (g per 100 g)	Phospho-lipid (mg per 100 ml)	Na (mg per 100 g)	K (mg per 100 g)	Ca (mg per 100 g)	Mg (mg per 100 g)	Whey-protein fraction (g per 100 ml)	"Casein" fraction (g per 100 ml)
T. a. multiaculeatus										
122	44·0		25·7							
208	50·0		—							
No. 1 mother { 321	{ 47·0 / 25·8a		20·6						2·9	4·4
386	49·0		—							
130	48·7		—							
149	48·7		35·0							
No. 2 mother { 124 (at death)	52·0	2·55	—							
—(9 days after death of young one)	53·0	2·66	—							
T. a. aculeatus										
570	—		—							
590	47·0		14·81 (g per 100 ml)	92	—	—	—	—		
630	—		—							
850	—	—	—	—	120·0	116·0	208·0	19·1		

a Milk obtained at the end of a sampling.

far richer than that which flows subsequently. For example, an initial sample of 7 ml contained 47·0 g per 100 g solids but a further 3 ml contained only 25·8 g per 100 g, moreover this particular sample of milk proved to be different in so far as the proportion of lipid to total solids was higher than that found in other samples (Table 11); the fatty acid complement of that lipid, however, was the same as in three other samples analysed (Table 12).

The milk samples were taken from echidnas who were suckling pouch young at the stages of growth shown in Table 11. From this it is seen that the milk fed to young ones weighing between 120 and 600 g had practically the same concentration of total solids, i.e. about 48 g per 100 g. A substantial proportion of those solids was lipid—14·8 to 35·0 g per 100 g in our samples, while Marston found 19·6 g per 100 g. This author failed to detect short-chain fatty acids in the lipid and he was close to the truth when he found that the fat was triolein; the modern aids of thin-layer chromatography and gas chromatography show that 95% of the lipid is triglyceride (Griffiths, 1965b) and that the fat consists of a mixture of triglycerides of long-chain fatty acids of which oleic acid ($C_{18:1}$) is in high concentration (Table 12). Under ordinary conditions of gas chromatography short-chain fatty acids C_4–C_{11} are not found but with careful temperature programming small and variable amounts can be detected (Table 12). In this respect echidna milk is unlike those of ruminants since they exhibit considerable quantities of C_4, C_6, C_8 and C_{10} acids, but echidna milk is quite like that of man and the pig. The milk of the former has little or no C_4, C_6, C_8 and C_{10} acids, 23% C_{16} and 37% $C_{18:1}$ (oleic) acids, the latter has about 1% each of C_4, C_6, C_8 and C_{12} acids, 27% C_{16} and 37% $C_{18:1}$ acids (Ling, Kon, and Porter, 1961).

As a matter of interest it may be mentioned, although the figures are not given in Table 12, that all samples contained C_{13} and C_{15} branched-chain fatty acids, but since their identification is based on retention times only, these results are regarded as tentative for the present.

The high levels of linoleic ($C_{18:2}$) acid in all samples, and of linolenic ($C_{18:3}$) and arachidonic ($C_{20:4}$) acids in the lipids of *T. a. aculeatus*, deserve comment. The high concentrations again emphasize the similarity of the lipids of human and pig milks to echidna milk since these contain 8, 15, and 7·27–10·2% of linoleic acid respectively, whereas the milks of various ruminants contain 1–5%

TABLE 12

Component fatty acids of milk fat from one specimen of Tachyglossus aculeatus aculeatus *and two specimens of* T. a. multiaculeatus

Saturated g per 100 g

Subspecies and weight of young one (g)	C_4	C_6	C_8	C_{10}	C_{12}	C_{14}	Iso C_{14}	Ante iso C_{14}	C_{15}	C_{16}	Iso C_{16}	Ante iso C_{16}	C_{17}	C_{18}	Ante iso C_{18}	C_{19}	C_{20}
T. a. aculeatus 630		Not detected			0·16	1·75	—	—	0·29	24·54	—	—	tr.	7·14	—	—	—
T. a. multiaculeatus 122	Nil	1·6	tr.	0·1	0·4	3·6	1·3	1·1	1·5	21·6	0·1	0·2	0·2	7·7	tr.	tr.	tr.
321	Nil	tr.	tr.	0·2	0·5	3·3	0·5	1·0	0·8	22·1	1·0	0·2	0·2	7·5	tr.	tr.	tr.
124 (at death)	Nil	0·4	0·9	0·1	0·6	3·1	0·7	1·3	0·7	23·8	1·4	0·7	0·9	7·4	tr.	tr.	tr.

Unsaturated g per 100 g

Subspecies and weight of young one (g)	Monoethenoid C_{14}	C_{16}	C_{18}	Diethenoid C_{17}	C_{18}	Triethenoid C_{18}	Tetraethenoid C_{20}
T. a. aculeatus 630	tr.	5·5	51·19	tr.	7·27	0·16	1·43
T. a. multiaculeatus 122	—	4·6	45·5	—	9·0	tr.	tr.
321	—	5·6	46·3	—	9·4	tr.	tr.
124	—	4·7	42·3	—	10·2	tr.	tr.

only. Linoleic, linolenic, and arachidonic acids are not usually synthesized by animals but they are essential for growth, so they must be ingested like vitamins. However, in echidnas fed milk, eggs, blood, and liver, the body fat contains only traces of linoleic, and no linolenic and arachidonic acids (Bolliger and Shorland, 1963). This raises the question of the source of the essential fatty acids found in the echidna milks; one possible source is the termite ration included in the custard fed to our suckling echidnas. No determinations of the fatty acids in *Nasutitermes exitiosus* have been made yet but it is known that other insects contain large amounts of polyunsaturated fatty acids—diene and triene C_{18} acids accounting for 54–88% of the total fatty acids found in some insect fats (Gilmour, 1961). Furthermore, it will be recalled that the fat of *Iridomyrmex detectus* virgin queens was liquid at ordinary temperatures suggesting a high degree of unsaturation (p. 25). It is entirely possible therefore, that insect-fed echidnas would have a body fat containing much higher amounts of linoleic acid than Bolliger and Shorland's echidnas did.

The mineral content of echidna milk presents nothing notable (Table 11). Concerning the amount of iron in echidna milk, it was stated (Griffiths, 1965b) that it was barely detectable, as judged by the method of atomic absorption, in a very small sample of milk taken from *T. a. aculeatus* when the young one weighed 850 g. Nevertheless, determinations of haemoglobin in the blood of that young one, made throughout the observation period, showed no sign of an anaemic condition. The levels observed were 15·0, 10·8, 9·6, 12·7, and 10·7 g per 100 ml and the average haemoglobin content of the mother's blood was 15 g per 100 ml. Likewise the young of *T. a. multiaculeatus* had normal haemoglobin concentrations while it was under observation, the values were: 11·7, 9·8, 10·1, and 11·3 g per 100 ml; the average for the mother was 12·5 g per 100 ml. These concentrations of haemoglobin are practically the same as those found by Kaldor and Ezekiel (1962) in the blood of the pouch young of *Setonix brachyurus*, a macropodid marsupial. The values observed ranged from 9·6 g to 13·6 g per 100 ml. *Setonix*, however, has ample quantities of iron in its milk for most of the lactation period but at weaning time the iron content falls precipitately (Kaldor and Ezekiel) —something like this may happen in *Tachyglossus* at weaning which may account for the trace quantity of iron found in the milk when the pouch young weighed 850 g and it is not unlikely that echidna milk at earlier stages of lactation will prove to have ample quantities of iron.[1]

Information on the carbohydrates is inconclusive and conflicting. Marston found that the reducing power of the carbohydrate fraction of his sample was equivalent to 2·81 g "lactose" per cent and he prepared from that fraction what appeared to be a lactosazone. However, recently Kerry and Messer (pers. comm.) failed to detect lactose chromatographically in a sample of echidna milk. Nevertheless, the milk had a reducing value equivalent to 2·8 g lactose per 100 g milk. They will investigate the identity of the reducing substances in the milk when more samples become available. Should all echidna milks prove to have little or no lactose, this will not be unusual since lactose, although it is present, is not the predominant sugar in the milk of marsupials (Jenness, Regehr, and Sloan, 1964); these milks contain considerable quantities of glucose, galactose, and various oligosaccharides. However, the composition varies with the stage of lactation and no doubt echidna milks will also prove to be variable in composition as far as carbohydrates are concerned.

Doctors H. Mackenzie and W. H. Murphy of the department of Physical Biochemistry, Australian National University, have made a preliminary examination of the proteins in the sample of milk taken from one of the *T. a. multiaculeatus* females when the pouch young weighed 386 g (Table 11). They found that the total protein content was 7·3 g per 100 ml and that about 60% of that protein was precipitable at pH 4·6. This precipitate is casein as defined by Sloan, Jenness, Kenyon, and Regehr (1961) and the supernatant is the whey protein fraction. Comparison of starch-gel electrophoretic pattern of the whey proteins with those of bovine whey proteins showed that none of the echidna proteins had the same mobility as any one of the bovine whey proteins. The starch-gel electrophoretic pattern of skim milk treated with 6·6 mol. urea—0·2 mol. mercaptoethanol revealed the presence of about 14 bands moving anodically and one band cathodically (probably an immunoglobulin). Comparison of these patterns with those of bovine skim milk, bovine α_s–casein and bovine β–caseins indicated no close similarity in patterns. This is not remarkable since Sloan *et al.* found that the electrophoretic patterns of whey and casein fractions of the milks of 40 species of mammals were different in each species; whey proteins in particular showing much variation, e.g. the whey of *Dama dama* exhibited two bands

[1] See Appendix II.

whereas six were detected in that of *Equus quagga*; the band patterns
of the caseins were also different in the various species.

The identification of the whey proteins in echidna milk will await
further electrophoretic and immunological examinations coupled
with comparison with blood serum proteins. Mackenzie and Murphy
intend to continue this work on echidna milk when more samples
come to hand.

CHAPTER 10

CIRCULATORY SYSTEM AND BLOOD

THE CIRCULATORY SYSTEM

The heart is four-chambered so that there are two completely separate circulations. Since the ventricle is divided into two, all venous blood from the right auricle goes into the pulmonary arch and all the arterial blood from the left ventricle into the systemic aorta.

The sinus venosus is incorporated into the wall of the right auricle and the three great veins (left and right venae cavae superior and the vena cava inferior) open directly into the auricular cavity. Sinu-auricular valves are as well developed in the heart of *Tachyglossus* as they are in those of the Sauropsida. The pulmonary veins open separately into the left auricle since their common stem is absorbed into its wall.

The atrioventricular valves are extraordinarily interesting. The right atrioventricular ostium is guarded by a valve which consists for the most part of a large muscular flap arising from around the ostium; its movement is limited not by chordae tendiniae but by extensions of the papillary muscles from the ventricle wall and these actually invade the muscular substance of the distal portions of the valve. There are three of these papillary muscles: the great anterior muscle column, right anterior muscle column, and the left conal column. The left atrioventricular ostium is surrounded by a tricuspid valve, the flaps of which are thin and membranous and are controlled in their extent of movement by papillary muscles extending out from the ventricular wall. As in the right ventricle there are no chordae tendiniae but the membranous flaps of the valve are not invaded by the substance of the musculi papillares; they are simply attached to the flap and do not spread through it. According to Lankester (1883) there is no septal flap at the right atrioventricular ostium, but Röse (1890), on the other hand, did find one, and that finding was confirmed by Hochstetter (1896). The septal flap valve is said to be very like that in the crocodile heart, and as a matter of fact, the fleshy right atrioventricular valve is also very like that found in the hearts of the Sauropsida.

Although Prototherians and birds have both achieved two completely separate circulations in the heart they have done so by different means. This is best understood from Hochstetter's descriptions of the development of the arterial arches in *Tachyglossus*. As we have already seen (p. 124), the pharynx during the course of its development produces a series of branchial pouches, and related to these pouches are a series of arteries, the aortic arches, which connect the ventral aorta with the dorsal aortae or trunks. The latter fuse to form one aorta conducting the blood posteriorly.

At the earliest stage (40) of development that Hochstetter examined, three pairs of arterial arches are present, numbers 3, 4, and 6; only rests of the first two pairs of arches are apparent, but the basal stem of each pair on each side is present; these two stems become the external carotid artery of each side. No trace of the 5th pair of arches is detectable. The 6th arch, which arises at the truncus arteriosus, has a branch on each side leading back to the lungs and a dorsal connection with the aortal trunk of each side; this connection is the ductus arteriosus or ductus Botalli.

At stage 42 the three pairs of arterial arches are still evident but the right partner of the 4th pair is clearly smaller than its partner on the left. Likewise the right dorsal aorta is much smaller than the left and that part of the right aorta between arches 3 and 4 is beginning to atrophy. The anterior dorsal part of arch 3 on either side becomes the internal carotid, and the very short ventral part of the arch posterior to the level of origin of the internal carotid becomes the common carotid artery.

The ventral aorta is divided into a dorsal pulmonary and a ventral aortic (carotid-systemic) channel by a septum; this subdivision is carried back through the truncus arteriosus to its origin at the ventricles, the right ventricle leading into the pulmonary part of the truncus and the left into the systemic channel.

The two subclavian arteries arise from the dorsal aortae, near their union which forms the dorsal aorta, at the level of the 7th cervical segment.

Stage 43 shows little difference from 42 save that those parts of the dorsal aorta between arches 3 and 4 are reduced to fine threads and the ductus Botalli on the left side shows signs of atrophy. At stage 44,

212   ECHIDNAS

the ductus Botalli, on the right side, as well as that on the left is beginning to undergo atrophy. The right dorsal aorta caudal to the origin of the right subclavian is now a shrunken remnant of a blood vessel.

At stage 45 the right dorsal aortal trunk having disappeared, the right common carotid and subclavian arise from an arteria innominata which in turn arises from the remnant of the right 4th arch. The left common carotid and the left subclavian arise separately from the left 4th arch which is now called the aortic arch. At birth, stage 46, the remaining ductus Botalli is obliterated so that all blood from the right ventricle is now directed solely to the lungs and all

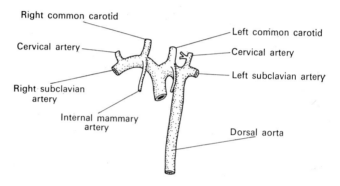

FIG. 90. Systemic arch of adult *Tachyglossus aculeatus*. After Hochstetter (1896).

blood from the left ventricle passes to the left systemic-carotid arch. The anatomy of the arterial system in this and in stage 47 corresponds in all essential respects with that of the adult (Fig. 90). It is also like the arterial system in any other mammal but is quite unlike the arterial system in birds, which have achieved separation of venous and arterial blood by obliteration of the left 4th arterial arch so that all arterial blood from the left ventricle is directed into the right 4th arch.

The arterial supply to the kidneys and their typically mammalian venous drainage have already been described; the circulation of *Tachyglossus* presents little else of interest, speaking in a phyletic sense. Those interested in descriptions of the fine anatomy of the circulatory system should consult the monographs of Hyrtl (1853) and

Hochstetter (1896), and the paper by Shellshear (1930) on the circulation in the head of *Tachyglossus*.

BLOOD

The red blood cells of *Tachyglossus aculeatus setosus* were shown to be of the non-nucleated mammalian type by Davy (1840); he thought his echidna was the species *hystrix* but since he says it came from Van Diemen's Land it must have been the subspecies *setosus*. Owen (1845) confirmed Davy's report that "the blood discs were of the true mammalian type in number, size, and form". He found that they were flat and circular and had an average diameter of $\frac{1}{3200}$ in. Briggs (1936) apparently rediscovered the mammalian nature of the erythrocytes and Bolliger and Backhouse are under the impression that they have confirmed Briggs' discovery.

Bolliger and Backhouse (1960) have made a thorough study of the haematology of blood samples from 43 echidnas. In 13 of these animals deemed to be normal, average haemoglobin value was found to be 17·4 g per 100 ml with a range of 16·5–19·4 g. They are of the opinion that this level is higher than that encountered in most other mammals. However, wild eutherians and metatherians exhibit higher haemoglobin values than these (Griffiths, Calaby, and McIntosh, 1960; Ealey, 1967); moreover, Bolliger and Backhouse found that echidnas kept in captivity for several months have a haemoglobin content 1–6 g% lower than the normal range.

The erythrocyte is a non-nucleated biconvex disc the diameter of which is approximately the same as that of a human erythrocyte. Nucleated red cells in the form of normoblasts were found when the haemoglobin content was 4 g less than the average normal value. Anisocytosis was detectable under those conditions. The red cell counts varied from 6·8 to 9·2 million/mm³ and the mean corpuscular haemoglobin content varied from 21 to 25 gamma gamma (av. 23).

The granular leucocytes are of the mammalian polymorphonuclear type but the nuclei of the neutrophils show a larger number of lobes than those in man. In echidnas suffering from pyogenic infections, neutrophils account for 50% of the total leucocyte count and, in extreme cases, 90%. The relative proportions of the various white cells in the blood of normal echidnas are given in Table 13; from this it is seen that basophils are absent and eosinophils are practically so.

As far as blood serum proteins are concerned, Roberts and Seal

TABLE 13

Blood counts on 13 normal echidnas. From Bolliger and Backhouse (1960)[a]

	Hgb.	R.B.C.	W.B.C.	N.	E.	B.	L.	Mo.	M.C.H.
1	16·5	6·9	8·7	12	0	0	87	1	23
2	16·7		6·6	40	0	0	57	3	
3	17·6	7·0	9·9	44	0	0	54	2	25
4	17·6	7·3		28	0	0	68	4	23
5	18·4			24	1	0	74	1	
6	16·6	6·9	5·0	15	0	0	84	1	24
7	18·6		7·6	32	0	0	67	1	
8	17·8								
9	17·5	7·5							22
10	19·4	9·2							21
11	16·6	6·8							24
12	16·5	7·0	7·8	34	0	0	65	1	24
13	17·5	7·0							25
Mean	17·4	7·3	7·6	29	0·1	0	69	1·8	23

Abbreviations: Hgb., Haemoglobin g per 100 ml; R.B.C., red cell count in millions/mm³; M.C.H., mean corpuscular haemoglobin in micromicrograms; W.B.C., leucocyte count in thousands/mm³; N., neutrophils; E., eosinophils; B., basophils; L., lymphocytes; Mo., monocytes, all in per cent.

[a] Reproduced by permission of the Zoological Society of London.

(1965) studied protein components resolvable by ultracentrifugal analysis and they concluded that the three groups of mammals Prototheria, Metatheria, and Eutheria contrasted with other classes of vertebrates have a common pattern of protein components in their sera. What is very much needed right now is an electrophoretic analysis of echidna serum and identification of the proteins especially in connection with studies of synthesis of milk proteins.

Average normal values of various constituents of the blood have been published: fasting blood sugar level in adults varies from 50 to 98 mg per 100 ml and in pouch young from 102 to 292 mg% (Griffiths, 1965a and b). The blood sugar in that work was determined by the Hagedorn–Jensen method which measures total reducing value, however, in protein-free filtrates of blood treated with glucose oxidase, 92% of the reducing value was found to be due to glucose so the Hagedorn–Jensen method gives a reasonably good estimate of the true blood sugar level. Plasma uric acid concentration varied from not detectable to 0·9 mg per 100 ml (Denton, Reich, and Hird, 1963; Griffiths, 1965a) and the average blood urea level is 50 mg%

in adults (range 29–92) and varies from 128 mg% to 67 mg% in pouch young. Reduced glutathione in the blood of adults varies from 6·4 to 35·0 mg per 100 ml (Griffiths, 1965a) and the ionic composition of echidna plasma has been determined by Denton, Wynn, McDonald and Simon (1951); the figures expressed as mg per 100 ml compared with those from man show that there is a close similarity.

	Na^+	K^+	Ca^{++}	Mg^{++}	Cl^-	PO_4^{---}
Man	344·0	20·0	10·0	2·7	370·0	—
Tachyglossus	319·7	19·4	11·2	1·1	369·2	12·0

Fantl (1961) has studied some factors that influence clotting time in the blood of various vertebrates including echidnas. No evidence of consistent relationships between phyletic status and the rates of the various reactions involved in coagulation was found. For example, the relative rates of the thrombin–fibrinogen reaction in various vertebrates were found to be as follow:

Man	100
Trout	80
Tiger snake	66
Toad	28
Lizard	25
Echidna	20
Tortoise	12

CHAPTER 11

AFFINITIES OF THE PROTOTHERIA

THE determination of the relationships of monotremes to other mammals is not easy for the reasons that the monotreme fossils are of Pleistocene age and are not very different from present-day forms, and that extinct primitive mammals are classified largely on the morphology of their teeth; this is not helpful since tachyglossids have no teeth and *Ornithorhynchus* exhibits the degenerate remains of molars only during the early stages of growth.

Simpson (1945) in his *Principles of Classification and a Classification of Mammals* considered that there are only two reasonable theories of the relationships of monotremes:

> that they have evolved independently and in isolation from a very early period of mammalian history, perhaps even from the reptilian ancestry, and that they were derived from very early marsupials and owe their peculiar nature to divergent specialisation, retention of ancient marsupial characters, some degeneration, and perhaps also reversion. There is much to be said for the latter view, but the former seems more probable, is more commonly held, and is reflected in this and in almost all other classifications.

I should like to consider the two sets of evidence that support these different views of the affinities of the monotremes.

As we have seen the essentially mammalian Prototheria exhibit a profuse array of what, doubtless, are therapsid reptilian characters: pilae antoticae and separate trabeculae in the chondrocranium; cartilaginous scleral cup in the eye, lagenar macula in a virtually uncoiled cochlea; precoracoids, coracoids, and interclavicle in the pectoral girdle, vestige of a post-temporal fossa in the skull (*Ornithorhynchus* only); Zwergkanälchen in the kidney; pars intercalis encephali and dorsally located ambiguus and hypoglossal nuclei in the brain; intra-abdominal testes; macro- and micro-chromosomes; large yolk-laden egg, meroblastic cleavage, and yolk navel; oviparity; and a muscular valve in the right ventricle of the heart. The notion that monotremes are closely related to early Mesozoic mammals and have achieved, by parallel evolution, characters like those of

216

other living mammals, stems from the fact that in late Triassic deposits in many parts of the earth fossils are found which also exhibit mammalian and therapsid characters. The line of demarcation between therapsid reptile and mammal is an arbitrary one and necessarily so since there are many skeletal characters that distinguish mammals from reptiles, but the evidence of the fossil record shows that they did not all arise at once. In fact, some "mammalian" characters are discernible in fossils of the late Carboniferous, but as late as the early Cretaceous the occurrence of incus, malleus, and single dentary in some animals otherwise considered to be mammals, was not universal. Consequently, the convention has been adopted that if a squamoso-dentary suspension is present, the animal is a mammal; if a quadrato-articular suspension is exhibited, the animal is deemed to be a mammal-like reptile, i.e. if other mammal-like characters, such as a single arch between maxilla and squamosal or a soft palate and so on, are present. There has been some discussion about this recently (Valen, 1960; Reed, 1960) and a proposal was made to include the Therapsida in the class Mammalia. Simpson (1960, 1961), supported by Patterson and Olson (1961), maintained that this arrangement was just as arbitrary and lacked the merit of providing a sharply defined single anatomical criterion of mammalian status; there the matter rests.

The order Therapsida is made up of two divergent groups, the herbivorous Anomodontia, and the carnivorous Theriodontia (Watson and Romer, 1956). Both these groups acquired gradually, to use Olson's (1959) apt expression, "suites of characters" that were mammalian in nature and which do not occur in other reptilian groups. The anomodonts culminated in the Dicynodontia which, as we have noted, had pectoral girdles like those of monotremes (p. 74). The Theriodontia were represented by a number of forms including the members of the infra-orders Bauriamorpha and Cynodontia. These apparently followed parallel lines of evolution so that in the lower Triassic the members of both infra-orders exhibited secondary palates, elimination of the post-orbital bar, and heterodont dentition which consisted of incisors, canines, and cheek-teeth. In the bauriamorphs the latter were simply tall, peg-like cylinders somewhat broadened medio-laterally with flattened grinding surfaces. In the cynodonts, however, there were well developed and numerous cheek-teeth which exhibited a radiation of crown development analogous to that seen in later mammals, i.e. the cynodont "molar" presented an expansion inward from a primary cusp in the upper jaw and an expansion outward in the lower jaw.

Two other infra-orders of the Theriodontia, the Ictidosauria and the Tritylodontia, which flourished in the late Triassic and Triassic–Jurassic respectively, displayed such a mosaic of reptile and mammal characters that they are treated simultaneously, but amiably, as Therapsida by Romer (1961), and as mammals by Simpson (1961). One of the Ictidosauria, *Diarthrognathus*, appears to have had both articular-quadrate and incipient squamoso-dentary articulation of the lower jaw (Crompton, 1958).

Although the tritylodonts were practically primitive mammals, they were specialized at the same time, especially as far as their teeth were concerned. These were differentiated into large multicuspidate molars and enlarged incisors which were separated from the molars by a diastema. In the ictidosaurs the molars were transverse with one main cusp, and, in some teeth, a small accessory cusp. Both Romer and Simpson feel that the structures of the teeth of tritylodonts and of the ictidosaurs do not suggest affinities with other Mesozoic mammals. Similarly, the advanced bauriamorphs and cynodonts appear to be specialized end forms but Romer states:

> We cannot rule out the possibility of mammalian origins from smaller and less specialised members of either—or both—groups. Both show a drift towards mammalian status in parallel fashion . . . Here then are two groups from one or both of which it is not unreasonable to believe all mammals may have arisen. But despite gradual advances in knowledge in recent years we are little farther along in working out a detailed phylogeny than we were several decades ago.

If he were really pushed to choose, "on the basis of the feeble evidence yet available", between the Bauriamorpha and the Cynodontia as ancestors of the Mesozoic mammals, Romer would put his money on the Cynodontia.

In spite of the multiple crossings of the mammal–reptile line there is a poor muster of fossilized remains of Mesozoic mammals, mostly in the form of teeth, jaw bones, bones of the pectoral girdle, and of skull fragments. These have been classified by Patterson (1956) and Kermack and Musset (1958) as follow:

Subclass Theria
  Infraclass Pantotheria
    Order Symmetrodonta
    Order Pantotheria (Eupantotheria of Kermack and Musset)

Infraclass Metatheria
  Order Marsupialia
Infraclass Eutheria
  Order Insectivora, etc.
Subclass Allotheria
  Order Multituberculata
Subclass Eotheria
  Order Docodonta
Mammalia of uncertain subclass
  Order Triconodonta

Among other insinuations, the monotremes stand accused of being related to the docodonts, so the relevant anatomy of these fossils will be dealt with in some detail.

The first Docodonta discovered were assigned to two genera, *Docodon* and *Peraiocynodon*, and were known only from upper and lower jaws. It appears, however, that the diagnosis of *Peraiocynodon* was based on milk-teeth (Butler, 1939; Simpson, 1961) and that *Peraiocynodon* may be synonymous with *Docodon*. The latter is found associated with pantothere remains in late Jurassic deposits in England and the United States. The docodonts used to be classified with the pantotheres but since the upper and lower molars are irregularly quadrate with a crushing occlusion rather than triangular with the embrasure-trigonid occlusion characteristic of pantotheres, Patterson (1956) removed the docodonts from the order Pantotheria and made them into an order of uncertain subclass. The lower jaw of the docodonts exhibits a ventral process resembling the therian angular process; Patterson (1956), however, argues that it is not homologous with the therian angle because it does not serve for the attachment of the pterygoideus muscle. Patterson may or may not be right about the nature of this angle, but I cannot agree with his reasons for rejecting it as a homologue of the therian angle since function has nothing to do with the concept of homology; one might argue on those lines that the quadrate and the incus are not homologous because they have different functions. However, to continue with the jaw structure of docodonts. Above the angle running along the medial aspect of the jaw-bone is a broad trough or sulcus. This commences at the jaw margin above the posterior end of the angle and runs forward to the mandibular foramen where it terminates. Dorsally the trough is separated from the pterygoid fossa by a ridge.

Oligokyphus, a bauriamorph, has a lower jaw furnished with a similar ridge and trough and in Therapsida it is known that it houses the articular (Watson, 1942), which, with the quadrate, forms the jaw hinge. However, *Docodon* has a well-developed dentary condyle, which articulates with the glenoid facet of the squamosal, but unlike the condyles of Prototheria, Metatheria, and of Eutheria, those of *Docodon* face posteriorly and are not elevated above the level of the long axis of the jaw. From the comparison with the *Oligokyphus* jaw, it is surmised that the articular was still present in the docodont lower jaw and that the jaw, therefore, was doubly hinged. Recently Kermack and Musset (1958) have described the jaw articulation in *Morganucodon* which had originally been classified as a triconodont (Kermack, Kermack, and Musset, 1956) on the basis of its tricono-dont-like teeth in the upper jaw. Patterson (1956), however, disagreed with this diagnosis and suggested that *Morganucodon* and *Docodon* might be related since they had similar jaw structures. Kermack and Musset in their reassessment of the affinities of *Morganucodon* came to the same conclusion. The lower jaw of *Morganucodon* exhibits evidence of vestigial articular-quadrate hingeing as well as of a robust dentary-squamosal suspension; indeed in one specimen of *Morgan-ucodon* the trough on the medial aspect of the jaw was found to be roofed by a broken bone which is taken to be, at the suggestion of D. M. S. Watson, the anterior end of the pre-articular or of the angular.

Although the molars of morganucodonts resemble those of tricondonts, the similarity of the structures of the jaws in *Docodon* and *Morganucodon* seems to be the over-riding consideration, so the two genera are included by Kermack and Musset in the order Docodonta of the subclass Eotheria. This is somewhat confidently diagnosed by these authors as "distinguished from all other sub-classes of the Mammalia in that the malleus and the incus form a subsidiary part of the jaw suspension, the major part of this being formed by the squamosal and dentary in a typically mammalian manner".

The members of this subclass are thought to be related to the monotremes because Kermack *et al.* (1956) considered that the petrosal (periotic) of *Morganucodon* is strikingly like that of mono-tremes in that it forms a thin anterior lamina perforated by a foramen for the passage of the mandibular branch of the trigeminal (V) nerve. In accordance with the nomenclature used for the monotreme skull they called this the foramen pseudo-ovale. These authors feel that those relations indicate affinity between docodonts and monotremes and that together they represent a side-branch of the main line of mammalian evolution. The reason advanced for this is that the petrosal plate has no adaptive significance and therefore it seems unlikely to have arisen independently in *Morganucodon* and in the monotremes! Be that as it may I feel that the main argument is untenable since the sphenoparietal fissure in echidnas, at least, is filled by an alisphenoid which is perforated by the foramen ovale; for this reason the foramen has been labelled ovale in Fig. 23 and not pseudo-ovale.

This criterion of the relations of the foramen ovale was used *inter alia* to distinguish *Morganucodon* from the triconodont, *Sinoconodon rigneyi* by Patterson and Olson (1961). *Sinoconodon* was found in late Triassic deposits in China and is one of the earliest mammals known; the lower jaw, however, is less reptilian than that of *Morganucodon*. The periotic, on the other hand, is similar in the two animals, but in an apparently young *Sinoconodon* (specimen C.U.P. No. 5), Patterson and Olson found evidence of a suture between the base of the alisphenoid and the periotic, and this suture can be traced above the foramen ovale. Patterson and Olsen conclude that:

> There is reason, therefore, to believe that the foramen in *Sinoconodon* is a true foramen ovale, completely or almost completely surrounded by alis-phenoid. If this is correct and if Kermack and Musset are also correct, as seems very likely, then there is a marked difference between *Sinoconodon* and the Pant morganucodontid in this area, in spite of the fact that the topographic relationships of the major structures are otherwise very similar.

Since the alisphenoid and foramen ovale can only be diagnosed in young echidnas weighing between 2 and 3 kg, the sutures between the periotic and the alisphenoid fusing together in older echidnas, it is possible that this is the case with the periotic of *Morganucodon*; I am willing to lay a shade of odds that, when a young specimen of *Morganucodon* turns up, it will exhibit relations of the foramen ovale identical with those of *Sinoconodon*, specimen C.U.P. No. 5. There is then, at present, no evidence that monotremes are related in any special way to any docodont; admittedly both the docodonts and the monotremes have coracoids and precoracoids in their pectoral girdles but this distinction would relate monotremes to any of the Therapsida as much as it would to Docodonta or, probably, to any other of the subclasses of early Mesozoic mammals.

This conclusion leaves for consideration the second proposition of Simpson (1945) to the effect that monotremes are related to ancient marsupials. It should be noted, however, that Simpson (1959, 1964), some 19 years after he admitted that this was a rational theory, no longer regards it as a possibility, and he has summarized his present position in the following:

> The phenomenon of parallel trends may be illustrated by a particularly striking large-scale example. The living mammals, monotremes excepted, are clearly of monophyletic derivation from reptiles. Long ago I suggested that the known Mesozoic mammals are not. That idea has been strongly supported by later studies and now seems well-established. At least six different lineages probably crossed the conventional line providing the usual distinction between reptiles and mammals at about the same time and each one independently: tritylodonts, multituberculates, triconodonts, symmetrodonts, docodonts, and pantotheres. The marsupials and placentals are derived from the pantotheres (*sensu lato*, at least). The monotremes may be derived from one of the other Mesozoic orders or may represent still another separate crossing of the line.[1]

Exclusion of ancient marsupials from close relationship to monotremes seems to date from Patterson's (1956) paper on the structure of the teeth and jaws of early Cretaceous mammals. Both Patterson and Simpson (1961) express a high degree of confidence in the concept that early Cretaceous marsupials and eutherians, and their descendants, are members of a taxon—the Theria, since these all have tribosphenic molars and their jaws are furnished with angles which in the case of the metatherians are inflected. Of the tribosphenic molars Simpson (1936) says:

> . . . the tribosphenic dentition must have been typically developed at the time when the marsupial and placental stocks separated, for the earliest marsupial and insectivore or creodont molars agree in so many respects and such minute details that it is almost inconceivable that this can be the result of parallelism or convergence.

The Pantotheria are also included in the Theria since their molars, although not tribosphenic, are related to those of Metatheria and Eutheria and since the pantotherian lower jaw also has an angle (uninflected) considered by Simpson (1961) to be "clearly homologous with that of later Theria", a statement of some confidence in this context of parallel evolution involving multiple, independent transformations of jaw-bones into intricate sets of ear ossicles.

The transitory molars of young platypuses, the one monotreme

---

[1] Quoted from G. G. Simpson, *This View of Life, the World of an Evolutionist*, Harcourt Brace and World (1964).

that has teeth, not surprisingly exhibit little relationship to the adult molars of members of the above groups: Gregory (1947) found a superficial resemblance of the molars of young wombats to those of the platypus and Butler (1961) detected resemblances of the occlusion pattern of the molars of triconodonts, symmetrodonts, and of pantotheres to that of *Ornithorhynchus*.

The lower jaw of the platypus has no angle but a vestige of one is present in *Tachyglossus* (Fig. 91). The reduction in size of the angle is due, presumably, to the atrophy of the jaw musculature analogous to that found in the little nectar-eating marsupial, *Tarsipes spenserae*; here there is no trace of angle or coronoid process in the lower jaw. It is probable, however, that an inflected angle was present in the jaw-bones of the conventional forebears of *Tarsipes* and it is possible that

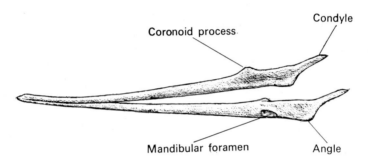

FIG. 91. Lower jaw of *Tachyglossus a. aculeatus*.

the angle was inflected in the ancestors of *Tachyglossus* but this can no longer be determined in the descendants. Patterson (1956) is of the opinion that the echidna angle and that of therians were evolved independently; this may be true but again I cannot subscribe to his conviction that the two angles are analogous rather than homo-logous, for the consideration that they subserve different functions.

On the face of it, the evidence of morphology of molars indicates that Metatheria and Eutheria are closely related and that Prototheria are not related to either of these groups. However, this conclusion is based on but one line of evidence and, as Simpson (1945) advocates, the evidence from genetics, embryology, anatomy, physiology, zoo-geography, etc., should be enlisted for the determination of phylo-geny and classification. If this is attempted in the case of the living Metatheria and Eutheria, it can be seen that they have a large number of characters in common which, apparently, are of phylogenetic significance since they are not exhibited by the Prototheria:

1. The posterior portion of the jugal participates in the formation of the glenoid cavity.
2. The cochlea is coiled.
3. Dentition is tribosphenic.
4. The pectoral girdle has clavicles, reduced coracoids, no pre-coracoids, and no interclavicle.
5. All the atrioventricular valves of the heart are membranous and are anchored by chordae tendiniae.
6. Sphincter colli differentiated into superficial and deep layers.
7. The testes are housed in a scrotum.
8. The adrenals have a central medulla surrounded by a cortex differentiated into zones.
9. The pons Varolii is situated anterior to the emergence of the trigeminal nerve.
10. The eggs are small, cleavage is holoblastic, and the embryos are nourished by placentas.
11. Birth is viviparous.
12. The mammary glands discharge through teats.
13. The chromosomes are macrochromosomal, and hetero-gamety is of the XY-type.

The phylogenetic significance of some of these characters is more apparent than real; I will discuss those that are of equivocal significance, i.e. numbers 4, 7, 10, 11, 12, and 13.

4. The pectoral girdles in adult eutherians and metatherians are identical but that in the marsupial pouch young passes through a condition resembling the monotreme pectoral girdle. This does not occur in the young eutherian.

7. The scrotum may or may not be homologous in the two infra-classes since in the Metatheria it is always situated anterior to the penis. As far as I know this happens in only one order of the Eutheria —the Lagomorpha. Some Eutheria lack scrotums.

10. The metatherian egg is different from that of the eutherians in that it is surrounded by albumen and a shell membrane. Although the metatherian egg contains yolk, cleavage is holoblastic but this is followed by extrusion of the yolk and the formation of a monotreme-like unilaminar blastocyst. A bilaminar blastocyst is then formed by processes that are similar in the monotremes and marsupials.

Formation of the embryo in both groups is inhibited until the bilaminar blastocyst is fully formed and at no stage is a morula formed. In the early stages of development nutriment is supplied to the embryos of monotremes and marsupials in the form of uterine secretions absorbed by bilaminar omphalopleure, and, later in the marsupials, by trilaminar omphalopleure as well. In most of the marsupials studied so far the shell membranes persist until term or for a large part of the gestation period. In the Peramelidae, however, allantoic placentas comparable in structure to those of Eutheria are formed, but Sharman (1965) is of the opinion that the union of the allantois with the serosa in *Phascolarctos* is also to be regarded as an allantoic placenta. It is inferred from this that allantoic placentation has arisen in the Phalangeridae and the Peramelidae independently. This parallels the remarkable instance of independent evolution of allantoic placentation in scincid lizards; two distantly related skinks, *Lygosoma* and *Chalcides* have similar types of allantoic placenta yet oviparous and viviparous species with allantoic placentas are found in the same subgenus, *Liolepisma*. Eutherians, of course, have allantoic placentation but one cannot say that this is homologous with that of Peramelidae.

It has been suggested, however, that marsupials have descended from viviparous ancestors with allantoic placentation and that intra-uterine life became abbreviated in those ancestors so that birth occurs near the termination of a period of functional activity of the yolk-sac placenta (Jones, 1923). Sharman (1965) argues against this view and points out that its protagonists have never attempted to explain the presence of the shell membrane which, as we have seen, persists in some marsupials almost until birth.

Finally, it may be mentioned that the monotreme and the marsupial reproductive systems are built on the same ground plan.

The inference of this discussion is, as far as embryological and reproductive processes are concerned, the marsupials have much in common with the monotremes and little with the eutherians.

11. Viviparity. The metatherian and the prototherian larvae exhibit similar caenogenetic adaptations related to birth in an immature condition and to a prolonged sojourn on a diet of milk. Eutherian viviparity exhibits nothing that can be compared to this situation, nor do eutherians display a relic of the egg-tooth during ontogeny as the marsupials do.

12. Eversion of the nipple occurs in the adult metatherian.

Before this takes place the mammary gland of the metatherian passes through a stage of development that resembles closely the structure of the monotreme mammary gland, even to the formation of mammary hairs. With eversion of the marsupial nipple the mammary hairs are shed. In eutherians mammary hairs are never evident but hair anlagen do appear fleetingly; the simple process of heterochronic retardation (de Beer, 1930) may account for the absence of differentiated mammary hairs during eutherian ontogeny, but we can only accept the evidence at its face value which suggests that the marsupial mammary gland is more closely related to the monotreme than it is to the eutherian gland. If this is so the possibility that the teats of Metatheria and Eutheria have evolved independently cannot be discounted.

13. The chromosomes of Metatheria are large and few in number, diploid numbers varying between 11 ♂ : 10 ♀ and 24 (Sharman, 1961). There is a possibility that one species has a diploid number of 28 (Drummond, 1933). The average number of chromosomes in the large number of species studied to date, is 18 but, as Sharman points out, no marsupial has 18 chromosomes (with the exception of the hybrid *Macropus hagenbecki*), but there is a bimodal distribution of chromosome numbers with peaks at 14 and 22. In eutherians the average number of chromosomes is 47 with a unimodal distribution, the modal number being 48. In general eutherian chromosomes are smaller than those of marsupials, thus on the evidence of the number and morphology of their chromosomes the Eutheria and Metatheria are as distinct from one another as they both are from the Prototheria with their XO heterogamety[1] and differentiation into macro- and micro-chromosomes.

As well as the structures already discussed, monotremes and marsupials also enjoy two or three other structures in common which they do not share with Eutheria: the marsupial bones of the pelvis are patently identical in the two groups; all marsupial and monotreme spleens are tripartite in structure; the ear ossicles in both groups show a hammer with a large handle, and a large open tympanic while the stapes is columelliform (as is the case in the eutherian, *Manis javanica*). The metatherian ear is distinct, however, from that

[1] Bick and Jackson (*Nature*, 1967; **214**, 600–601) have recently admitted the possibility that the echidna sex determining mechanism may be of the nature of $X_1X_1X_2X_2$, X_1X_2Y rather than XX, XO. Since the former configuration is known to occur in Metatheria and Eutheria, the force of this part of the argument is decreased somewhat.

of the Prototheria and the Eutheria in that a backwardly directed flap of the alisphenoid covers the middle ear.

The brains of Metatheria and Prototheria lack the third commissure, the corpus callosum, linking together the two halves of the eutherian neopallium, but all three groups of mammals are distinct as far as the relations of the sensory and motor areas of the cortex are concerned.

Gregory (1947) was so impressed with the likeness between marsupials and monotremes that he proposed that they should be included in a taxon, the Marsupionta, the class Mammalia being classified as follows:

Class Mammalia
  Subclass Marsupionta
    Order Marsupialia
    Order Monotremata
  Subclass Monodelphia (Placentalia)

This classification ignores the fact that the Metatheria and Eutheria enjoy a lot of characters in common, yet it does suggest that all may not be well with the taxon Theria. To my mind there is little justification for the erection of either Theria or Marsupionta and if one accepts Simpson's view of the progressive, independent, acquisition of advanced mammalian characters by the Prototheria (as I believe one should), the above evidence indicates that those characters were equally independently acquired by marsupials and by eutherians. This distressing, apparent failure of the ancestors of the mammals to fossilize extends even to the ancestry of man; 46 years ago de Chardin (1965) wrote:

> Neither for us nor for other living creatures can evolution be represented by a few simple strokes: it resolves itself into innumerable lines diverging from so great a distance that they seem almost parallel. These lines certainly touch somewhere—of this we are more and more certain—but so far away we cannot see where.

These words, I feel, sum up the present position of the phylogeny of the living mammals.

This viewpoint may be hard to swallow if one believes that the evolution of mammals is due to a process that by and large consists of chance changes in the structure of deoxyribonucleic acid, which are eventually selected (if they have adaptive significance) in a non-random way so that the resultant structural adaptations become part of the genotype of whole populations. One's mind is indeed entitled to boggle at the notion, for example, that the multiple, independent, evolution of ear ossicles, along with the differentiation of the corpus trapezoideum and the projection of its messages onto an independently evolved auditory area of neopallium via the same thalamic way stations, have arisen by initially chance processes.

This, and many similar examples of parallel evolution, have led to expression of dissatisfaction with the concept of natural selection as a causal explanation of mammalian evolution. Olson (1959) in his sensitive essay on the evolution of mammalian characters has expressed his "uneasiness" and that of others including myself, "with regard to the current genetic–selective concepts of evolution". He points out that this has induced some paleontologists to propose one or another form of purposive vitalistic causation, a tendency that Olson himself and Simpson (1964) quite rightly deplore since the purposive element usually postulated involves a force that lies outside the realm of material scientific investigation. The labelling of these forces with names like "entelechy", "élan vital", and so on simply covers up ignorance and as Simpson says "We may indeed be ignorant of the causes of trends, or the causes may indeed be transcendental but naming our ignorance does not alleviate it, and postulating the transcendental always stultifies inquiry."

Postulating the transcendental may stultify scientific inquiry but conscious exploration of the transcendental is quite another matter. Within our era of scientific research, in the eighteenth century, two men demonstrated that they were endowed with a peculiar type of consciousness which enabled them to describe events, in an extra-sensory realm, accompanying natural phenomena; these men were Johann Wolfgang Goethe (see Steiner, 1928) and Emanuel Swedenborg (Dingle, 1958). Of Swedenborg's contributions to physics, chemistry, and physiology, Dingle writes:

. . . considered on the purely intellectual level, there is no doubt that Swedenborg was a very remarkable man. His versatility manifests the breadth, as his original discoveries show the profundity of his concern with natural phenomena. As would be expected, he did not allow the intensity of his search for knowledge to destroy his sense of the importance of understanding what that search signified. . . Why is it that such a gifted and successful investigator has left so small a mark on scientific history? The number of his discoveries that have had to be repeated later before being recognized as such is probably greater than that of any other man, and the lack of recognition was not because they were in any way inaccessible. How has such a remarkable thing happened?

I think it is because his eyes were fixed on a point too far ahead. He leaped
to the goal by intuition, but was unable to explain the way in such terms that
his contemporaries could tread it. To contribute to scientific progress you
must see ahead of your fellows, but not too far ahead.

Swedenborg himself, however, states the matter more explicitly:
"It has been granted me, now for several years, to be constantly and
uninterruptedly in company with spirits and angels, hearing them
converse with each other, and conversing with them." It was also
given to Goethe and Steiner to enjoy similar faculties; it is the contention of Steiner that Swedenborg and Goethe were exhibiting a
type of consciousness that will arise by evolution and will be exhibited
more and more by future generations of men. Since I am convinced
of this I feel justified in invoking the transcendental as a causal
explanation of the facts of parallel evolution, indeed of purpose in
evolution, without qualms that this viewpoint will stultify research
into the mechanisms of evolution. Biologists are not obliged to
believe that their mechanistic interpretation of evolution and living
processes is the only one possible; mechanism is a philosophy
appropriate for our present stage of evolution but I am convinced
that the purposive elements of gene mutation will be definable only
in terms of the transcendental and that the unravelling of these
processes will await the researches of future Swedenborgs and
Steiners.

ANATOMICAL SPECIALIZATIONS

Anatomical specializations, connected with capture and
ingestion of ants and termites, in *Myrmecobius fasciatus*
and some eutherian anteaters compared with those of
Tachyglossus aculeatus

AT THE beginning of this book it was related that the basis of Shaw's
(1792) tentative diagnosis of the "ant-eating porcupine" as a species
of the genus *Myrmecophaga* was the exhibition of like anatomical
structures in the two animals (now known to be the result of convergent evolution) and of putatively similar food habits. The characters in question, and some others that could not be studied by Shaw,
are as follow:

> Extensile vermiform tongues.
> Large salivary glands secreting a sticky mucus for lubricating
> the tongue.
> Long snouts and palates.
> Jaws with grossly modified or with no teeth.
> Anomalous stomachs.
> Forelimbs adapted for digging in hard substrata to expose insect
> prey.

These characters are present in a more or less consistent and
well-developed fashion in echidnas, *Myrmecobius fasciatus*, some
edentates, Pholidota, and in Tubulidentata.

Myrmecobius, the numbat, is a member of one of the most
primitive living families of the Marsupialia. Like the beduin's mare
(Doughty, 1888), the numbat "all shining beautiful and gentle of
herself, she seemed a darling life, . . . without gall towards mankind".
This harmless little animal, once widespread in Australia, is now
found only in a very few places in the southern part of the state of
Western Australia; its decline in numbers is not in the main due
to direct persecution by man or by introduced predators, like the

fox, but rather to destruction of its woodland habitat to make farming land (Calaby 1960).

Besides *Myrmecobius* and the eutherians mentioned above, many other eutherians, including a hyena, *Proteles cristata,* catch and eat a variety of insects but they are not specialized for the capture and wholesale ingestion of rapidly moving ants and termites, either or both of which comprise the main sustenance of the anteaters *sensu stricto.* The classification (Simpson, 1945) of the eutherian anteaters selected for this comparison of convergent anatomy and food habits, is as follows:

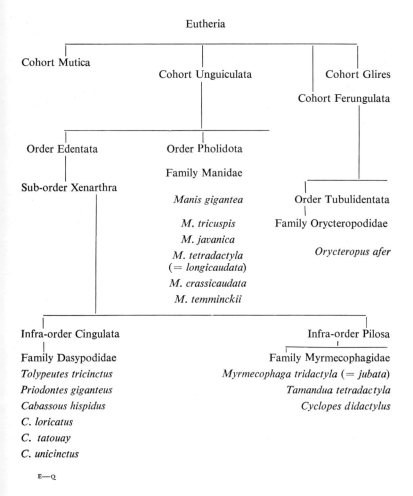

Of the many species of armadillos only three kinds, the *Cabassous* species, *Priodontes giganteus* (Kühlhorn, 1939, 1952), and *Tolypeutes tricinctus* (Eisentraut, 1952) could be termed ant- or termite-eaters. The other armadillos, although they can ingest termites and ants, are not specially adapted for their capture; they are omnivores and, in the case of *Dasypus novemcinctus*, even carrion eaters.

Cabassous hispidus occurs in eastern Brazil; *C. loricatus* in the Matto Grosso of Brazil, the Gran Chaco and northern Argentina; *C. tatouay* in southern Brazil and northern Argentina; and *C. unicinctus* in the Guianas and eastern Brazil.

Priodontes is found in the tropics of South America; it is especially common in the Matto Grosso and in the Gran Chaco, but it also inhabits open savannah country. *Tolypeutes tricinctus* comprises three subspecies (Sanborn, 1930) with a very wide distribution in South America from north-eastern Brazil to Patagonia. Cabrera (1957), however, recognizes two species: *T. tricinctus* and *T. matacus*.

Seven species of pangolin are recognized and their distributions (see Ellerman and Morrison-Scott, 1951; Krieg and Rahm, 1961) are as follow:

> *Manis pentadactyla*, through Hainan, Formosa, southern China from Yunnan to Fukien, Kiangsu, Burma to Sikkim, and Nepal.
>
> *M. crassicaudata*, Ceylon, the peninsula of India to Kutch and Bengal.
>
> *M. javanica*, Burma, Indo-China, Siam, Malaya, Sumatra, Java, Borneo to the Phillipines.
>
> *M. tetradactyla* (= *longicaudata*), Senegal, Guinea, north Congo.
>
> *M. tricuspis*, Senegal to north Angola.
>
> *M. gigantea*, east Africa and South Africa.
>
> *M. temminckii*, South Africa, east Africa, Sudan.

There is but one species of *Tamandua tetradactyla*[1] (three subspecies; Allen, 1904), and its range extends throughout the warmer parts of America from Paraguay to Mexico. There is only one species of *Myrmecophaga tridactyla* and of *Cyclopes didactylus*: the range of the former is from Guatemala to Paraguay and northern Argentine, whereas *C. didactylus* comprises several subspecies found in the Guianas, Venezuela, Columbia, eastern Peru, northern Brazil, and

---

[1] Cabrera (1957) inclines to the view that there are two species: *T. tetradactyla* and *T. longicaudata*.

part of Bolivia. Reeve (1940), however, in his study of allometric growth in the ant-bears makes no reference to subspecies.

Orycteropus afer is confined to Africa and its distribution resembles that of the African pangolins. Many species and subspecies have been described but the consensus (see Simpson, 1945) is that there is only one good species with three reasonably well-defined subspecies, *O. afer aethiopicus* from east Africa and Abyssinia, *O. a. senegalensis* from west Africa and *O. a. capensis* from South Africa.

The various convergent adaptations and food habits of the above animals will be discussed individually rather than comparing one kind of animal with another.

TONGUES

Without exception these are elongated, extensile, vermiform structures in all the anteaters and their function is apprehension of ants and termites.

In *Myrmecophaga tridactyla* the tongue internally has a bifid structure, as it does in echidnas, due to the presence of two longitudinal musculi sternoglossi and, as in echidnas, these are attached to the sternum (Pouchet, 1874; Windle and Parsons, 1899a and b; Kühlhorn, 1939). The latter records that the tongue can be extended 47–50 cm beyond the end of the snout. Extrusion is achieved by a combination of two mechanisms: firstly by contraction of the median unpaired genioglossus muscle which is inserted, in part, on the mandibular symphysis, and in part, via two long fascicles of muscle fibres, onto the sternoglossi around which the genioglossal bundles are wound spirally; secondly, by contraction of intrinsic musculature which produces deformation of the tongue. Retraction is achieved by contraction of the sternoglossi. Upon retraction into the buccal cavity the tongue is folded on itself.

Windle and Parsons (1899a) state that the tongue of *Tamandua tetradactyla* has sternoglossal muscles, and that the matter has not been determined in *Cyclopes didactylus*. Kühlhorn (1939), however, is of the opinion that the "Zurückziehen der Zunge wird durch die Mm sternoglossi bewirkt, deren Ursprung zwecks Verlängerung bei den Myrmecophagidae bis zu Innenseite des Proc. xiphoideus des Sternums verschoben ist"; which implies that all Myrmecophagidae, including *Cyclopes*, have sternoglossal muscles.

The mouth in *Priodontes* and in *Tolypeutes* is small and the tongue is correspondingly narrow. That of *Priodontes* is cylindrical (Kühl-horn, 1939) but the tongue of *Tolypeutes* is flattened dorso-ventrally and is of an elongated conical shape (Murie, 1875). This author says of *Tolypeutes*: "in partaking of food they employ the tongue much which is rapidly protruded and withdrawn ant-eater fashion, but of course with nothing like the elongate thrust and spiral recoil peculiar to *Myrmecophaga*". He could not detect sternoglossal muscles in

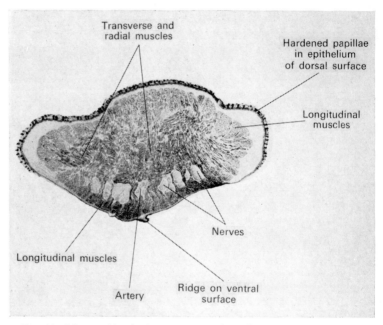

FIG. 92. *Myrmecobius fasciatus.* Cross-section of tongue taken at a level about 2 cm from the tip. Heidenhain's iron haematoxylin. ×19.

Tolypeutes but he did observe the presence of relatively voluminous sternohyoidei and sternothyroidei.

The presence or absence of sternoglossi in *Priodontes* has not been determined.

The tongue of *Orycteropus afer* is like that of *Tolypeutes*, being flattened dorso-ventrally and having the shape of a very long isoceles triangle (Sonntag, 1923). This author, incidentally, describes the positions and lists the numbers of vallate papillae in the tongues of many of the eutherian anteaters.

The extrinsic muscles of the *Orycteropus* tongue consist of a hyoglossus and of paired genioglossi which arise from the inner aspects of the anterior parts of the mandible. The fibres come together and pass to the tongue and basi-hyal (Sonntag, 1925).

The tongue and the attachments of its extrinsic muscles have not been described, as far as I know, in *Myrmecobius* but very recently I had the opportunity to dissect a specimen which had been preserved in alcohol. An elongated cylindrical appearance of the tongue in the live animal has been commented on by Fleay (1942); Fleay states that it is at least 4 in. long and speaks of it "flickering with lightning-like rapidity deep into every crevice of termite-riddled wood, its tip shooting out at all angles, inches away from the animal's snout". Actually the tongue is not cylindrical but is flattened dorso-ventrally and in cross-section it can be seen to consist of bundles of longitudinal muscles between which dorso-ventral transverse and radially arranged muscle bundles interpenetrate (Fig. 92). The longitudinal muscles which are responsible for retraction of the tongue are arranged around the periphery of the tongue just beneath the dermis, while the transverse, radial, and dorso-ventral muscle bundles are concentrated centrally. Contraction of these brings about deformation of the tongue leading to extrusion. This peripheral arrangement of the retracting muscles is the opposite to that found in echidnas. There are no sternoglossal muscles in *Myrmecobius*.

As far as internal structure is concerned the tongue of *Manis javanica* (Oppel, 1899) is very like that of *Myrmecobius* in that bundles of longitudinal muscles are arranged around the periphery of the tongue, and the musculature of extrusion, consisting of transverse and radial bundles, is centrally placed. The tongues of the pangolins have a sternoglossus muscle, but it is median and unpaired and is attached to a specially elongated and strengthened xiphisternal plate of the sternum.

SALIVARY GLANDS

The salivary glands of the anteaters are enlarged, but they are modified in the various forms in different ways. In echidnas they occur as discrete parotid, submaxillary, and sublingual glands, whereas in *Myrmecophaga* the parotids and submaxillary glands of each side are fused into one enormous gland stretching from the articulation of the jaw all over the neck and chest; it takes the form of a lobulated sheet of glandular tissue lying beneath the muscles of the skin of that region. According to Pouchet (1874) the sublingual glands are absent and in their stead are found numerous buccal glands which open into the mouth cavity. Dalquest and Werner (1952) refer to the salivary glands in *Tamandua tetradactyla* as parotids; since they do not mention the presence or absence of the other salivary glands, nor do they quote the work of Chatin (1870) on the salivary glands of *Tamandua*, it is likely that their parotid is identical with the composite gland of *Myrmecophaga*. They described the cytology of the gland and made the interesting observation that when cut it exuded a thick transparent liquid of the consistency of Canada balsam. I have made a similar observation on the sublingual glands of *Tachyglossus*, in fact about 1 ml of sticky honey-like fluid can be squeezed from the ducts emerging from the anterior ends of the glands. This secretion lubricates the tongue and renders it sticky so that the ants and termites adhere to it.

The parotids and sublinguals of *Tolypeutes* are small (Murie, 1875) but the two submaxillary glands are enlarged and reach back to the sternum. In *Tolypeutes* and in *Myrmecophaga* (Forbes, 1882) the submaxillary duct of each side leads into an extraordinary dilation which serves as a salivary reservoir. From each reservoir a duct passes forwards conveying the stored saliva to the buccal cavity. In *Myrmecophaga* the terminal reservoirs lie just above the long thin median tendon of the genio-hyoid muscle, the contraction of which may, by compressing the floors of the reservoirs, aid in ejaculation of the stored saliva. The salivary glands of *Cyclopes didactylus* also discharge into reservoirs (Owen, 1868).

Sonntag (1925) found that the salivary glands of *Orycteropus* consist of discrete parotid, submaxillary, and sublingual moieties. The two former are small but the submaxillary glands are large, bow-shaped, and extend from the angle of the mandible almost to the manubrium sterni. Posteriorly the two glands are in contact and at their anterior ends two ducts on each side pass forwards. The two ducts unite to form one on each side. There are no salivary reservoirs as there are in edentate anteaters, but there is an increase in the calibre of each duct where it crosses the posterior belly of the digastric muscle. Anterior to the digastric the duct passes to the inner side of the mandible and it becomes surrounded by muscle fibres which are fused with those of the genio-glossus. Sonntag feels that these muscle fibres may also act as a propelling agent driving the saliva to the mouth.

The sublingual glands of *Orycteropus* are thin and elongated.

The salivary glands of pangolins appear to have been ignored except for Eggeling's (1899) detailed description of the submaxillary glands in *Manis javanica*. These stretch from the anterior part of the neck and breast down to the level of the mammary teats which are situated just posterior to the forearms. Each salivary gland is shaped like an elongated kidney and is composed of numerous ramifying tubules lined with the epithelium of typical *Schleimspeicheldrüsen*. He considered that the structures of nuclei and protoplasm of the cells indicated a process of lively (*lebhafter*) secretion. There are no secretion reservoirs as in edentate anteaters.

Lang (see Bequaert, 1922) states that the salivary glands of *M. gigantea* attain the size of a goose egg.

STOMACHS

These, without exception, in *Myrmecobius* and the eutherian ant-eaters are different from that of *Tachyglossus*; in place of its non-glandular, thin-walled sac one finds glandular stomachs of varying degrees of specialization for trituration and digestion of ants and termites. The stomach of *Myrmecobius* (already described, p. 41), however, exhibits little or no specialty that might be associated with termite eating; it is like that of any carnivorous metatherian. On the other hand, the stomachs of Myrmecophagidae, the armadillos, *Orycteropus*, and of the Pholidota are all remarkable for the extra-ordinary development of the submucosae and muscular coats at their posterior ends.

In *Tolypeutes* there is a substantial development of the pyloric parietes (Murie, 1875) but in the Myrmecophagidae there is a hypertrophy of longitudinal, circular, and oblique muscles to form a sort of gizzard. Of this Owen (1857) remarks that the internal cavity is small and is lined with a dense epithelial lining and that:

> ... a very small proportion only, of food can enter at one time into this cavity to be subjected to the triturating force of its parietes, operating with the aid of swallowed particles of sand in the comminution of the unmasticated or imperfectly masticated termites.

Forbes (1882) agrees in general with that description but feels that the pyloric folds are softer and more vascular, than he was led to believe from Owen's account.

In *Orycteropus* the hypertrophy of the pyloric musculature is such that the gizzard takes the form of a large globe of muscle (Sonntag, 1925). That of *Manis javanica* is even more bizarre since the epithelium lining the gizzard is equipped with a series of keratinous teeth for the grinding of its insect prey (Weber, 1891; Oppel, 1896b). The stomach of *M. gigantea* has an hypertrophied pylorus but it lacks the keratinous tooth-like structures of that in *M. javanica* (Lang, see Bequaert, 1922). The stomach of *M. gigantea* is also different in that the large gastric gland (see p. 41) does not open via a single orifice into the stomach as it does in *M. javanica* "but it presents an even surface, the individual follicles of the oval patch secreting directly into the stomach". Many small pebbles, the largest not exceeding 5 mm in diameter, were found in the stomachs of *M. gigantea*; they probably assist the triturating action of the thick pyloric walls. The pylori of the stomachs of *M. tetradactyla* and *M. tricuspis* also lack keratinous teeth.

As we have seen, echidnas grind their food with keratinous spines on a knob at the base of the tongue; *Myrmecobius*, however, has no special organs for grinding up termites and it appears to swallow its prey whole. Fleay (1942) found that when large termites like the soldier caste of *Calotermes* (=*Neotermes*) *insularis* were offered they were subjected to rapid and audible mastication by the animal's peculiar teeth. However, Calaby (1960) points out that large termites are not found within the natural range of the animal. Despite the lack of specific anatomical specializations for triturating termites, *Myrmecobius* makes a good job of comminution since Calaby found that numbat scats nearly always contained termites that had been well broken up during passage through the gut. Apparently this is achieved by the grinding action of coarse sand which was detected in the scats.

SNOUTS AND PALATES

The skulls of the anteaters are prolonged rostrally to form elongated snouts and this extension gives rise to elongation of the palates which lack vacuities. The epithelia clothing the palates are not smooth but exhibit transverse ridges of varying degrees of development. Those in echidnas are well defined and bear backwardly directed keratinized teeth; my *Myrmecobius* specimen[1] exhibited

[1] *Myrmecobius* has a large mouth and a true gape, in fact it can yawn (Calaby, 1960).

13–14 such ridges, the first 4 being robust whereas the others were smaller and less well defined. The latter were confined to the arched posterior portion of the palate, the concavity no doubt serving as accommodation for the retracted tongue. The palatal ridges in *Myrmecobius* bear no teeth.

Forbes (1882) found that the palate of *Myrmecophaga* exhibits about 7 ill-defined and irregularly arranged transverse ridges. Those of *Tamandua* are even more ill-defined (Sonntag, 1925); this author also records that the palates of *Orycteropus* and *Manis tricuspis* exhibit 12 and 5 transverse ridges respectively and according to Murie (1875) there are 12 such on the palate of *Tolypeutes*.

Apparently the function of these ridges is to scrape ants off the tongue, when it is thrust out to catch more, and so retain them within the buccal cavity.

Along with the elongation of jaws, development of long tongues, and ingestion of insects and dirt, teeth became modified or even disappeared in the anteaters. The gradation of modification is as follows:

Myrmecobius teeth are degenerate, slender, and sharp, even the molars have remarkable pointed and sharp cusps. The dental formula according to Tate (1951) is:

$$i_1^1 \; i_2^2 \; i_3^3 \; i^4 \; c_1^1 \; p_1^1 \; p_3^3 \; p_4^4 \; dp_4^4 \; m_1^1 \; m_2^2 \; m_3^3 \; m_4^4$$

Bensley (1903) has pointed out that the teeth are extremely variable even to the extent that the molars on the left and right sides of the skull can be different. As Calaby says this variation and the degenerate nature "strongly suggest that the pre-molars and molars are not used and are therefore not being subject to selection pressure".

Priodontes has 65–76 undifferentiated and stump-like teeth while *Tolypeutes* has 36 (Kühlhorn, 1939). The dentine of the teeth of these and other armadillos is tubular in shape and is covered with but a very thin layer of enamel (Martin, 1916).

Orycteropus. Has teeth unlike those in any other mammal. They are peg-like, have no enamel and consist of numerous hexagonal columns of dentine separated by tubes of pulp. There are about 20 of these teeth in the adult aard-vark.

Myrmecophagidae, Pholidota, and Tachyglossidae have no teeth whatever. In the tachyglossids the degenerate malar arch lacks a jugal bone; the Myrmecophagidae and the Pholidota lack malar arches; modifications no doubt connected with the fact that these animals grind their food by means other than that of mastication with toothed jaws.

FEEDING BEHAVIOUR AND FOOD HABITS

Apart from the work of Sweeney (1956) on *Smutsia* (=*Manis*) *temminckii* and of Calaby (1960) on *Myrmecobius*, no systematic detailed studies have been published on the food of anteaters. Eisentraut (1952) states that *Tolypeutes tricinctus* living in the Bolivian Chaco at the foothills of the Cordilleras ingests mound-building termites. Krieg and Rahm (1961) allege that *Priodontes giganteus* eats termites, ants, and the immature forms of both those insects. Kühlhorn (1952) is equally uninformative about species of termites and in what proportions they are ingested by *Myrmecophaga tridactyla* and *Tamandua tetradactyla* living in the south Matto Grosso of Brazil. *Tamandua* is facultatively arboreal and terrestrial and takes with ease termites from mounds on the ground and from those in trees; it is said to plunder bees' nests on the ground and in trees, whether for honey or insects is not certain (Krieg and Rahm, 1961).

Cyclopes didactylus is arboreal and appears to live on termites and "other insects".

The forelimbs of the two armadillos and the Myrmecophagidae mentioned above are all grossly modified for digging into or ripping termite and ant mounds. The skeletons of the forelimbs of *M. tridactyla* and *T. tetradactyla* are pentadactyl but there are varying degrees of development of the digits as the specific names indicate. In *C. didactylus* digit 5 has disappeared but in all three ant-bears, digit 3 and its claw are particularly well developed. The forelimb musculature of the terrestrial *M. tridactyla* is of noble proportions as is that of *Priodontes*. In this animal the claw on the third digit is hypertrophied and it is so large in *Tolypeutes* that the manus is no longer plantigrade but "onguligrade", the little animal trotting about, as far as its forelimbs are concerned, on the tips of its toenails.

The forelimbs of the pangolins are equally well adapted for tearing open ant and termite mounds. They are pentadactyl anatomically but functionally they are tridactyl exhibiting a strong development of the claw on the 3rd digit; numbers 1 and 5 are small, although number 5 is slightly larger in the arborial *Manis triscuspis* than it is in the ground-dwelling pangolins.

Sweeney (1956) has studied, at Kadugli in the Nuba Mountains of Sudan, the feeding habits of the ground pangolin, *Manis* (=*Smutsia*) *temminckii*. It is nocturnal and feeds exclusively on ants and termites. Sweeney had fairly tame specimens to work with and he found that they could be persuaded to eat some immature stages but not the worker castes of the following ants: *Camponotus sericeus, C. maculatus, C. rufoglaucus cinctellus, Pheidole crassinoda, Tetramorium sericeiventre, Acantholepis capensis,* and *Cataglyphis viaticus bicolor.*

When these pangolins were released and followed (at night) it was observed that they would search for and eat only two species of ant, hitherto unseen by Sweeney.[1] One was an undetermined species of *Crematogaster* which is subterranean and was found in cracking clay soil; the other was a formicine ant, also undetermined, and also found in the same habitat. Twenty identified species of ant in addition to the above listed ants were common in the area; they were all ignored by the pangolins.

Sweeney also observed that ground pangolins seldom troubled to dig out a termite mound, but when they did it was invariably the nest of an *Odontotermes* or a *Microcerotermes* species in spite of the fact that the mounds of other species of termite were available. In the main these pangolins preferred to feed on termites where only a little scraping was necessary to reach them. Other species taken in this fashion were *Ancistrotermes periphrasis, Amitermes hastatus, Amitermes* sp., *Microtermes aluco, M. thoracalis,* and *Microtermes* sp.

Sweeney made some fascinating observations of the feeding habits of his pangolins, not the least of which is the following:

> When dealing with termites which are active in dung or small pieces of wood, etc., the Pangolin has the curious but sensible habit of grasping the cow-pat or wood with its front-claws and at the same time rolling over on its back still holding on to it. It then rests the cow-pat (now, of course, reversed and disclosing the termites) on its ventrum, and still grasping it with the claws, it raises its head, extrudes the tongue, and catches the termites scurrying about on the moist side of the cow-pat or wood with this organ. Having done this it either discards the cow-pat as being of no further interest, or breaks it up (still in the same position) and catches the termites with the long flexible tongue as they drop on its body. Having finished, it rolls the right way up again and proceeds to the next cow-pat. In this manner it may clear of termites as many as 25 or 30 cow-pats an hour.

---

[1] Pangolins appear to be good at this sort of collecting; Forel (*Ann. Soc. Ent. Belgique* **43**, 58–63, quoted by Bequaert, 1922) found eleven different species of ant in the stomach of a specimen of *Manis gigantea* from the lower Congo, several of which were at that time new to entomologists.

Manis tricuspis and *M. longicaudata* (=*tetradactyla*) are tree-climbers; both of these species break into the tree nests of *Microcerotermes* and *Nasutitermes* species, and feed on the inmates (Krieg and Rahm, 1961). These pangolins cling to bough or trunk adjacent to a nest, with the hind limbs and with the long tail which can be wrapped around the bough. This leaves the forelimbs free to burrow into the nest. The stomachs of tree-living pangolins rarely contain the little pebbles ("Steinchen") characteristic of the stomach of *Manis gigantea*, which argues that their main food supply lives in trees.

Information on what aard-varks eat is scanty and unsatisfactorily documented. They eat both ants and termites but apparently they often specialize and only eat the one or the other. According to Sjöstedt (quoted in Hegh, 1922, p. 551), *Trinervitermes trinervius* is a termite favoured by *Orycteropus* and according to Fuller (same source) *Termes natalensis* is eaten with equal gusto.

Apparently *Orycteropus* does not invade termite mounds *per se* but digs around the base to get at the termites in the galleries raying out from the mounds. In this way most of the surroundings of the mound will be ripped up with the tetradactyl forefeet; the first digit of the manus being absent. The claws are large and powerful as is the musculature of the forelimbs. The claw on the second digit ends in a point whereas the others are blunt.

The feeding behaviour of *Orycteropus* amounts to a type of termite farming as the following description from Bigourdan (quoted from Rahm, 1961) indicates:

> Ses promenades nocturnes constituent de véritables circuits auxquels il se tient aussi longtemps qu'il n'est pas troublé et que la population des insectes lui assure un ravitaillement copieux. On dirait vraiment que l'oryctérope possède un programme de soirée. Sa trace passe toujours au même endroit, chemine sans hâte entre les obstacles, dessinant de nombreux méandre et reliant les unes aux outres toutes les termitières du pays. . . . Ainsi tout la nuit, la promenade alimentaire se poursuit. Le circuit total est court, soit de 2 à 4 km, car l'oryctérope n'est pas rapide, il s'arrête souvent sauf sur terrain mort, par exemple les endroits très humides récemment inondés que les termites ont dû évacuer. L'oryctérope les traverse alors en marchant d'assurance et en ligne droite pour gagner un autre champ d'action. Le plus curieux caractère de ces circuits est assurément leur periodicité. Si l'animal suit mèthodiquement un programme arrêté d'avance ce programme change chaque jour de la semaine ou plutôt chaque nuit. Passé la nuit dernière à telle termitière de son parcours, il n'y reviendra sûrement pas las nuit suivante sachant d'expérience qu'il n'y trouverait plus de victimes. Le fait est très constant et facile à vérifier en marquant sur un calendrier les dates successives de passage. On peut ainsi prévoir à peu près la prochaine venue

du visiteur. Le cycle de visites s'échelonne entre 5 et 8 jours et l'oryctérope pourrait être comparé à un apiculteur prévoyant occupé a l'examen périodique de ses ruches avec l'évident souci de ménager les insectes qui le font vivre. Ainsi les "ponctions" se suiventelles presqu' à jour fixe avec mèthode et modération. Cette exploitation est si rationelle qu'il paraît s'établir une sorte d'équilibre entre le mangeur et le mangé, car il est certain qu'un même oryctérope sejourne des mois et peut-être des années sur un même terrain sans l'épuiser.

Numbat food and feeding habits have been described in detail by Calaby (1960). Favourite feeding places of numbats are the bases of wandoo trees where the soil is usually loose, contains bark and leaf litter, and is well stocked with termites. It does not break open the nests of termites, but occasionally it digs a few shallow pits in the mounds of *Amitermes obeuntis*; its usual method of feeding is to dig in the upper 2 in. of soil and to turn over sticks and small pieces of wood. Feeding is diurnal. When food is located by scent, according to Calaby, the numbat

> squats on its hind feet and digs very rapidly with both front feet. The tongue is flicked in and out gathering up exposed termites and the process is then repeated. Meanwhile the tail lies flat on the ground. The animal may move on a few inches and repeat the process or it may leave the spot and trot away to begin searching for another feeding place.

The forelimb in *Myrmecobius* is pentadactyl but digits 1 and 5 are vestigial. The nails on 2, 3, and 4 are long and slender and are of approximately equal length; although not adapted for muscular tours de force, as the forelimbs of echidnas and ant-bears are, those of numbats are admirably adapted for rapid digging in loose earth or for raking over bark, leaf mould, and other litter of a woodland floor, to expose their prey.

Entomological analysis of scats (252 scats from Dryandra, W.A.) showed that the numbat feeds largely on termites, only about 15% of the diet consisting of ants and only in eight scats did ants equal or outnumber termites. As we have seen this is not the case with *Tachyglossus aculeatus aculeatus* living on the southern tablelands of New South Wales (p. 25), but Western Australian echidnas may prove to present a different feeding pattern. The most important termites in the diet of numbats were *Coptotermes acinaciformis* and *Amitermes obeuntis* and these were by far the most abundant species in the study area. The former inhabits living and dead wandoo and powder-bark trees but its galleries run out through the soil where the numbats can detect them and expose them with their slender claws. *Amitermes obeuntis* makes a mound nest but it is also abundant just below the surface of the soil where it attacks dead wood in contact with the ground. In addition to the above two species of termite 23 other species were eaten by numbats including three of those eaten by echidnas (see Table 4), namely *Heterotermes ferox, A. neogermanus*, and *Nasutitermes exitiosus*. As well as the large number of termite species some 26 species of ants are ingested by *Myrmecobius*.

CONCLUSIONS

It is certain that anteaters exhibit many similar anatomical characters but the anatomy is never identical; perhaps the tongues of echidnas and Myrmecophagidae come nearest to one another, but grinding techniques, stomach structures, and forelimb anatomy take different paths, nevertheless, all lead to the goal of assimilation of ant and/or termite flesh. Even the stomachs of the pangolins exhibit considerable variation within the family Manidae, but they are unmistakably laid down to the same specification. Their tongues, superficially very like those of echidnas and ant-bears, are fundamentally different from these and indeed they are quite like that of *Myrmecobius* except that the latter lacks a sternoglossus for retraction. *Myrmecobius* is the least specialized of the anteaters. Like the termite-eating hyena, *Proteles cristata* (see Hegh, 1922), its teeth are still differentiated (but much reduced in number in the hyena), it has a wide gape and it is active, having normal plantigrade extremities. Both these species are amateur anteaters, so to speak, and there would appear to be no anatomical obstacle to them taking to eating beetles, large cockroaches, soft fruits, or even succulent plants; the *Myrmecobius* stomach would be quite capable of assisting in digestion of these items. It would be most interesting to compare N_2 balance and digestibility and rates of passage of termites in *Myrmecobius* with these entities in the most "professional" anteater, *Tachyglossus*.

REFERENCES

ALLEN, J. A. (1904) The *Tamandua* anteaters, *Bull. Amer. Mus. Nat. Hist.* **20**, 385–98.

BENSLEY, B. A. (1903) On the evolution of the Australian Marsupialia, *Trans. Linn. Soc. London*, Ser. 2, **9**, 83–215.

BEQUAERT, J. (1922) The predaceous enemies of ants, *Bull. Amer. Mus. Nat. Hist.* **45**, 271–331.

CABRERA, A. (1957) Catalogo de los mamiferos de America del sur, *Rev. Mus. Argentino Ciencias nat.* "*Bernardino Rivadavia*", vol. 4.

CHATIN, J. (1870) Observations sur les glandes salivaires chez les Fourmilier *Tamandua, Annal. Sc. Natur. V. Ser. Zool.*, vol. 13.

DALQUEST, W. W. and WERNER, H. J. (1952) The parotid gland of an ant-eater, *Tamandu tetradactyla, Am. Midl. Nat.* **48**, 250–2.

DOUGHTY, C. M. (1888) *Arabia Deserta*, Cambridge University Press.

EGGELING, H. (1899) Ueber die Stellung der Milchdrüsen zu den übrigen Haut-drüsen. 1. Mitteilung: Die ausgebildeten Mammardrüsen der Monotremen und die Milchdrüsen der Edentaten nebst Beobachtungen über die Speichel-drüsen der letzteren, *Denk. Med. Naturwiss. Ges. Jena* **7**, 79–104.

EISENTRAUT, M. (1952) Vom Kugel-Gürteltier (*Tolypeutes conurus*), *Natur und Volk* **82**, 43–8.

ELLERMAN, J. R. and MORRISON-SCOTT, T. C. S. (1951) *Checklist of Palaearctic and Indian Mammals*, Trustees of the British Museum, London.

FLEAY, D. (1942) The numbat in Victoria, *Victorian Naturalist* **59**, 3–7.

FORBES, W. A. (1882) On some points in the anatomy of the great ant-eater (*Myrmecophaga jubata*), *Proc. Zool. Soc. London*, for the year 1882, pp. 287–302.

HEGH, E. (1922) *Les Termites*, Bruxelles (no publisher given).

KRIEG, H. and RAHM, U. (1961) Das Verhalten der Xenarthren (Xenarthra) und das Verhalten der Schuppentiere (Pholidota), *Handbuch der Zoologie*, vol. 8, no. 27, Walter Gruyter & Co., Berlin.

KÜHLHORN, F. (1939) Beziehungen zwischen Ernährungsweise und Bau des Kauapparates bei einigen Gürteltier-und Ameisenbärenarten, *Gegenbaurs Morph. Jahrb.* **84**, 55–85.

KÜHLHORN, F. (1952) Termitenfeinde, *Natur und Volk* **82**, 49–53.

MARTIN, B. E. (1916) Tooth development in *Dasypus novemcinctus, J. Morphol.* **27**, 647–91.

MURIE, J. (1875) On the habits, structure, and relations of the three-banded armadillo (*Tolypeutes conurus*, Is. Geoff.), *Trans. Linn. Soc. London* **30**, 71–132.

OWEN, R. (1857) On the anatomy of the great ant-eater *Myrmecophaga jubata* (Linn.), Part. II, *Proc. Zool. Soc. London*, for the year 1857, pp. 22–3.

OWEN, R. (1868) *On the Anatomy of Vertebrates*, vol. 3, Longmans, Green, & Co., London.

POUCHET, G. (1874) *Mémoir sur le grand fourmilier (Myrmecophaga jubata)*, Masson édit., Paris. Quoted by Grassé, P. *Ordre des Edentés in Traité de Zoologie*, vol. XVII, Masson & Cie, Paris.

RAHM, U. (1961) Das Verhalten der Erdferkel (Tubulidentata), *Handbuch der Zoologie*, vol. 8, no. 27, Walter de Gruyter & Co., Berlin.

REEVE, E. C. R. (1940) Relative growth in the snout of ant-eaters, *Proc. Zool. Soc. London* **110**, 47–80.

SANBORN, C. C. (1930) Distribution and habits of the three-banded armadillo (*Tolypeutes*), *J. Mammal.* **11**, 61–8.

SONNTAG, C. F. (1923) The tongues of the Edentata, *Proc. Zool. Soc. London* 515–23.

SONNTAG, C. F. (1925) A monograph of *Orycteropus afer*. I. Anatomy except the nervous system, skin, and skeleton, *Proc. Zool. Soc. London*, Pt. 2, 331–437.

SWEENEY, R. C. H. (1956) Some notes on the feeding habits of the ground pangolin, *Smutsia temminckii* (Smuts), *Ann. Mag. Nat. Hist.* **9**, 893–6.

TATE, G. H. H. (1951) The banded ant-eater *Myrmecobius* Waterhouse (Mar-supialia), *Amer. Mus. Nov.*, No. 1521, 1–8.

WEBER, M. (1891) Beiträge zur Anatomie und Entwıckelungsgeschichte der Genus *Manis*, *Zoologische Ergebnisse einer Reise in Niederländisch-Ostindien*, vol. 2, E. J. Brill, Leiden.

WINDLE, B. C. A. and PARSONS, F. G. (1899a) On the myology of the Edentata. Part I. Muscles of the head, neck, and fore limb, *Proc. Zool. Soc. London* 314–38.

WINDLE, B. C. A. and PARSONS, F. G. (1899b) On the myology of the Edentata. Part II. Muscles of the hind limb; and summary of conclusions respecting the musculature of the order, *Proc. Zool. Soc. London* 990–1017.

IRON CONTENT OF ECHIDNA MILK

THAT echidna milk can contain ample supplies of iron at certain stages of lactation is apparent from some results that have just come to hand. Dr. I. Kaldor of the University of Western Australia has very kindly carried out some estimations of iron, by a modification of the method of E. Ezekiel (*Biochem. Biophys. Acta* **107**, 511; 1965) in aliquots of the samples of milk of *Tachyglossus aculeatus multiaculeatus* specified in Table 11. The results are set out in Table 14.

TABLE 14

Animal	Date of milking	Body weight of young (g)	Iron concentration of whole milk (mg per 100 ml)
T. a. multiaculeatus	1.10.65	130	4·78
	8.10.65	149	4·25
	13.10.65	Dead	4·36
	22.10.65	Dead	4·75
T. a. multiaculeatus	22.10.65	208	3·00
	8.11.65	321	2·37

These suggest that as lactation proceeds the amount of iron in echidna milk decreases as it does in the marsupial *Setonix brachyurus* (p. 207). It is possible, however, that the high values found in the milk of one of the echidnas are abnormal since this mother refused to suckle the young one after October 8, 1965. However, by comparison with published figures for rat and for quokka milk (0·3–1·3 mg per 100 ml and 0·8–3·2 mg per 100 ml respectively; Kaldor and Ezekiel, 1962), it is quite apparent that echidna milk contains a great deal of iron and that it approaches the milk of a marsupial in this regard rather than that of eutherians (the average concentration of iron in human and bovine milks is about 0·05 mg per 100 ml). One

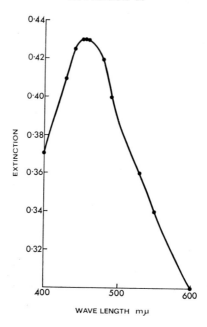

FIG. 93. Absorption spectrum of whey of echidna milk. Sample diluted with
distilled water to give suitable optical density.

might have anticipated this in view of the long sojourn on a diet of
milk alone, enjoyed by the two kinds of larvae.

Dr. Kaldor indicated to me that in the milk taken on November
8, 1965, 36% of the total iron was in the whey fraction. This iron
is very likely in the form of lactotransferrin since the whey has a
colour resembling that of a strong solution of oxidized cytochrome
C. The absorption spectrum (Fig. 93) of this pigment, however, is
identical with that of human serum transferrin which has an absorption maximum at a wavelength of 460 m μ (Roberts, Makey, and Seal,
J. Biol. Chem. **241**, 4907–13, 1966).

APPENDIX III

KIDNEY FUNCTION

THE notion that the echidna kidney is essentially a mammalian organ
has been substantiated by the data of an important paper, just
published, by Bentley and Schmidt-Nielsen (*Comp. Biochem.
Physiol.* **20**, 285–90; 1967). They studied the role of the kidney of
Tachyglossus aculeatus in water balance and found that, unlike the
reptilian kidney, it could form a hypertonic urine, as does the kidney
in Metatheria, Eutheria, and birds. When echidnas were deprived of
food and water the urine volume was small and the concentration
rose as high as 2300 m Osm/kg water whereas the plasma concentration was 281 m Osm/kg water; a urine: plasma concentration ratio
of about 8. Sodium and potassium and their accompanying anions
made up only about 20% of the total solute excreted. The observed
osmolarities in echidnas are higher than those found in man; are
similar to those of rabbits, dogs, and the macropodid marsupial
Setonix brachyurus; but they are lower than in rats, sheep, and various
desert rodents.

Urine volume may be changed in three main ways: by alterations in
glomerular filtration rate, by changes in absorption of water from
the tubules, or by a combination of these two. The results of a study
of endogenous creatinine excretion of echidnas suggested that at low
urine flow there is a decrease in glomerular filtration rate, though at
higher rates of flow, changes in tubular reabsorption must also take
place. This is also the case in all mammals that have been studied.
In man, however, tubular reabsorption is solely responsible for the
control of urine volume.

Zarnik's (1910) observations of the tubular-loop arrangement of
the nephrons in echidna kidneys are in agreement with the observed
ability to form a hypertonic urine. In mammals this arrangement
according to Wirz (Paper in *The Neurohypophysis*, ed. H. Heller,
Butterworths Scientific Publications, London, 1957) allows of the
formation of hypertonic urine by two processes: flow along a tube
that doubles back on itself (hairpin counter-current) and an active

249

process setting up a small osmotic pressure difference between the two limbs of the tube. Wirz adduces evidence suggesting that the antidiuretic hormone, vasopressin, acts at three sites in the mammalian nephron: at the descending limb of the loop allowing the tubular fluid to equilibrate with the hypertonic extracellular fluid thus inducing the counter-current concentration mechanism; at the distal convoluted tubules allowing the rate of water reabsorption to equal the rate of distal sodium reabsorption; and at the collecting ducts where a transfer of water to the hypertonic surroundings would concentrate the urine above isotonicity. Since the echidna pars nervosa elaborates vasopressin (p. 122) this schema presumably would be applicable to the echidna nephron.

As far as the ecological significance of the results is concerned it was calculated by Bentley and Schmidt-Nielsen, from published data of Griffiths (1965a) and of Schmidt-Nielsen, Dawson, and Crawford (1966), that in the termite-fed echidna living in dry air at 25–33·5°C the kidney can maintain a positive water balance without additional water intake by the echidna. From this Bentley and Schmidt-Nielsen surmise that echidnas are well adapted to survive in arid areas.

RESPIRATION

BENTLEY, Herreid, and Schmidt-Nielsen (Bentley, P. J., Herreid, C. F. and Schmidt-Nielsen, K., *Am. J. Physiol.* **212**, 957–61, 1967) have once again made good a deficiency in our knowledge of echidna physiology, this time on the characteristics of respiration of *Tachyglossus aculeatus*.

They found that the parameters of respiration in this animal are similar to those of Eutheria in that the concentrations of CO_2 in alveolar or end-tidal air are of the same order: man $5·95\%$; dog $5·68$; seal $6·3$; echidna $5·49$; the corresponding O_2 concentrations being $14·0$, $13·6$, $11·6$, and $14·4\%$ for the echidna.

Similarly tidal and minute volume values observed in their echidnas were of the order of magnitude found in eutherians. Also the extraction of O_2 from inspired air is comparable with that of eutherians in spite of the facts that echidnas have a body temperature of about 31°C and an O_2 consumption about half that of eutherians of the same size.

Alterations in respiratory minute volume in the echidna, however, are related to alterations in the respiratory rate, whereas in other mammals the changes in minute volume are brought about by a change in respiratory rate and tidal volume. However, when the respiratory minute volume of the echidna is increased by forcing it to inspire a high concentration of CO_2 the change is due to increased tidal volume while the respiratory rate is unchanged.

Bentley *et al.* further noted that echidnas voluntarily stay put in situations where the CO_2 concentrations range as high as $6·9\%$. One other mammal at least, the wild rabbit, *Oryctolagus cuniculus*, voluntarily withstands equally high CO_2 concentrations in its burrows (Hayward, J., *J. Mammal.* **47**, 723–4, 1966) and in fact the CO_2 concentrations found in the nesting chambers containing the litters range from 7 to 14%. It would be of great interest to compare the minute volumes of rabbits and echidnas at various CO_2 concentrations.

INCUBATION PERIOD
OF THE EGG IN THE POUCH

A FEMALE specimen of *Tachyglossus aculeatus aculeatus* weighing 4450 g was taken on August 18, 1967 in the company of two large males weighing 4100 and 4250 g respectively. The female exhibited a well-developed pouch which had thick tumescent lips; she was segregated from the males and kept in a dark metal container on a substratum of fine loose earth and soft absorbent paper. She was offered daily the usual custard containing *Nasutitermes exitiosus,* and just prior to feeding each day she was picked up for examination of the pouch. The temperature of the room in which she was housed was maintained at a steady 70°F and about 50 % relative humidity.

At 9.00 a.m. on September 3 the pouch was empty, but at 9.00 a.m. on September 4 it was found to contain an egg. It was noted that when the animal was picked up the cloaca could be everted about 1–1·25 cm, practically reaching into the posterior end of the pouch; if the animal was allowed to curl up, the cloaca did indeed reach the pouch suggesting that the egg could be deposited therein in this way.

This egg was not stuck to hairs, but was quite loose being found, from time to time, located in different parts of the pouch apparently retained there by apposition of the lips of the pouch. This seemed to occur only when the animal was allowed to adopt a position of rest which consisted of a sort of crouch with the back well arched. However, when she was picked up there was an alarming propensity of the egg to fall out, in fact during photography the egg was retained only by manipulation of the hairs on the lips of the pouch (Fig. 94).

Eight days after laying, the egg was removed and measured, the diameters being 16·5 mm × 13·0 mm; it was a creamy yellow in colour and had a rubber-like feel when held in the fingers. On the ninth day of incubation, at an inspection at 10.00 a.m., the egg had a dried-out and dimpled appearance. At 8.40 a.m. (September 14) on the tenth day, it was found that the egg had hatched and that

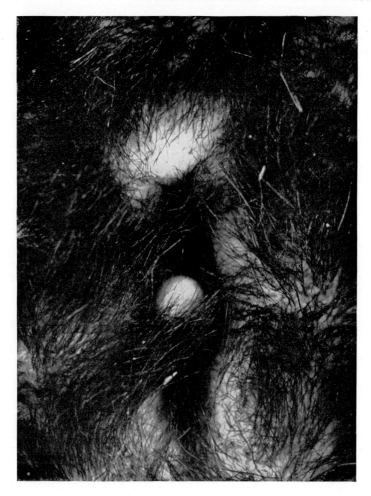

Fig. 94. Echidna egg in pouch at eighth day of incubation. ×1·2.

live pouch young was adherent to one of the milk areolae; the squashed egg shell was still present in the pouch. From this it is concluded that the incubation period is of the order of 10–10·5 days; in this instance the temperature of the incubatorium being 32·5° and that of the cloaca 32·0°C.

The young one was removed from the pouch, not without difficulty since it clung with its strong forelimbs to the numerous hairs in the pouch, so that it could be weighed and measured. It was 378 mg in weight and the crown–rump measurement was 1·47 cm. Externally it looked very like Semon's stage 46 echidna, save that the egg tooth was still evident. As far as its weight is concerned, it is very close to that of the neonatuses of some of the marsupialia, e.g. *Potorous tridactylus*, 333 mg; *Bettongia lesueur*, 320 mg; *Setonix brachyurus*, 340 mg (see Waring, Moir, and Tyndale-Biscoe, *Advances in Comp. Physiol. and Biochem.* **2**, 337, 1966).

The young one was returned to the pouch but apparently the manipulation was too much for it since it failed to find the milk areola again and it was found dead clinging to externally lying hairs of the pouch some four hours later. The next day about 2·5 ml of milk was taken from the mother after she had been injected with 22 IU of oxytocin. This milk contained 11·95 % solids, total N_2 being 1·23 g/100 ml whole milk, whereas the total solids and total N_2 concentration of mature milk of *T. a. aculeatus* are about 47 % and 2·6 g/100 ml respectively. Currently the component fatty acids are being determined in the 1-day milk, and the structure of the mammary gland at this stage will be studied.

REFERENCES

ABBIE, A. A. (1934) The brain stem and cerebellum of *Echidna aculeata*, *Phil. Trans. Roy. Soc. London*, B, **224**, 1–74.

ABBIE, A. A. (1938) The excitable cortex in the Monotremata, *Aust. J. Exp. Biol. Med. Sci.* **16**, 143–52.

ABBIE, A. A. (1940) Cortical lamination in the Monotremata, *J. Comp. Neurol.* **72**, 429–67.

ALEXANDER, G. (1904) Entwickelung und Bau des inneren Gehörorganes von *Echidna aculeata*, *Denkschr. Med. Naturwiss. Ges. Jena* **6**, Part 2, 3–118.

ALMEIDA, M. and FIALHO, A. (1924) Métabolisme, température et quelques autres déterminations physiologiques faites sur le Paresseux (*Bradypus tridactylus*), *C.R. Soc. Biol.* **91**, 1124–5.

BACKHOUSE, T. C. and BOLLIGER, A. (1959) *Babesia tachyglossi* n. sp. from the echidna *Tachyglossus aculeatus*, *J. Protozool.* **6**, 320–2.

BAILEY, A. M. (1951) Tasmanian spiny anteater withstands low temperature, *J. Mammal.* **32**, 116–17.

BARER, R., HELLER, H. and LEDERIS, K. (1963) The isolation, identification and properties of the hormonal granules of the neurohypophysis. *Proc. Roy. Soc. London*, B. **158**, 388–416.

BARRETT, C. (1942) The echidna's secret, *Wildlife* **4**, 350.

BASIR, M. A. (1932) The histology of the spleen and suprarenals of *Echidna*, *J. Anat.* **66**, 628–49.

BAYLIS, H. A. (1930) Four new trichostrongyle nematodes from Queensland, *Ann. Mag. Nat. Hist.* **6**, 1–18; **6**, 550.

DE BEER, G. R. (1926) Studies on the vertebrate head. II. The orbito-temporal region of the skull, *Quart. J. Micr. Sci.* **70**, 263–370.

DE BEER, G. R. (1930) *Embryology and Evolution*, Oxford, Clarendon Press.

DE BEER, G. R. and FELL, W. A. (1936) The development of the Monotremata Part III. The development of the skull of *Ornithorhynchus*, *Trans. Zool. Soc. London* **23**, 1–43.

VAN BEMMELEN, J. F. (1901) Der Schädelbau der Monotremen, *Denkschr. Med. Naturwiss. Ges. Jena* **6**, Part 1, 729–98.

BENDA, C. (1906) Die Spermiogenese der Monotremen, *Denkschr. Med. Naturwiss. Ges. Jena*, vol. **6**, Part 2, 413–38.

BENNETT, G. (1860) *Gatherings of a Naturalist in Australasia*, John van Voorst, London.

BICK, Y. A. E. and JACKSON, D. W. (1967) A mammalian X—O sex-chromosome system in the monotreme *Tachyglossus aculeatus* determined from leucoyte cultures and testicular preparations. *The American Naturalist* **101**, 79–86.

BOLLIGER, A. and BACKHOUSE, T. C. (1960) Blood studies on the echidna *Tachyglossus aculeatus*, *Proc. Zool. Soc. Lond.* **135**, 91–7.

BOLLIGER, A. and SHORLAND, F. B. (1963) Investigation on fats of Australian mammals, *Aust. J. Sci.* **25**, 453–6.

BOURLIÈRE, F. and PETTER-ROUSSEAUX, A. (1953) L'homéothermie imparfaite des certains Prosimiens, *C.R. Soc. Biol.* **147**, 1594–5.

BOURLIÈRE, F., PETTER, J. J. and PETTER-ROUSSEAUX, A. (1956) Variabilité de la température centrale chez les lémuriens, *Mém. Inst. Scient. Madagascar*, Série A, **10**, 303–4. (Quoted by Kayser, *The Physiology of Natural Hibernation*, 1961, Pergamon Press, Oxford.)

BOURNE, G. H. (1949) *The Mammalian Adrenal Gland*, Oxford, Clarendon Press.

BREMER, J. L. (1904) On the lung of the opossum, *Am. J. Anat.* **3**, 67–73.

BRESSLAU, E. (1907) Die Entwickelung des Mammarapparates der Monotremen, Marsupialier und einiger Placentalier. Ein Beitrag zur Phylogenie der Säugethiere. I. Entwickelung und Ursprung des Mammarapparates von *Echidna, Denkschr. Med. Ges. Jena* **7**, 455–518.

BRESSLAU, E. (1912a) Die Entwickelung des Mammarapparates der Monotremen, Marsupialier und einiger Placentalier. Ein Beitrag zur Phylogenie der Säugethiere. II. Der Mammarapparat der erwachsenen Echidna-Weibchens, *Denkschr. Med. Ges. Jena* **7**, 631–42.

BRESSLAU, E. (1912b) Die Entwickelung des Mammarapparates der Monotremen, Marsupialier und einiger Placentalier. Ein Beitrag zur Phylogenie der Säugethiere. III. Entwickelung des Mammarapparates der Marsupialier, Insectivoren, Nagethiere, Carnivoren, und Wiederkäuer, *Denkschr. Med. Ges. Jena* **7**, 653–874.

BRESSLAU, E. (1920) *The Mammary Apparatus of the Mammalia*, Methuen & Co. Ltd., London.

BRIDGWATER, R. J., HASLEWOOD, G. A. D. and TAMMAR, A. R. (1962) Bile salts of monotremes and observations on glycine conjugation, *Biochem. J.* **85**, 413–16.

BRIGGS, E. A. (1936) The red blood corpuscles of primitive mammals, *Nature* **138**, 762.

VAN BRINK, J. M. (1959) L'expression morphologique de la digamétée chez les Sauropsides et les Monotremes, *Chromosoma* **10**, 1–72.

BRODMAN, K. (1909) *Vergleichende Lokalizationslehre der Grosshirnrindl*, Leipzig. Quoted by Abbie (1940) and Kappers, Huber, and Crosby (1960).

BROEK, A. J. P. (1910) Untersuchungen über den Bau der männlichen Geschlechtsorgane der Beuteltiere, *Morph. Jahrb.* **41**, 347–436.

BROOM, R. (1895) Note on the period of gestation in *Echidna, Proc. Linn. Soc. N.S.W.* **10**, 576–7.

BROOM, R. (1897) On the existence of a sterno-coracoidal articulation in a foetal marsupial, *J. Anat.* **31**, 513–15.

BROOM, R. (1909) Observations on the development of the marsupial skull, *Proc. Linn. Soc. N.S.W.* **34**, 195–214.

BUCHANAN, G. and FRASER, E. A. (1918) The development of the female urogenital system in the Marsupialia with special reference to *Trichosurus vulpecula, J. Anat.* **53**, 35–95.

BURRELL, H. (1927) *The Platypus*, Angus & Robertson, Sydney.

BUTLER, P. M. (1939) The teeth of the Jurassic mammals, *Proc. zool. Soc. London* **109**, 329–56.

BUTLER, P. M. (1961) Relationships between upper and lower molar patterns. In: Vandebroek, G. (ed.) *International Colloquium on the Evolution of Lower and Non-specialized Mammals*, Paleis der Academien, Brussels.

CABRERA, A. (1919) *Genera Mammalium Monotremata Marsupialia*, Museo Nacional de Ciencias Naturales, Madrid.

CALABY, J. H. (1960) Observations on the banded ant-eater, *Myrmecobius f. fasciatus* Waterhouse (Marsupialia), with particular reference to its food habits, *Proc. Zool. Soc. Lond.* **135**, 183–207.

CALABY, J. H. (1966) *Mammals of the Upper Richmond and Clarence Rivers*, Div. of Wildl. Res. Techn. Paper No. 10. CSIRO. Australia.

CALABY, J. H. (1968) The Platypus (*Ornithorhynchus anatinus*) and its venomous characteristics. In: *Venomous Animals and their Venoms*, Academic Press, N.Y.

CALABY, J. H. and WIMBUSH, D. J. (1964) Observations on the broad-toothed rat, *Mastacomys fuscus* Thomas, CSIRO *Wildl. Res.* **9**, 123–33.

CALDWELL, W. H. (1884) Telegram, "Monotremes oviparous, ovum meroblastic". Read at meeting of the British Association at Montreal, Sept. 2, 1884. Brit. Assoc. Rep. Montreal Meeting, 1884.

CALDWELL, W. H. (1887) The Embryology of Monotremata and Marsupialia. Part I, *Phil. Trans. Roy. Soc. London*, B, **178**, 463–86.

CARPENTER, T. M. (1938) The partition of urinary nitrogen of fasting and hibernating woodchucks (*Arctomys monax*), *J. Biol. Chem.* **122**, 343–7.

DE CHARDIN, P. T. (1965) *The Appearance of Man*, Collins, London.

CHEW, R. (1965) Water metabolism of mammals. In: *Physiological Mammalogy*, vol. 2, Academic Press, New York.

COLEMAN, E. (1935) Hibernation and other habits of the echidna under domestication, *Vict. Naturalist* **52**, 55–61.

COLEMAN, E. (1938) Notes on the hibernation, ecdysis, and sense of smell of the echidna under domestication, *Vict. Naturalist* **55**, 105–7.

COLLETT, R. (1885) On *Echidna acanthion* from Northern Queensland, *Proc. Zool. Soc. London*, 148–61.

COSTIN, A. B. (1954) *A Study of the Ecosystems of the Monaro Region of New South Wales with special Reference to Soil Erosion*, Government Printer, Sydney.

CROMPTON, A. W. (1958) The cranial morphology of a new genus and species of ictidosauran, *Proc. Zool. Soc. London*, **130**, 183–216.

DAVIS, H. (1957) Biophysics and physiology of the inner ear, *Physiol Revs.* **37**, 1–48.

DAVY, J. (1840) Notice sur la forme des globules du sang chez *l'Echidna hystrix*, *L'institut*, **8**, 441.

DEL RIO-HORTEGA, P. (1921) *Boln. R. Soc. esp. Hist. nat.* **21**, 63.

DENKER, A. (1901) Zur Anatomie des Gehörorgans der Monotremata, *Denkschr. Med. Naturwiss. Ges. Jena* **6**, Part 1, 637–62.

DENTON, D. A., REICH, M. and HIRD, F. J. (1963) Ureotelism of echidna and platypus, *Science* **139**, 1225.

DENTON, D. A., WYNN, V., MCDONALD, J. R., and SIMON S. (1951) Renal regulation, *Acta Medica Scandinavica*, **140**, 1–201.

DIENER, E. and EALEY, E. H. M. (1965) Immune system in a monotreme, *Nature* **208**, 950–3.

DIENER, E. and EALEY, E. H. M. (1966) Phylogenetical development of the immune system with special reference to the primitive mammals, echidna and platypus. Presented at the Plenary Session of the XIth International Congress of Haematology, Sydney, 1966.

DILLON, L. S. (1962) Comparative notes on the cerebellum of the monotremes, *J. Comp. Neurol.* **118**, 343–53.

DINGLE, H. (1958) The scientific work of Emanuel Swedenborg, *Endeavour* **17**, 127–32.

DOBRORUKA, L. (1960) Einige Beobachtungen an Ameisenigeln, *Echidna aculeata* Shaw, *Zeit. f. Tierpsychologie* **17**, 178–81.

DOBRORUKA, L. (1961) Einige Bemerkungen über dem Brutbeutel des Ameisenigels, *Echidna aculeata*, *Zoologische Garten* **26**, 111–13.

258 REFERENCES

DOMROW, R. (1962) The mammals of Innisfail 2. Their mite parasites, *Aust. J. Zool.* **10**, 268–306.

DORAN, A. H. G. (1879) Morphology of the mammalian ossicula auditus, *Trans. Linn. Soc. London*, **1**, 371–497.

DRUMMOND, F. H. (1933) The male meiotic phase in five species of marsupials, *Quart. J. Micr. Sci.* **76**, 1–11.

DUVERNOY, M. (1830) *Mém. de la Soc. d'Histoire Naturelle de Strasbourg*, pp. 1–16.

EALEY, E. H. M. (1967) Ecology of the euro *Macropus robustus cervinus* Thomas in north-western Australia. IV. Seasonal changes in nutrition, *CSIRO Wildl. Res.* In press.

ECCLES, J. C. (1953) *The Neurophysiological Basis of Mind*, Oxford, Clarendon Press.

EGGELING, H. (1907) Ueber die Stellung der Milchdrüsen zu den übrigen Hautdrüsen. Nachtrag zur II. Mittheilung: Neue Beobachtungen über die Mammardrüsenentwickelung bei *Echidna*, *Denkschr. Naturwiss. Ges. Jena*, **7**, 333–40.

FANTL, P. (1961) A comparative study of blood coagulation in vertebrates, *Aust. J. Exp. Biol. Med. Sci.* **39**, 403–12.

FERGUSON, D. R. and HELLER, H. (1965) Distribution of neurohypophysial hormones in mammals, *J. Physiol.* **180**, 846–63.

FERNANDEZ, C. and SCHMIDT, R. S. (1963) The opossum ear and evolution of the coiled cochlea, *J. Comp. Neurol.* **121**, 151–60.

FEWKES, J. W. (1877) Contributions to the myology of *Tachyglossa* (sic) *hystrix*, *Echidna hystrix*, *Bull. Essex Inst. Salem* **9**, 111–37.

FLINDERS, M. (1798) *A Voyage to Terra Australis*, G. W. Nichol, London, pub. 1814.

FLYNN, T. T. (1923) The yolk-sac and allantoic placenta in *Perameles*, *Quart. J. Micr. Sci.* **67**, 123–83.

FLYNN, T. T. and HILL, J. P. (1939) The development of the Monotremata. Part IV. Growth of the ovarian ovum, maturation, fertilization, and early cleavage, *Trans. Zool. Soc. Lond.* **24**, 445–622.

FLYNN, T. T. and Hill, J. P. (1947) The development of the Monotremata. Part VI. The later stages of cleavage and the formation of the primary germ-layers, *Trans. Zool. Soc. Lond.* **26**, 1–151.

FOLLETT, B. K. (1963) Mole ratios of the neurohypophyseal hormones in the neural lobe, *Nature* **198**, 693–4.

FRANZEN, A. (1956) On spermiogenesis, morphology of the spermatozoon, and biology of fertilization among invertebrates, *Zoologiska Bidrag fran Uppsala* **31**, 355–482.

FUSE, G. (1926) *Arbeiten aus dem anatomischen Institut der Kaiserlich-Japanischen Universität zu Sendai*, Book 12. Quoted by Goldby (1939).

GAUPP, E. (1900) Das Chondocranium von *Lacerta agilis*, *Anat. Hefte* **14**, 433–595.

GAUPP, E. (1908) Zur Entwickelungsgeschichte und vergleichenden Morphologie des Schädels von *Echidna aculeata var typica*, *Denkschr. Med. Naturwiss. Ges. Jena* **6**, Part 2, 539–788.

GEGENBAUR, C. (1886) *Zur Kenntniss der Mammarorgane der Monotremen*, Wilhelm Engelmann, Leipzig.

GERVAIS, P. (1878) *Osteographie des Monotremes vivants et fossiles*, Librarie Scientifique et Maritime, Paris.

GILLESPIE, J. M. and INGLIS, A. S. (1965) A comparative study of high sulphur proteins from α keratins, *Comp. Biochem. Physiol.* **15**, 175–85.

GILMOUR, D. (1961) *Biochemistry of Insects*, Academic Press, New York, London.

GILMOUR, D. (1965) *The Metabolism of Insects*, Oliver & Boyd, Edinburgh and London.

GOLDBY, F. (1939) An experimental investigation of the motor cortex and pyramidal tract of *Echidna aculeata*, *Jour. Anat.* **73**, 509–24.

GÖPPERT, E. C. (1901) Beiträge zur vergleichenden Anatomie des Kehlkopfes und seiner Umgebung mit besonderer Berücksichtigung der Monotremen, *Denkschr. Med. Naturwiss. Ges. Jena* **6**, Part 1, 533–634.

GOODRICH, E. S. (1958) *Studies on the Structure and Development of Vertebrates*, Dover Publications Inc., New York.

GRAY, A. A. (1908) An investigation of the anatomical structure and relationships of the labyrinth in the reptile, the bird, and the mammal, *Proc. Roy. Soc. London*, B, **80**, 507–30.

GREAVES, T. (1939) The control of meat ants (*Iridomyrmex detectus* Sm.), *J. C.S.I.R.* **12**, 109–14.

GREGORY, W. K. (1947) The monotremes and the palimpsest theory, *Bull. Amer. Mus. Nat. Hist.* **88**, 7–52.

GREGORY, W. K. and NOBLE, G. K. (1924) The origin of the mammalian alisphenoid bone, *J. Morph. Physiol.* **39**, 435–63.

GRIFFITHS, M. (1940) The relationship between the secretory cells of the pars nervosa of the hypophysis and classical neuroglia, *Endocrinology* **26**, 1032–41.

GRIFFITHS, M. (1941) The influence of anterior pituitary extracts on the insulin content of the pancreas of the hypophysectomized rat, *J. Physiol.* **100**, 104–11.

GRIFFITHS, M. (1965a) Digestion, growth and nitrogen balance in an egg-laying mammal *Tachyglossus aculeatus* (Shaw), *Comp. Biochem. Physiol.* **14**, 357–75.

GRIFFITHS, M. (1965b) Rate of growth and intake of milk in a suckling echidna, *Comp. Biochem. Physiol.* **16**, 383–92.

GRIFFITHS, M., CALABY, J. H. and McINTOSH, D. L. (1960) The stress syndrome in the rabbit, *CSIRO Wildl. Res.* **5**, 134–48.

GRIFFITHS, M. and BARTON, A. A. (1966) The ontogeny of the stomach in the pouch young of the red kangaroo, *CSIRO Wildl. Res.* **11**, 169–85.

GRIFFITHS, M. and SIMPSON, K. S. (1966) A seasonal feeding habit of the spiny ant-eater, *CSIRO Wildl., Res.* **11**, 137–43.

HAACKE, W. (1885) On the marsupial ovum, the mammary pouch, and the male with glands *Echidna hystrix*, *Proc. Roy. Soc. London*, B, **38**, 72–4.

HACKMAN, R. H. (1960) Studies on Chitin., IV. The occurrence of complexes in which chitin and protein are covalently linked, *Aust. J. Biol. Sci.* **13**, 568–77.

HANSTRÖM, B. and WINGSTRAND, K. G. (1951) Comparative anatomy and histology of the pituitary in the egg-laying mammals, the monotremata. *Kungl. Fysiograf., Sällskap. Handl. Lund, Acta Univ. Lund N.F.* **62**, 1–39.

HARPER, A. E. (1964) *Amino Acid Toxicities and Imbalances, in Mammalian Protein Metabolism*, vol. II, Academic Press, New York–London.

HAUSMAN, L. A. (1920) A micrological investigation of the hair structure of the Monotremata, *Am. J. Anat.* **27**, 463–87.

HECK, L. (1908) *Echidna-Züchtung im Berliner Zool. Garten*, Ges. Naturforsch. Freunde. Berlin Sitzungsbericht, pp. 187–9.

HEUSER, C. H. (1921) The early establishment of the intestinal nutrition in the opossum. The digestive system just before and soon after birth, *Am. J. Anat.* **28**, 341–69.

HILL, C. J. (1933) The development of the Monotremata. Part I. The histology of the oviduct during gestation, *Trans. Zool. Soc. London*, **21**, 413–43.

HILL, C. J. (1941) The development of the Monotremata. Part V. Further observations on the histology and the secretory activities of the oviduct prior to and during gestation, *Trans. Zool. Soc. London*, **25**, 1–31.

HILL, J. P. (1898) The placentation of *Perameles*, *Quart. J. Micr. Sci.* **40**, 385–446.

HILL, J. P. (1900) On the foetal membranes, placentation, and parturition of the native cat (*Dasyurus viverrinus*), *Anat. Anz.* **18**, 364–73.

HILL, J. P. (1901) Contributions to the embryology of the Marsupialia. II. On a further stage in the placentation of *Perameles*, *Quart. J. Micr. Sci.* **43**, 1–22.

HILL, J. P. (1910) The early development of the Marsupialia, with special reference to the Native Cat (*Dasyurus viverrinus*), *Quart. J. Micr. Sci.* **56**, 1–134.

HILL, J. P. (1933) The development of the Monotremata. Part II. The structure of the egg-shell. *Trans. Zool. Soc. London*, **21**, 443–76.

HILL, J. P. and DE BEER, G. R. (1949) The development and structure of the egg-tooth and caruncle in the Monotremes and on the occurrence of vestiges of the egg-tooth and caruncle in Marsupials, *Trans. Zool. Soc. London*, **26**, 503–44.

HILL, J. P. and GATENBY, J. B. (1926) The corpus luteum of the Monotremata, *Proc. Zool. Soc. London*, Number 47, 715–63.

HILL, J. P. and HILL, W. C. O. (1955) The growth stages of the pouch young of the Native Cat (*Dasyurus viverrinus*) together with observations on the anatomy of the new-born young, *Trans. Zool. Soc. London*, **28**, 349–452.

HINES, M. (1929) The brain of *Ornithorhynchus anatinus*, *Phil. Trans. Roy. Soc. London*, B, **217**, 155–287.

HOCHSTETTER, F. (1896) Beiträge zur Anatomie und Entwickelungsgeschichte des Blutgefässsystems der Monotremen, *Denkschr. Med. Naturwiss. Ges. Jena* **5**, 191–243.

HODGE P. and WAKEFIELD, N. (1959) Echidna and its young, *Vict. Nat.* **76**, 64–5.

HOME, E. (1802) Description of the anatomy of the *Ornithorhynchus hystrix*, *Phil. Trans. Roy. Soc. London*, for the year 1802, 348–64.

HOPKINS, G. H. E. and ROTHSCHILD, M. (1953) *Catalogue of the Rothschild Collection of Fleas*, vol. I, Trustees of the British Museum.

HORNER, B. E., TAYLOR, J. M. and PADYKULA, H. A. (1965) Food habits and gastric morphology of the grass-hopper mouse, *J. Mammal.* **45**, 513–35.

HÜBER, E. (1930) Evolution of facial musculature and cutaneous field of trigeminus, *Quart. Rev. Biol.* **5**, 133–88.

HUGHES, R. L. (1965) Comparative morphology of spermatozoa from five marsupial families, *Aust. J. Zool.* **13**, 533–43.

HUGHES, R. L., THOMSON, J. A. and OWEN, W. H. (1965) Reproduction in natural populations of the Australian ringtail possum, *Pseudocheirus peregrinus* (Marsupialia: Phalangeridae), in Victoria, *Aust. J. Zool.* **13**, 383–406.

HYRTL, J. (1853) Das arterielle Gefässsystem der Monotremen. *Denkschr. der math.-naturwiss, Klasse der K. Akademie der Wissenschaften*, vol. 5.

IREDALE, T. and TROUGHTON, E. (1934) *A Check List of Mammals Recorded from Australia*, the Australian Museum Memoir 6, Sydney.

JENNESS, R., REGEHR, E. A. and SLOAN, R. E. (1964) Comparative biochemical studies of milks ii. Dialyzable carbohydrates, *Comp. Biochem. Physiol.* **13**, 339–52.

JOHNSON, D. H. (1964) Mammals of the Arnhem Land expedition. In: *Records of the American-Australian Scientific Expedition to Arnhem Land*, ed. C. P. Mountford, Melbourne University Press.

JOHNSTON, T. A. (1913) Cestodes and Acanthocephala. *Aust. Inst. Trop. Med. Rep.*, for the year 1911, 75–98.

JOHNSTONE, B. M. and JOHNSTONE, J. R. (1965) Interaction between two-tone pips in the cochlea of reptiles and mammals. Abs. No. 12A–2, *International Symposium on Comparative Neurophysiology Tokyo*.

JOHNSTONE, C. G., SCHMIDT, R. S. and JOHNSTONE, B. M. (1963) Sodium and potassium in vertebrate cochlear endolymph as determined by flame microspectrophotometry, *Comp. Biochem. Physiol.* **9**, 335–41.

JOHNSTONE, W. K. and EALEY, E. H. M. (1965) Reproduction in the Echidna, *Aust. Mamm. Soc. Bull.* **2**, 39.

JOLLIE, M. (1962) *Chordate Morphology*, Reinhold Publishing Corporation, New York.

JONES, F. W. (1923) *The Mammals of South Australia*, Part 1, The monotremes and the carnivorous marsupials, Government Printer, Adelaide.

JONES, I. C. (1957) *The Adrenal Cortex*, Cambridge University Press.

JORDAN, K. and ROTHSCHILD, N. C. (1922) *Ectoparasites*, vol. 1, p. 233, Hazell, Watson & Viney, London and Aylesbury.

KALDOR, I. and EZEKIEL, E. (1962) Iron content of mammalian breast milk: measurements in the rat and in a marsupial, *Nature, London*, **196**, 175.

KAPPERS, C. U. A., HUBER, G. C. and CROSBY, E. C. (1960) *The Comparative Anatomy of the Nervous System of Vertebrates Including Man*, The Macmillan Co., New York.

KAYSER, CH. (1961) *The Physiology of Natural Hibernation*, Pergamon Press, Oxford, London New York and Paris.

KEIBEL, F. (1904a) Zur Entwickelungsgeschichte des Urogenital apparates von *Echidna aculeata var. typica*, *Denkschr. Med. Naturwiss. Ges. Jena* **6**, Part 2, 151–206.

KEIBEL, F. (1904b) Zur Entwickelung der Leber, des Pankreas und der Milz bei *Echidna aculeata var typica*. *Denkschr. Med. Naturwiss. Ges. Jena* **6**, Part 2, 207–28.

KERMACK, K. A., KERMACK, D. M. and MUSSETT, F. (1956) New Mesozoic mammals from South Wales. *Proc. Geol. Soc. London*, No. 1533, 31.

KERMACK, K. A. and MUSSETT, F. (1958) The jaw articulation of the Docodonta and the classification of Mesozoic mammals, *Proc. Roy. Soc. London*, B, **149**, 204–15.

KLAATSCH, H. (1895) Studien zur Geschichte der Mammarorgane 1. Theil. Drüsenfeld der Monotremen, *Denkschr. Med. Naturwiss. Ges. Jena* **5**, 155–88.

KOHLS, G. M. (1960) *Ixodes* (Endopalpiger) *zaglossi*, n sp. from the long-beaked echidna of New Guinea (Acarina, Ixodidae), *Acarologia* **2**, 447–52.

KÖLLIKER, A. VON (1901) *Die Medulla Oblongata und die Vierhügelgegend von Ornithorhynchus und Echidna*, Engelmann, Leipzig.

KOLMER, W. (1925) Zur Organologie und mikroskopischen Anatomie von *Zaglossus bruijni, Zeitschr. f. wiss. Zool.* **125**, 448–82.

KOLMER, W. (1929) Zur Frage der Wärmregulation bei den Monotremen, *Pflügers. arch. f. Ges. Phys.* **221**, 319–20.

KONISHI, T., BUTLER, R. A. and FERNANDEZ, C. (1961) Effect of anoxia on cochlear potentials, *J. Acoust. Soc. Amer.* **33**, 349–56.

DE LANGE, S. J. (1918) Quoted by Kappers, Huber and Crosby 1960, vol. 1, 775.

LANKESTER, E. R. (1883) On the right cardiac valve of *Echidna* and *Ornithorhynchus, Proc. Zool. Soc. London*, for the year 1883, 8–14.

LARSELL, O., McCRADY, E. and ZIMMERMANN, A. A. (1935) Morphological and functional development of the membranous labyrinth in the opossum, *J. Comp. Neurol.* **63**, 95–118.

LAURIE, E. (1952) Mammals collected by Mr. Shaw Mayer in New Guinea 1932–49. *Bull. B.M. (Nat. Hist.) Zool.*, vol. 1, No. 10, London.

LENDE, R. A. (1963) Cerebral Cortex: A sensorimotor amalgam in the Marsupialia, *Science* **141**, 730–2.

LENDE, R. A. (1964) Representation in the cerebral cortex of a primitive mammal, *J. Neurophys.* **27**, 37–48.

VON LENDENFELD, R. (1886) Zur Brutpflege von Echidna, *Zool. Anz.* **9**, 9–10.

LING, E. R., KON, S. K. and PORTER, J. W. G. (1961) The composition of milk and the nutritive value of its components. In *Milk: The Mammary Gland and its Secretion*, **2**, 195–263, Academic Press, New York and London.

LINZELL, J. L. (1955) Some observations on the contractile tissue of the mammary glands, *J. Physiol.* **130**, 257–67.

LINZELL, J. L. (1959) Physiology of the mammary glands, *Physiol. Rev.* **39**, 534–76.

LYMAN, C. P. (1963) Hibernation in mammals and birds, *Amer. Scient.* **51**, 127–38.

MACKERRAS, J. M. (1958) Catalogue of Australian mammals and their recorded internal parasites, *Proc. Linn. Soc. N.S.W.* **83**, 101–60.

MACKERRAS, J. M. (1962) Filarial parasites (Nematoda: Filarioidea) of Australian animals, *Aust. J. Zool.* **10**, 400–57.

MARINE, D. (1932) In: *Cowdrey's Special Cytology* **2**, 799–855. Paul Hoeber, New York.

MARSTON, H. R. (1926) The milk of the monotreme—*Echidna aculeata multiaculeata*, *Aust. J. Exp. Biol. Med. Sci.* **3**, 217–20.

MARTIN, C. J. (1903) Thermal adjustment and respiratory exchange in monotremes and marsupials, *Phil. Trans. Roy. Soc. London*, B, **195**, 1–37.

MAURER, F. (1892) Hautsinnesorgane, Feder und Haaranlage, *Morphol. Jahrb.* **18**. Quoted by Römer (1898).

MAURER, F. (1899) Schilddrüse, Thymus, und sonstige Schlundspaltenderivate bei *Echidna* und ihre Beziehungen zu den gleichen Organen bei anderen Wirbeltieren, *Denkschr. Med. Naturwiss. Ges. Jena* **6**, Part 1, 403–44.

MCCRADY, E. (1938) *The Embryology of the Opossum*, The American Anatomical Memoirs No. 16, published by the Wistar Institute of Anatomy and Biology.

DE MEIJERE, J. C. H. (1893) *Over de Haren der Zoogdieren*, ed. E. J. Brill, Leiden.

MIKLOUHO-MACLAY, N. (1883) Temperature of the body of *Echidna hystrix*, *Proc. Linn. Soc. N.S.W.* **8**, 425.

MITCHELL, M. (1931) Observations on the composition of the urine and blood of *Echidna aculeata*, *Aust. J. Exp. Biol. Med. Sc.* **8**, 237–8.

NARATH, A. (1896) Die Entwickelung der Lunge von *Echidna aculeata*, *Denkschr. Med. Naturwiss. Ges. Jena* **5**, 247–74.

NEUMEISTER, R. (1898) Ueber den Harn von *Echidna aculeata*, *Z. Biol.* **36**, 77–9.

O'DAY, K. (1938) The visual cells of the Platypus, *Br. J. Ophthal.* **22**, 321–8.

O'DONOGHUE, C. H. (1911) The growth changes in the mammary apparatus of *Dasyurus* and the relation of the corpora lutea thereto, *Quart. J. Micr. Sci.* **57**, 187–234.

OLSON, E. C. (1959) The evolution of mammalian characters, *Evolution* **13**, 344–53.

OPPEL, A. (1896a) Ueber den Magen der Monotremen einiger Marsupialier und von *Manis javanica*, *Denkschr. Med. Naturwiss. Ges. Jena* **5**, 275–300.

OPPEL, A. (1896b) *Lehrbuch der vergleichende mikroskopische Anatomie der Wirbeltiere*, vol. 1, Gustav Fischer, Jena.

OPPEL, A. (1897) Ueber den Darm der Monotremen, einiger Marsupialier und von *Manis javanica*, *Denkschr. Med. Naturwiss. Ges. Jena* **5**, 401–33.

OPPEL, A. (1899) Ueber die Zunge der Monotremen, einiger Marsupialier und von *Manis javanica*, *Denkschr. Med. Naturwiss. Ges. Jena* **7**, 105–72.

OPPEL, A. (1900) *Lehrbuch der vergleichende mikroskopische Anatomie der Wirbeltiere*, vol. 3, Gustav Fischer, Jena.

OWEN, R. (1832) On the mammary gland of *Echidna hystrix*, *Proc. Comm. Zool. Soc. London* 179–81.

OWEN, R. (1839–47) *Monotremata in the Cyclopaedia of Anatomy and Physiology*, vol. 3, pp. 366–407. Longman, Brown, Green, Longmans and Roberts, London.

OWEN, R. (1845) *Proc. Zool. Soc. London* 80–82 (no title given).

OWEN, R. (1865) On the marsupial pouches, mammary glands, and mammary foetus of *Echidna hystrix*, *Phil. Trans. Roy. Soc. London*, **155**, 671–86.

PATTERSON, B. (1956) Early Cretaceous mammals and the evolution of mammalian molar teeth. *Fieldiana, Geol.* **13**, 1–105.

PATTERSON, B. and OLSON, E. C. (1961) A triconodontid mammal from the Triassic of Yunnan. In: Vandebroek, G. (ed.) *International Colloquium on the Evolution of Lower and Non-specialised Mammals*, Paleis der Academien, Brussels.

PEARSON, H. (1924) A dicynodont reptile reconstructed, *Proc. Zool. Soc. London*, **46**, 827–55.

PINKUS, F. (1906) Ueber die Haarscheiben der Monotremen, *Denkschr. Med. Naturwiss. Ges. Jena* **6**, Part 2, 459–80.

POULTON, E. B. (1884) The structures connected with the ovarian ovum of Marsupialia and Monotremata, *Quart. J. Micr. Sci.* **24**, Quoted by Flynn and Hill, 1939.

PRIESTLEY, H. (1915) *Theilia tachyglossi* (n.sp.) a blood parasite of *Tachyglossus aculeatus*, *Ann. Trop. Med. Parasit.* **9**, 233–8.

PUMPHREY, R. J. (1961) In: *Marshall's Biology and Comp. Physiology of Birds*, vol. 2, 69–74. Academic Press, New York and London.

RAMSAY, E. P. (1877) Note of a species of *Echidna* from Port Moresby, *Proc. Linn. Soc. N.S.W.* **2**, 31–3; **3**, 244 (1878).

RASMUSSEN, A. T. (1938) Innervation of the hypophysis, *Endocrinology* **23**, 263–78.

RASMUSSEN, A. T. and RASMUSSEN, G. B. (1917) The volume of the blood during hibernation and other periods of the year in the woodchuck (*Marmota monax*), *Amer. J. Physiol.* **44**, 132–48.

REED, C. A. (1960) Polyphyletic or monophyletic ancestry of mammals, or: what is a class? *Evolution* **14**, 314–22.

RETZIUS, G. (1906) Die Spermien der Monotremen, *Biol. Unters.* (N.F.) **13**, 75–6.

RICHARDSON, K. C. (1949) Contractile tissues in the mammary gland, with special reference to myoepithelium in the goat, *Proc. Roy. Soc. London*, B, **136**, 30–45.

RIENITS, R. and RIENITS, T. (1963) *Early Artists of Australia*, Angus & Robertson, Sydney.

ROBERTS, F. H. S. (1963) A systematic study of the Australian species of the genus Haemaphysalis Koch (Acarina: Ixodidae), *Aust. J. Zool.* **11**, 35–80.

ROBERTS, F. H. S. (1964) Further observations on the Australian species of *Aponomma* and *Amblyomma* with descriptions of the nymphs of *Amblyomma moreliae* (L. Koch) and *Amb. loculosum* Neumann (Acarina: Ixodidae), *Aust. J. Zool.* **13**, 288–313.

ROBERTS, R. C. and SEAL, U. S. (1965) Sedimentation analysis of vertebrate serum proteins. *Comp. Biochem. Physiol.* **16**, 327–31.

ROBINSON, K. W. (1954) Heat tolerances of Australian monotremes and marsupials, *Aust. J. Biol. Sci.* **7**, 348–60.

RÖMER, F. (1898) Studien über das Integument der Säugethiere. 2. Das Integument der Monotremen, *Denkschr. Med. Naturwiss. Ges. Jena* 6, Part 1, 189–241.

ROMER, A. S. (1961) Synapsid evolution and dentition. In: Vandebroek, G. (ed.) *International Colloquium on the Evolution of Lower and Non-specialized Mammals*, Paleis der Academien, Brussels.

RÖSE, C. (1890) Beiträge zur Vergleichende Anatomie des Herzens der Wirbelthiere, *Morphol. Jb.* 16, 27–96.

ROTHSCHILD, W. (1905) Notes on *Zaglossus* and description of a new subspecies of *Echidna hystrix*, *Nov. Zoologicae* 12, 305–6.

ROTHSCHILD, W. (1913) Some notes on the genera *Zaglossus* and *Tachyglossus*, *Nov. Zoologicae* 20, 188–91.

RUGE, G. (1895) Die Hautmusculatur der Monotremen und ihre Beziehungen zu dem Marsupial- und Mammarapparate. *Denkschr. Med. Naturwiss. Ges. Jena* 5, 75–153.

SAWYER, W. H., MUNSICK, R. A. and VAN DYKE, H. B. (1960) Pharmacological characteristics of neurohypophysial hormones from a marsupial (*Didelphis virginiana*) and a monotreme (*Tachyglossus* (*Echidna*) *aculeatus*), *Endocrinology* 67, 137–8.

SCHMIDT, R. S. (1963) Types of endolymphatic potentials, *Comp. Biochem. Physiol.* 10, 83–7.

SCHMIDT, R. S. and FERNANDEZ, C. (1963) Development of mammalian endocochlear potential, *J. Exp. Zool.* 153, 227–36.

SCHMIDT-NIELSEN, K., DAWSON, T. J. and CRAWFORD, E. C. (1966) Temperature regulation in the echidna (*Tachyglossus aculeatus*), *J. Cell. Comp. Physiol.* 67, 63–71.

SCHULMANN, H. J. (1906) Ueber die Ventrale facialismuskulatur einiger Säugetiere, besonders der Monotremen, *Festschrift für Palmen*, No. 18. Helsingfors.

SCHUSTER, E. (1910) Preliminary note upon the cell lamination of the cerebral cortex of the echidna, with an enumeration of the fibres in the cranial nerves. *Proc. Roy. Soc. London*, B, 82, 113–23.

SELENKA, E. (1887) *Studien ueber Entwickelungsgeschichte*, Bord I Viertes Heft, Das Opossum, C. W. Kreidels, Verlag, Wiesbaden.

SEMON, R. (1894a) Beobachtungen ueber die Lebensweise und Fortpflanzung der Monotremen, etc. *Denkschr. Med. Naturwiss. Ges. Jena* 5, 3–15.

SEMON, R. (1894b) Die Embryonalhüllen der Monotremen und Marsupialier, *Denkschr. Med. Naturwiss. Ges. Jena* 5, 19–58.

SEMON, R. (1894c) Zur Entwickelungsgeschichte der Monotremen, *Denkschr. Med. Naturwiss. Ges. Jena* 5, 61–74.

SEMON, R. (1899) *In the Australian bush*, Macmillan & Co. Ltd., London.

SEYDEL, O. (1899) Der Eizahn von *Echidna*, seine Entwickelung und sein Bau. *Denkschr. Med. Naturwiss. Ges. Jena* 6, Part 1, 519–32.

SHANKLIN, W. M. (1944) Histogenesis of the pituicytes in the chick, *J. Anat.* 78, 79–93.

SHARMAN, G. B. (1961) The mitotic chromosomes of marsupials and their bearing on taxonomy and phylogeny, *Aust. J. Zool.* 9, 38–60.

SHARMAN, G. B. (1961) The embryonic membranes and placentation in five genera of diprotodont marsupials, *Proc. Zool. Soc. London* 137, 197–220.

SHARMAN, G. B. (1965) Marsupials and the evolution of viviparity. In: *Viewpoints in Biology*, Butterworth & Co. London.

SHAW, G. (1792) *The Naturalist's Miscellany*, vol. 3, London.

SHELLSHEAR, J. (1930) A study of the arteries of the brain of the spiny ant-eater (*Echidna aculeata*), *Phil. Trans. Roy. Soc. London*, B, 218, 1–36.

SIMPSON, G. G. (1928) A catalogue of the Mesozoic mammals in the geological department of the British Museum (Natural History), London.

SIMPSON, G. G. (1936) Studies of the earliest mammalian dentitions, *Dental Cosmos* **78**, 791–800 and 940–53.

SIMPSON, G. G. (1938) Osteography of the ear region in monotremes, *Amer. Mus. Nov.*, number **978**, 1–15.

SIMPSON, G. G. (1945) The principles of classification and a classification of mammals, *Bull. Amer. Mus. Nat. Hist.* vol. 85, New York.

SIMPSON, G. G. (1959). Mesozoic mammals and the polyphyletic origin of mammals, *Evolution* **13**, 405–14.

SIMPSON, G. G. (1960) Diagnosis of the classes Reptilia and Mammalia, *Evolution* **14**, 388–92.

SIMPSON, G. G. (1961) Evolution of mesozoic mammals. In: Vandebroek, G. (ed.) *International Colloquium on the Evolution of Lower and Non-specialised Mammals*, Paleis der Academien, Brussels.

SIMPSON, G. G. (1964) *This View of Life, the World of an Evolutionist*, Harcourt Brace and World Inc., New York.

SLOAN, R. E., JENNESS, R., KENYON, A. L. and REGEHR, E. A. (1961) Comparative biochemical studies of milks. I. Electrophoretic analysis of milk proteins, *Comp. Biochem. Physiol.* **4**, 47–62.

SMITH, E. (1902) *Museum of the Royal College of Surgeons Catalogue of the Physiological Series 2*, 145–157.

SPENCER, B. and SWEET, G. (1899) The structure and development of the hairs of monotremes and marsupials, *Quart. J. Micr. Sci.* **41**, 549–58.

STEINER, R. (1928) *Goethe's Conception of the World*, Anthroposophical Publishing Co., London.

STURKIE, P. (1965) *Avian Physiology*, Comstock Publishing Associates, associated with Cornell University Press, Ithaca, N.Y.

TATE, G. (1952) Mammals of Cape York Peninsula with notes on the occurrence of rainforest in Queensland, *Bull. Am. Mus. Nat. Hist.* **98**, 567–616.

TERRY, R. (1917) The primordial cranium of the cat, *J. Morph.* **29**, 281–436.

THOMAS, O. (1885) Notes on the characters of the different races of *Echidna*, *Proc. Zool. Soc. London*, 329–39.

THOMAS, O. (1906) On mammals collected in South-west Australia for Mr. W. E. Ballston, *Proc. Zool. Soc. London*, 468–78.

THOMAS, O. and ROTHSCHILD, W. (1922) On a new subspecies of *Zaglossus* with remarks on the other species of the genus, *Ann. Nag. Nat. Hist.* **10**, 129–31.

THOMPSON, D. (1893) *Notes on a Tape Worm from Echidna (Taenia echidnae* n. sp.), J.R. Microscop. Soc. for the year 1893, 297.

TOBIN, G. (1792) Journal MS. A 562–3 in Mitchell Library, Sydney.

TUCKER, R. (1966) Comparative studies on the external acoustic meatus, *Proc. Linn. Soc. N.S.W.* **90**, 176–80.

VALEN, L. VAN (1960) Therapsids as mammals, *Evolution* **14**, 304–13.

VAZQUEZ-LOPEZ, E. (1942) The existence of microglia in the neurohypophysis, *J. Anat.* **76**, 178–86.

VOIT, M. (1906) Bau und Entwickelung der Cowperschen Drüsen bei *Echidna*, *Denkschr. Med. Naturwiss. Ges. Jena* **6**, Part 2, 401–12.

WALLS, G. L. (1942) *The Vertebrate Eye*, Cranbrook Institute of Science, Bulletin No. 19, Michigan, U.S.A.

WARDLAW, H. S. H. (1915) The temperature of *Echidna aculeata*, *Proc. Linn. Soc. N.S.W.* **40**, 231–58.

WATSON, D. M. S. (1916) The monotreme skull; a contribution to mammalian morphogenesis, *Phil. Trans. Roy. Soc. London*, B, **207**, 311–74.

WATSON, D. M. S. (1942) On Permian and Triassic tetrapods, *Geol. Mag.* *London*, **79**, 81–116.

WATSON, D. M. S. and ROMER, A. S. (1956) A classification of the therapsid reptiles, *Bull. Mus. Comp. Zool.* **114**, 35–89.

WEEKES, H. C. (1930) On placentation in reptiles. II, *Proc. Linn. Soc. N.S.W.* **55**, 550–76.

WEISS, M. and MCDONALD, I. R. (1965) Cortico-steroid secretion in the monotreme *Tachyglossus aculeatus*, *J. Endocrinol.* **33**, 203–10.

WEISS, M. and MCDONALD, I. R. (1966) Adrenocortical secretion in the wombat, *Vombatus hirsutus* Perry, *J. Endocrinol.* **35**, 207–8.

WESTLING, C. (1889) Anatomische Untersuchungen uber *Echidna*, *Bih. Svensk. Akad. Handl. Stockholm* **15**, 3–71.

WEVER, E. G., VERNON, J. A., PETERSON, E. A. and CROWLEY, D. E. (1963) Auditory responses in the tokay gecko, *Proc. Nat. Acad. Sci.* **50**, 806–11.

WILDMAN, A. B. and MANBY, J. (1938) The hair of the Monotremata with special reference to their cuticular pattern, *Trans. Roy. Soc. Edinburgh* **59**, 333–49.

WILSON, J. T. and HILL, J. P. (1907) Observations on the development of *Ornithorhynchus*, *Phil. Trans. Roy. Soc. London*, B, **199**, 31–168.

WILSON, J. T. and HILL, J. P. (1915) The embryonic area and so-called "primitive knot" in the early Monotreme egg, *Quart. J. Micr. Sci.* **61**, 15–25.

WRIGHT, A. and JONES, I. C. (1957) The adrenal gland in lizards and snakes, *J. Endocrinol.* **15**, 83–99.

WRIGHT, A., JONES, I. C. and PHILLIPS, J. G. (1957) The histology of the adrenal gland of the Prototheria, *J. Endocrinol.* **15**, 100–7.

YAMADA, H. (1938) *Arbeiten aus dem anatomischen Institut der Kaiserlich-Japanischen Universität zu Sendai*, vol. 21. Quoted by Goldby (1939).

ZARNIK, B. (1910) *Vergleichende Studien über den Bau der Niere von Echidna und der Reptilienniere*, Gustav Fischer, Jena.

ZIEHEN, T. (1897) Das Centralnervensystem der Monotremen und Marsupialier. I. Teil. Makroskopische Anatomie, *Denkschr. Med. Naturwiss. Ges. Jena* **6**, Part 1, 1–187.

ZIEHEN, T. (1905) Das Centralnervensystem der Monotremen und Marsupialier. III. Teil. Zur Entwickelungsgeschichte des Zentralnervensystems von *Echidna hystrix*, *Denkschr. Med. Naturwiss. Ges. Jena* **6**, Part 2, 229–96.

ZIEHEN, T. (1908) Das Centralnervensystem der Monotremen und Marsupialier. II. Teil. Mikroskopische Anatomie, *Denkschr. Med. Naturwiss. Ges. Jena* **6**, Part 2, 789–921.

ZSCHOKKE, F. (1899) Neue Studien an Cestoden der aplacentale Säugetiere. *Z. wiss. Zool.* **65**, 404–45.

AUTHOR INDEX

SUBJECT INDEX

280   SUBJECT INDEX

OTHER DIVISIONS IN THE SERIES IN
PURE AND APPLIED BIOLOGY

BIOCHEMISTRY

BOTANY

MODERN TRENDS
IN PHYSIOLOGICAL SCIENCES

PLANT PHYSIOLOGY